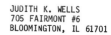

D1298778

EXPLORATIONS
1

Betty Coombs ◆ Lalie Harcourt

ILLUSTRATOR
Steve Pilcher

STORY/POEM EDITOR
Sue Ann Alderson

CONSULTANTS
Jennifer Travis
Nancy Wannamaker

ADDISON-WESLEY PUBLISHERS

Don Mills, Ontario • Reading, Massachusetts • Menlo Park, California
Wokingham, Berkshire • Amsterdam • Sydney • Singapore • Tokyo
Mexico City • Bogota • Santiago • San Juan

Explorations 1

Editorial Development

Dianne Goffin
Ricki Wortzman

Project Editor

Carol Ring

Design, Art Direction, and Illustration

Pronk & Associates

Design

Gord Pronk

Character Concept

"Ted the Troll" and associated characters conceived and illustrated by Steve Pilcher. All rights reserved.

Art Production

Mary Pronk
Walter Augustowitsch
Bruce Bond
Frank Zsigo

Photography

Birgitte Nielsen
Jeremy Jones *(Unit 2)*

Acknowledgements

The authors and publishers would like to express their appreciation for the invaluable advice and encouragement received from educators during the development of this program. We particularly wish to thank the following people:

Edith Biggs, Dianne Brow, Donna Burron, Janis Cleugh, Brendan Kelly, Roberta MacKean, Eileen Mansfield, Carolyn McCann, Bill Nimigon, Alexander Norrie, Gina Rae, and Kathy Willson.

In addition, we would like to say a special thank you to the staff and students of Cherokee Public School and Crestview Public School, Willowdale; Floradale Public School, Mississauga; McMurrich Junior Public School, Toronto; and Percy Williams Junior Public School, Agincourt.

Canadian Cataloguing in Publication Data

Coombs, Betty, 1931–
  Explorations 1

Bibliography: p.
ISBN 0-201-19112-1

1. Mathematics — 1961- 2. Mathematics — 1961- — Problems, exercises, etc.
I. Harcourt, Lalie, 1951- II. Title.
QA135.5.C66 1986 510 C85-099409-8

ISBN 0-201-19112-1

Printed and bound in Canada

D E F G H —BP— 93 92 91 90 89 88

About the Authors

Betty Coombs

Betty Coombs is a consultant in Primary Education with the Board of Education for the City of Hamilton. A graduate of McMaster University with a Master of Education from the Ontario Institute for Studies in Education, Mrs. Coombs has nearly twenty years of experience in both elementary and secondary education. As well, she has given guest lectures at Brock University on Early Childhood Education and on Mathematics And Children's Literature.

Lalie Harcourt

Lalie Harcourt is a teacher with the Halton Board of Education. A graduate of the University of Waterloo, she holds a Bachelor of Education from Queen's University and a Master of Education from the Ontario Institute for Studies in Education. In addition to her ten years of teaching experience, Ms. Harcourt is an experienced author, having collaborated with Dr. Brendan Kelly on 5 titles in the *Math Clues* series published by Hayes Publishing.

About the Illustrator

Steve Pilcher

Steve Pilcher has created characters and illustrations for children's publications since 1973. He has had several gallery showings of his fine art and many of his works hang in public and private collections. Mr. Pilcher has published several books for the trade market, including *Norbert Nipkin* and *Elfabit*. He currently works with Pronk & Associates Inc. as an illustrator and creative director for the primary school level.

About the Story/Poem Editor

Sue Ann Alderson

Sue Ann Alderson is Associate Professor in the Creative Writing Department of the University of British Columbia, where her special interest is a course in writing children's literature. Ms. Alderson is an accomplished author in her own right, with 10 published titles to her credit. Books such as *Bonnie McSmithers you're driving me dithers* have long delighted young children.

Table of Contents

Sequencing Your Program vi

Scope and Sequence vii

Explorations: The Theory and The Practice x

A Guide to *Explorations* xiv

Implementing the Program xviii

Suggested Materials List xxiv

The Role of Language in *Explorations* xxviii

Introducing the Story Characters 1

Introductory Story: Who Stole the Cookies? 2

Unit 1 Sorting and One-to-one Correspondence 4

Unit 2 Patterning 40

Unit 3 Number to 10 64

Unit 4 Measurement 106

Unit 5 Addition and Subtraction to 5 136

Unit 6 Geometry 172

Unit 7 Addition and Subtraction to 10 194

Unit 8 Geometry and Fractions 220

Unit 9 Number to 99 244

Unit 10 Measurement 280

Unit 11 Addition and Subtraction to 12 304

Sample Letters to Parents 317

Annotated Bibliography 318

Sequencing Your Program

Explorations 1 is a complete mathematics program for Grade 1. The objectives have been organized into eleven units. Although the time spent on any unit will vary with the needs of the children, the following general guidelines will help to pace the year's work.

Term 1	Units 1 to 4, pages 4–135
Term 2	Units 5 to 7, pages 136–219
Term 3	Units 8 to 11, pages 220–316

As you work through the program with your children, no doubt you will see the potential for alternative sequences. It is important to remember that the sequence provided in this book is only one of several ways to organize these mathematical objectives. Your own preferences or the interests of the children may prompt you to alter the sequence. Feel free to do so, provided that you maintain the sequence of objectives within each strand. One alternative sequence is offered in the chart below. This sequence may be a preferred one if you would rather develop the different strands concurrently.

Term 1

Problem Solving	Number	Measurement	Operations	Geometry
Sorting: **Unit 1** *Section 1* *pages 12-23*	One-to-one Correspondence: **Unit 1** *Section 2* *pages 24-31*	Time and Length in Non-standard Units: **Unit 4** *Sections 1 and 2* *pages 112-127*	Addition and Subtraction to 5: **Unit 5** *Sections 1-3* *pages 142-170*	Geometric Solids: **Unit 6** *Section 1* *pages 178-184*
Patterning: **Unit 2** *Section 1* *pages 48-55*	Number to 5: **Unit 3** *Section 1* *pages 70-83*			
Graphing: **Unit 1** *Section 3* *pages 32-37*				

Term 2

Patterning: **Unit 2** *Section 2* *pages 56-61*	Number to 10: **Unit 3** *Sections 2 and 3* *pages 84-103*	Mass and Capacity: **Unit 4** *Section 3* *pages 128-133*	Addition and Subtraction to 10: **Unit 7** *Sections 1 and 2* *pages 200-218*	Geometric Figures: **Unit 8** *Section 1* *pages 226-235*
Graphing: **Unit 6** *Section 2* *pages 185-191*				

Term 3

Graphing: **Unit 10** *Section 3* *pages 298-301*	Number to 99: **Unit 9** *Sections 1-3* *pages 250-275*	Time to the Hour and Length in Non-standard Units: **Unit 10** *Sections 1 and 2* *pages 286-297*	Addition and Subtraction to 12: **Unit 11** *Section 1* *pages 310-315*	Geometry continues to be referenced through Five Minute Math Activities: *pages 197, 247, 307*
Patterning: **Unit 9** *Section 3* *pages 276-277*	Fractions: **Unit 8** *Section 2* *pages 236-241*			

Scope and Sequence

Explorations 1

Number

Matching to determine equivalent sets *26-27*
Matching to create equivalent sets *28-29*
Estimating and identifying a set with more/less *30, 43*
Creating a set with more/less *31*
Counting on and counting back *7, 42, 66, 108, 138, 174, 282, 306*
Recognizing numerals *7, 42*
Printing numerals *8, 43*

Creating a set of 1, 2, 3, 4, 5, and 0 *74-78*
Labelling a set of 1, 2, 3, 4, 5, and 0 *78-83*
Creating a set of 6, 7, 8, 9, and 10 *86-87*
Labelling a set of 6, 7, 8, 9, and 10 *88-91, 104-105, 108*
Identifying ordinal position *95-96*
Identifying the number before/after/between *97-98, 108*
Identifying the greater/lesser number *99-101*
Ordering numbers to 10 *101-103*

Identifying fair shares *239-240*
Identifying halves, fourths, and tenths *240-241*

Counting by twos *196*
Counting by tens *222, 306*
Counting by fives *246, 306*
Grouping by fours and fives *252-253*
Grouping by tens *254-255*
Trading pennies for a coin *256*
Recording a ten and ones *260-261*
Counting and recording groups of 10 *262-263*
Counting sets to 50 or 100 *264-265*
Recording a 2-digit number *265-267*
Identifying the greater/lesser number *272-273, 282*
Identifying the number before/after/between *274-275*
Creating and recording number patterns *276-277*

Explorations 2

Number

Counting on and counting back
Counting by twos
Counting by fives
Counting by tens

Grouping by fours and fives
Grouping and counting by groups of 10
Recording a ten and ones
Counting and recording sets to 99
Creating and recording number patterns
Identifying ordinal position
Identifying the number before/after/between
Identifying the greatest/least number

Identifying fair shares
Identifying one half, one third, one fourth, and one tenth
Identifying tenths

Grouping and counting groups of 100
Counting and recording sets to 999
Representing numbers to 999
Identifying the number before/after/between
Identifying the greatest/least number
Counting money: dollars and cents
Estimating number

Explorations 1

Geometry

Manipulating geometric solids *180-181, 192-193, 197*
Sorting geometric solids *181-182*
Relating real-world objects to geometric solids *183-184, 193*
Identifying geometric solids *180-184*

Relating faces of geometric solids to geometric figures *228*
Sorting and identifying geometric figures *229, 247*
Relating real-world objects to geometric figures *230*
Patterning with geometric figures *231-232*
Identifying sides and corners *233*
Tiling a surface *234-235*
Creating and recognizing symmetrical figures *238-239, 242-243*

Measurement

Reading the calendar *6, 42, 66, 108, 138, 175, 196, 246, 306*
Ordering the days of the week *138, 282*
Ordering the months of the year *222, 246, 282*

Discussing weather and temperature *6, 66, 197, 246*
Reading a thermometer *138, 306*

Recognizing time names *6, 138, 197*
Sequencing events *113-115*
Estimating and measuring time in non-standard units *116-117, 138*
Telling time to the hour *287-289, 306*
Recording time to the hour *289-291*

Estimating and comparing length *120-122, 196-197, 222, 306*
Ordering by length or height *122-127, 134*
Estimating and comparing length in non-standard units *293-297*

Estimating and comparing capacity *129-130, 135, 138*
Estimating and comparing mass *131-133, 135, 138*

Identifying and counting coin collections *109, 139, 222, 246-247, 283*
Making change *217-218*

Explorations 2

Geometry

Relating real-world objectives to geometric solids
Sorting and manipulating geometric solids
Identifying faces, edges, corners
Constructing models of geometric solids

Relating faces of geometric solids to geometric figures
Relating real-world objects to geometric figures
Identifying sides and corners
Identifying congruent figures
Sorting geometric figures
Patterning with geometric figures
Creating and recognizing symmetrical figures

Measurement

Reading the calendar
Ordering days of the week and months of the year

Discussing weather and temperature
Reading the thermometer

Sequencing events
Estimating and measuring time in non-standard units
Telling time to the hour and half-hour
Telling time to 5 minute intervals

Estimating and comparing length
Estimating and measuring in non-standard units
Estimating and measuring in metres (yards)
Estimating and measuring in centimetres (inches)

Estimating and comparing capacity
Estimating and measuring capacity in non-standard units
Estimating and measuring capacity using a litre (quart)
Estimating and comparing mass
Estimating and measuring mass in non-standard units
Estimating and measuring mass using a kilogram (pound)

Tiling a surface in non-standard units

Counting money
Making change

Explorations 1

Problem Solving

Sorting and re-sorting a collection   *17-22, 38-39, 44, 66-67, 83, 100, 121, 130, 132-133, 181-182, 197, 229, 247*

Identifying the sorting rule   *23, 44, 67, 109, 139, 175, 223, 283, 307*

Identifying likenesses and differences   *8, 44, 67, 109, 139, 223, 283*

Developing observation and listening skills   *9, 44-45, 67, 175, 247, 283*

Identifying patterns   *51-52, 175*

Extending patterns   *52-55, 223, 247, 307*

Creating patterns   *58-63, 66, 89, 109, 231-232, 247*

Creating and solving story problems   *45, 109, 139, 175, 197, 207-208, 223, 247, 283*

Creating and interpreting a concrete graph   *34-37, 183*

Creating and interpreting a pictograph   *186-191, 196*

Creating and interpreting a bar graph   *299-301*

Operations

Combining sets to 3, 4, and 5   *146-147*

Creating and solving addition story problems   *148-149, 167-169*

Recording addition sentences   *150-153*

Solving addition sentences   *153-155, 169-170*

Separating sets to 3, 4, and 5   *159-160*

Creating and solving subtraction story problems   *161-162, 167-169*

Recording subtraction sentences   *163-164*

Solving subtraction sentences   *164-165, 169-170*

Combining and separating sets to 6, 7, 8, 9, and 10   *203-206*

Recording sums and differences to 6, 7, 8, 9, and 10   *206-207*

Creating and solving story problems   *207-208*

Adding with 3 addends   *209-211*

Solving number sentences to 10   *212-213*

Combining and separating sets to 11 and 12   *312*

Recording sums and differences to 11 and 12   *313*

Creating and solving story problems   *314*

Solving number sentences to 12   *315*

Explorations 2

Problem Solving

Sorting and re-sorting a collection

Identifying the sorting rule

Sorting into overlapping sets

Identifying and extending patterns

Creating patterns

Translating patterns

Creating and interpreting a concrete graph

Creating and interpreting a pictograph

Creating and interpreting a bar graph

Creating and solving story problems

Looking for possibilities

Identifying likenesses and differences

Developing observation and listening skills

Interpreting information

Operations

Combining and separating sets to 10

Creating and solving story problems

Identifying related addition and subtraction number sentences

Finding missing numbers

Solving number sentences to 10

Adding with 3 addends

Combining and separating sets to 11, 12, ... , 17, and 18

Creating and solving story problems

Solving number sentences to 18

Adding 2-digit numbers

Creating and solving addition story problems

Subtracting 2-digit numbers

Creating and solving subtraction story problems

Creating and solving addition and subtraction story problems

Adding and subtracting 2-digit numbers

Identifying and creating equal groups

Creating and solving multiplication story problems

Recording multiplication sentences

Dividing a collection

Explorations:
The Theory and The Practice

Explorations for Early Childhood and Explorations 1, and *2* form a complete mathematics program for grades kindergarten through 2. This activity-based program makes it possible to put the solid theoretical underpinnings of experiential learning into practice. Activities are carefully sequenced to promote the development of concepts in each of the main strands of primary mathematics: Problem Solving, Number, Measurement, Operations, and Geometry.

Theory

Because most primary children are at a pre-operational stage of development, they learn mathematics best through manipulating concrete materials and interacting with their environment. That environment should be carefully planned to encourage the development of mathematical concepts.

Practice

Children explore sorting concepts using a variety of concrete materials. Note that the materials are easily accessible and clearly labelled so that children can pursue the task independently.

Theory

Children must manipulate materials and see the results of their activity to develop a solid grasp of mathematical concepts. Only after children have participated in a wide range of activities using a variety of materials will they have a complete understanding. Only then should symbols be introduced as labels to represent the concrete activity. Introducing symbols as a tool to represent concepts rather than to teach them reflects the belief that learning proceeds in a continuum from concrete to pictorial to symbolic.

Practice

After children have created sets concretely they begin to keep a record of their actions by creating a pictorial representation. When the concept is firmly established they express their understanding by labelling their work with symbols.

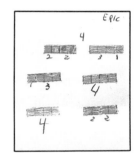

Theory

Experiences and learning styles of children in any given class vary considerably. Activities must be designed to accommodate individual needs.

Practice

Children play an addition game at their own levels of development. One pair of children is manipulating and verbalizing combinations of 4 while another child is recording all the different ways he can combine a set of 5 objects.

Theory

Problem-solving skills and strategies are developed best when integrated into all facets of the primary mathematics program.

Practice

Problem-solving activities are interwoven into each strand: Number, Geometry, Measurement, and Operations. This photo shows children using their sorting skills as they predict whether objects are longer than, shorter than, or the same length as a given object. They then check their prediction by measuring.

Theory

The internalization of mathematics concepts and the development of language skills are two aspects of a child's intellectual growth which can and should reinforce each other. Activities should offer children opportunities to discuss their discoveries and questions.

Practice

Children have many opportunities to verbalize as they engage in creating and acting out stories on story boards. Children are encouraged to report the results of their activities to their classmates.

Theory

Mathematics is an exciting and far-reaching element of the child's world with relevance to virtually every aspect of that world. It is important to encourage children to search their environment for examples of concepts under consideration.

Practice

Children search their environment for real-world objects similar to the geometric solids they have investigated in class.

Theory

Children's feelings about themselves as learners and about their experiences with mathematics can greatly influence their success with the subject. By providing an environment that is accepting, encouraging, stimulating and enjoyable, a program can foster a strong self-image and a positive attitude towards mathematics.

Practice

Children engage in a familiar type of hide and seek game as they identify ordinal position.

A Guide to *Explorations*

In designing *Explorations*, utmost consideration was given to making the book as inviting and easy to use as possible. The next few pages describe those features of the book which will help you to organize your program.

Reproduced below and overleaf are 4 typical unit planner pages from *Explorations 1*.

Lists sequentially all the unit objectives.

Describes the mathematical background for each concept developed in the unit. The development of the concept within the context of the program is also discussed.

Patterning

Unit Objectives

Section 1

A Identifying Patterns
B Extending Patterns

Section 2

C Creating Patterns

About this Unit

Patterning

Patterning, the repetition of a sequence, is a skill which touches virtually every aspect of a child's life. When infants recognize the human face as a regular arrangement of eyes, nose, and mouth, they are beginning to see pattern. The toddler who automatically brings a storybook at bedtime has recognized (or is seeking to establish) a pattern.

Recognition of pattern will continue to be a requisite skill throughout a child's academic life. Mathematics, literature, the arts, and the sciences all demand the recognition and creation of patterns.

This unit leads children through a sequence of activities which allows them to experience patterns visually, auditorially, and kinesthetically. Exploring the materials gives children the opportunity

to focus on interesting characteristics of the materials provided. Some children may pattern spontaneously in the course of their exploration. The activities begin by having the children identify and then extend a simple pattern using concrete materials such as block, bead, block, bead, block, bead. They progress to extending more complex patterns, first with concrete materials and sounds, then with pictures. The second section of the unit gives children opportunities to create patterns with many different materials at both the concrete and pictorial levels. The patterns created may be as simple or as sophisticated as the child's abilities and imagination dictate.

Throughout the unit it is emphasized that children should have opportunities to read and read again in other ways the patterns they extend and create. Reading patterns aloud helps children focus their attention on the pattern, provides a way of checking the pattern, and is especially beneficial for auditory learners.

Problem Solving

As the children participate in the activities of this unit, they develop problem-solving skills. In each activity, the children

• identify, extend, and/or create patterns.

They always have the opportunity to "read" their pattern aloud. The children are also encouraged to think of different possible ways to read these patterns. These patterning activities provide the children with opportunities to apply their sorting skills. In addition, activities provided in Five Minute Math, page •• develop the following problem-solving skills:

• sorting
• identifying likenesses and differences
• developing observation and listening skills
• creating stories

Vocabulary

• Next
• Pattern

Planning Ahead

The next unit focusses on number to 10. It is suggested that you assess the children's understanding of number while you progress through the current unit so that you will have the information you need to provide an appropriate program when you are ready to begin the number work. See page •• for a suggested assessment technique.

*Highlights the problem-solving skills developed in the unit. Identifies all activities which present the children with the opportunity to further develop their problem-solving skills. (Those activities identified have the logo **PS** to the right of the activity title.)*

Lists the vocabulary children should be encouraged to use as they participate in the unit.

Alerts the teacher when it is necessary to plan ahead for the work of the following unit. This may involve assessing children or collecting materials.

Ongoing Objectives

- Reading the calender
- Counting on and counting back
- Recognizing time names
- Discussing temperature
- Problem solving

  - Sorting
  - Identifying, extending, and creating patterns
  - Identifying likenesses and differences
  - Developing observation and listening skills

Five Minute Math

Calendar Activities

- Direct the children's attention to last month's calendar. These questions can form the basis of your discussion:

  - Did it rain (snow) last month?
  - What day was Adam's birthday? What was the date?
  - How many birthdays were in (September)?
  - Did we go on a class trip in (September)? When? Where did we go?
  - Did we have a bake sale last month?

- Create a monthly mural to record current events. Have each child who has an event to share record it on the mural.

Counting Activities

- Have the children count aloud as they bounce a ball to a partner or jump a skipping rope.
- Frequently draw the children's attention to the Cumulative Record of Days in School. Have them count aloud as you point to each numeral starting at 1. On another day, have them count back from 10 as you point to the corresponding numerals.
- On a signal, have the children count silently as they pat their knees 3 times and then count on aloud to 10. Have the children generate ideas for different actions to perform during the silent counts. Begin counting on from 3 and extend the number of silent counts as children feel more confident and comfortable. On another day, adapt this activity. Have the children count back silently from 10 as they pat their knees 3 times and then count back aloud to 0. For example, Pat, pat, pat, 7, 6, 5, 4, 3, 2, 1, 0. (Blast off.)
- Tap a pencil and ask the children to count to themselves a designated number of taps. At the designated number, have them all continue to count aloud.

66   UNIT 3

Measurement Activities

- Make frequent, incidental references to time so that children become familiar with the time of the day's events. For example, these references are appropriate and help children develop a frame of reference for daily events.

  - Let's start our school day. It's 9 o'clock.
  - Clean up, get ready for recess. It's almost 10:30.
  - 12 o'clock, time for lunch!
  - Afternoon recess . . . yes, it's already 2:30.
  - Let's start to pack up. We go home at 3:30.

- Place catalogues and old magazines at a center. Have the children cut out pictures showing hot and cold objects during their free time. After the children have had ample opportunity to search for pictures, have them compare the pictures according to temperature. Display some of the pictures. Hold up a picture, e.g., ice cream and ask, Is there a picture of something that is warmer than this ice cream? Is there another picture of something warmer? Is there a picture of something that is colder?

  On another day, you could post 3 to 5 of these pictures and ask the children to put them in order from coldest to hottest.

Problem Solving Activities

Sorting

Have the children sit in a circle so that they can see each other easily. Decide on a sorting rule which involves 2 criteria and state it aloud. For example, say, If you are wearing running shoes and a short sleeve shirt, stand at the front of the room. When everyone is assembled, say, Does everyone standing here belong? Choose a child who did not join the group and ask, Should Leah be in this group? Why not?

Identifying, Extending, and Creating Patterns

- Any of these games: Tap a Pattern, page 51; Whisper a People Pattern and Plip, Plip, Plop!, page 52; and Magic Pattern Makers, page 53 can easily be played in 5 minutes to reinforce and review pattern skills.
- Have the children identify those children wearing a patterned item of clothing such as shirts, socks, pants, or sweaters. Read the patterns aloud with the children, Blue stripe, white stripe, blue stripe, white stripe.

- Draw 3 repetitions of a pattern with different colored chalk on the chalk board. Have the children, in turn, select a piece of chalk and extend the pattern. Invite children to begin a chalk pattern for others to create.

Identifying Likenesses and Differences

- Display 2 books which are familiar to the children. Ask, How are these books the same? After the children have described a number of similarities ask, How are these books different? Encourage the children to consider the size, color, thickness, titles, and number of pages. Children may suggest similarities and differences in content.
- Display a collection of Pattern Blocks, Parquetry Tiles, or Attribute Blocks. Hold up a block so that all children can see it and, say, Find me a block from this collection that is the same color. Invite several children to select a block in response to your statement. Display another block and, say, Find me a block from this collection that has the same shape (size, or thickness). If children respond comfortably to these directions, continue with statements such as these:

  - Find me a block with the same shape and color.
  - Find me a block that is the same color but which has a different shape.

Developing Observation and Listening Skills

- Ask a volunteer to stand in front of a group of children. Tell the children to observe the child very carefully. After a few moments, ask the children to close their eyes. Change something about the child's appearance. (For example you could: untie a shoe, have the child roll up/down her or his sleeves, remove a cardigan, untuck a shirt, put her or his shoes on the wrong feet, etc.) Invite the children to open their eyes, and observe the child to determine what change took place.
- Display a concrete object such as a paintbrush and say, I'm going to tell you about this paintbrush. Make a number of statements about the paintbrush. Include 1 or 2 false statements and ask the children to identify them. For example, you could say, This is a paintbrush. You use it to paint pictures. It is brown and black. You sharpen it when it is dull. It is long and thin. Have the children identify the false statement and then ask, What other correct details can you tell me about the paintbrush?

Using the Story

The story With a Hum and a Hum and a Ho introduces creating sets through the action of adding one more. A practical situation of packing a bag is used. Ted is preparing for a picnic and is verbalizing the number of items he will need, I'll pack one for me and one more for you. These actions confirm through one-to-one correspondence that he will have enough for Troll-teddy and himself. This situation forms the basis of the activity Pack Your Bag, page 74.

The story also refers to Ted's practice of having a picnic in the meadow every Monday. You may wish to discuss weekly classroom or personal routines and post them on the calendar, e.g., gym is every Tuesday and Thursday, library is every Friday.

When discussing the story, you may wish to introduce the ordinal vocabulary stressed in this unit by using some of these questions.

- What did Ted put in his bag first? Second? Third?
- What did Ted take out of his bag first? Second? Third?
- What was the first thing Ted did to get ready for the picnic?

The children may enjoy drawing pictures of the events or of the series of objects and sequencing them according to the story.

With a Hum and a Hum and a Ho

Supplementary Material

Ted is my Friend: Mathematics Activity Book, pages 7-10 and 20-26; story boards, pages 39-42 and 51-54; and game boards; pages 45-48.

NUMBER TO 10   67

The pages from Explorations 1 reproduced below illustrate the features of a typical section.

Provides an overview of the section's activities. Activities are defined as being at the concrete, pictorial and/or symbolic level. A suggestion for group size is offered for each activity.

- *whole group* 👤👤👤👤👤👤
- *small group or partners* 👤👤👤👤
- *individual* 👤

Additional ideas for material preparation, group management, and classroom organization are also suggested.

Identifies the activity's objective. The chart at the top of the page links this letter to an objective.

Lists the unit objectives sequentially. Each objective is assigned a letter. This letter appears to the right of each activity title to identify the purpose of the activity.

Suggests appropriate materials for the activities in the section. Note that materials considered to be classroom supplies such as scissors, glue, and paper are not referenced.

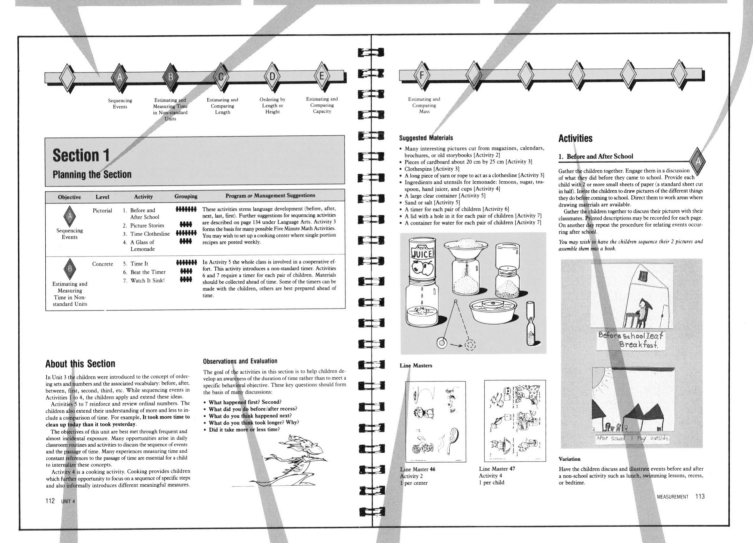

References line masters used in activities of the section, and specifies appropriate quantities.

Describes any mathematical background specific to the concepts under consideration in the section. Suggestions for management and materials are also provided when appropriate.

Lists key questions for the teacher to ask children as he or she circulates among them. In most cases an activity-based assessment task and typical responses are also described. Suggestions for teacher direction are provided.

Suggests a number of activities to meet the objectives of the section. It is not intended that each and every activity be used. Teachers should select those activities which are appropriate for their children.

These pages from Explorations 1 illustrate additional ideas offered at the end of each unit.

Suggests a number of ways to integrate the mathematical concept under consideration into other curriculum areas. These ideas can be introduced to reinforce and/or extend the concept when children are involved in subsequent units.

Describes a project which presents children with the opportunity to apply the concepts presented in the unit. This should be pursued independently by children who have demonstrated a solid grasp of the unit material.

Patterning Across the Curriculum

Language Arts

• Develop printing readiness by having children extend patterns such as this.

OOIIOOIIOOII

• Develop letter recognition and formation skills by having children read and reproduce or extend this kind of pattern. Use a variety of media: sand, salt trays, finger paint, as well as pencils.

abc abc abc

• Have the children use their ability to recognize their names to read a word pattern.

Julia Kim Julia Kim Julia Kim

• Children use letters or words cut from magazines, newspapers, or greeting cards to create patterns.
• In conjunction with this unit, you may wish to read any of these stories (see page 318 for an annotated bibliography):
  – *Drummer Hoff* by Barbara Emberley
  – *Bears* by Ruth Krauss
  – *Brown Bear* by Bill Martin, Jr.
  – *I Love the Morning* by Seiji Yabuki
  – *Bonnie McSmithers you're driving me dithers* by Sue Ann Alderson

Art

This unit provides opportunities to explore a variety of art materials. Be on the lookout for patterns occurring spontaneously in the children's art work. Invite the children to talk about these patterns.

• The children may wish to make a patterned frame or border for their favorite piece of artwork.

• Have the children make rubbings of different patterned surfaces such as leaves, corrugated cardboard, the soles of their shoes, brick walls, or imprints on cutlery. Note that the children should be shown how to hold (or tape) a sheet of paper over the surface. Encourage them to experiment rubbing the surface with the side of a crayon. Invite the children to do many rubbings. These can be cut out and used to create a picture or a pattern.

• Cut 2 colors of felt squares (an even number of each). Distribute a square to each child. Encourage the children to decorate their pieces by cutting and pasting scrap pieces of felt on them. When all the children have finished decorating their squares, gather them together. As a group, arrange the squares to form a patterned quilt. Post them in the pattern on a bulletin board with tacks. Note that you can substitute paper for felt.

Science

Have the children make patterns with natural objects such as pebbles, leaves, twigs, or seeds.

Social Studies

• Take the children on a pattern walk to find examples of patterns in the school or neighborhood. Draw their attention to the floor tiles, wallpaper, brick walls, fences, gardens, etc.
• Have the children bring in patterns they find on wrapping paper, ribbons, fabric scraps, wallpaper or floor tile samples, etc. These patterns can be collected into a class book, posted on a bulletin board, or the children may keep personal scrapbooks.

Music

• Prepare a tape of sound patterns. Leave space on the tape between patterns so that the children can extend the patterns.
• Have children create and tape record their own sound patterns.
• Have the children identify and extend rhythm patterns, such as snap, snap, - ; snap, snap, - ; snap, snap, - . After some experience with a variety of these, some children may wish to create rhythm patterns.
• Have pairs of small groups of children create sound patterns using musical instruments for other children to identify.
• In conjunction with this unit, you may wish to teach these songs:
  – Row, Row, Row Your Boat
  – The Hokey Pokey
  – Head and Shoulders
  – Frère Jacques
  – This Old Man
  – The Farmer in the Dell

Physical Education

• Groups of children make body patterns in the gym or other large areas. Encourage the children to describe each pattern in a variety of ways.

Stretch   Bend   Stretch   Bend   Stretch   Bend
or
Pole   Bridge   Pole   Bridge   Pole   Bridge

• The children move around the gym using repetitive movements such as: hop, hop, step; hop, hop, step. Invite children to create their own sequence.

Extension Project

Identify different ways in which the children contribute patterns to decorate the classroom. For example, they could create:

• patterned strips for a bulletin board or large calendar trim
• patterned book covers for their personal notebooks or class library books
• patterns to cover a large surface such as the door, filing cabinet, or cupboard doors.

At a large center place long strips of paper, large sheets of newsprint, construction paper cut in different shapes, crayons, templates; and any other materials which the children could use to create these patterns. Have the children (the designers) sign their patterns.

Implementing the Program

To successfully implement an activity-based program, it is essential to provide an organized environment that is rich in materials and experiences. Careful planning is necessary to ensure that your classroom provides such an environment. Here are some questions you will want to consider.

How do I establish math centers in my classroom?

It is common for teachers to store containers of math-related materials in one area of the room. Since containers are portable, any place can become a math center. Initially, you may wish to place the containers in certain areas and direct specific groups of children to them.

However, there are simple systems which you can introduce so that small groups of children can proceed independently to work areas. For example, you can hang colored cards from the ceiling or prop colored signs on table tops to designate the color of the container that should be placed in each area. The containers can be color-coded using labels or markers.

As an alternative to portable centers, you may wish to establish a more permanent type of work area such as the one illustrated.

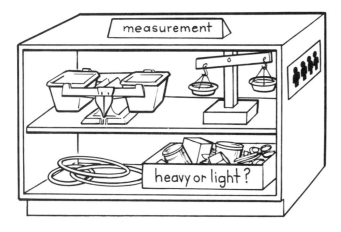

The maximum number of children at any center can be specified by posting a sign. If children are unable to count, you can accomplish this by placing "necklaces" in a box at a center. Children take a necklace as they come to the center; when all the necklaces are gone, the area is full.

How do I establish groups in my class?

The way in which you choose to begin implementing an activity-based mathematics program in your classroom depends on your teaching style and the needs of your children. A reasonable start may be to withdraw a small group of 3 to 8 students after you have engaged the class in an activity. This small group can then return to participate in the activity introduced to the large group and you can work with another small group. As the children become familiar with the procedures and with your expectations, they will be able to work independently in small groups with minimum direction. For specific suggestions on how to manage several small groups efficiently, refer to the Planning the Section charts at the beginning of each section.

At the end of an activity period (or day) it is a good practice to call the whole group together to discuss briefly the activities the children participated in and the discoveries they made, to pose new questions, and to discuss any problems which may have arisen. As children listen to their peers describe their experiences, they are often motivated to participate in new activities. Often, the children's explanations may also introduce an activity and recording procedures to children who have not yet tried it.

How can I schedule children into the various activities or centers?

There are several methods of accomplishing this. Here are some ideas.

A *pocket chart* is a useful rotation schedule. The center cards can be rotated while the groups remain fixed, or the group make-up can be altered by students or teacher while the center cards remain fixed.

	Joe	Pam	Dino	Mary
Bin 1 ☺☺☺				
Bin 2 ▭▭▭				
Bin 3 ☗☗				
Bin 4 ∘∘∘∘				
Bin 5 ▭▭▭				
Bin 6 ☗☗				

A *rotation wheel* has a fixed inner circle. It identifies the activities or centers. The outer circle rotates. The children's names are affixed to it by clothespins. This allows you to easily change the group members.

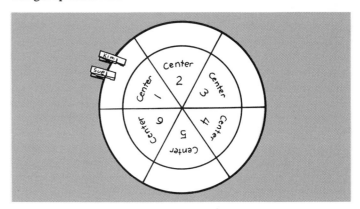

A *sign up sheet* is a chart listing the various centers and the activity days and is another way to keep track of children's activities. The children can sign up for the activity of their choice or the teacher may determine their placement. Name cards with photocopied photographs of the children help children identify each other's names.

	Mon.	Tues.	Wed.	Thurs.	Fri.
Center 1					
Center 2					
Center 3					
Center 4					

How can I establish effective classroom routines?

Well-established consistent routines are essential to the management of any classroom. An activity-based program promotes more movement, verbal interaction, activities, and materials than may be found in traditional programs. Attention must be directed to effective classroom procedure and routines early in the year. Expectations must be clearly stated and consistently reinforced. As with any new skill, routines take time, experience, and practice before they are understood and consolidated; be patient, consistent, and positive.

It is useful to post a chart of those routines which have been discussed. This visual reminder helps children recall the established routines.

Here are some simple routines which you may wish to try.

Stop those imps! is a quick game which can be used to introduce and reinforce your signal calling for attention. Explain to the children the signal you will use when you want them to stop what they are doing and listen, e.g., tones on the xylophone. Suggest that the children quietly scurry about the room just like the imps sneaking about Ted's room. Signal them to stop and give an oral instruction, e.g., **Put your hands on your knees and listen for Ted!** Reinforce how quickly they stopped when they heard the signal and how well they listened to the instruction. Repeat the game several times.

It is important that the children learn to stop and listen when asked. This will ensure a safe and efficient learning environment. Sound the tone once only and wait for all children to stop and listen. The children usually alert those who are causing them to wait. This also reinforces the idea that instructions will be given only once. It is recommended that you play this game at different times in the day in order to firmly establish this routine.

Traffic light is an easy-to-make signal which can help control the noise level in the classroom. Post a large spinner divided into 3 colored sections; green, yellow, and red. Explain to the children that when the spinner points to green, they are free to go on with their activities. When the spinner points to yellow, then the noise level is becoming too high, and they should be more quiet to prevent the spinner moving into the red area, at which point all conversation must stop.

Work mats are useful devices for establishing children's working space. In some cases, the mats will be specific to the activity (e.g., sorting, graphing, or place value mats). In other instances, an appropriately-sized sheet of construction paper or newsprint can be used. Discuss with the children the need to respect each other's work areas, and how they would feel if another child walked over their work space.

Tidy-up timers can be used to encourage the children to clear their work space quickly and efficiently. A homemade sand timer works well as you can adjust the amount of sand to allow a reasonable time for children to complete the task. You may wish to record the results of each day's efforts by making a simple graph. Color in 2 squares if the children beat the timer, 1 square if they took the same time as the timer, and none if they were slower.

How do I assess the children's progress?

The main assessment tool for the teacher at the primary level is observation. As children are involved in an activity, observe the child under consideration to identify strengths, weaknesses, interests, work habits, and learning needs. These observations should be recorded to establish a continuous record of the child's development and progress. It is important that the actual observed behaviours be recorded, not inferences you may draw. These observations are most useful as they help chart behaviour patterns, attitudes towards work and towards other children, interests, difficulties which have been overcome, and areas of success and weakness. It is important to remember that recorded observations are not an end in themselves but merely provide a window into the child's thinking processes and how he or she relates to the program of instruction. Observations provide a basis on which to plan an appropriate program to meet the children's needs.

The teacher should spend much of the student activity time circulating, observing, questioning, assisting, fostering inquiry, and recording observations. To assist in this task, suggestions for observation and evaluation are included at the beginning of each section of *Explorations 1*. Frequently, a chart is included which describes typical types of behaviours and responses, and offers some suggestions for teacher direction.

In addition, a list of key questions is provided to assist in assessing a child's grasp of a specific objective. When appropriate, an informal evaluation task for individuals or small groups is described. When asking questions or initiating evaluation tasks with an individual or small group, the format should be:

test or question → teach → test or question.

This format provides further insights into a child's understanding of the concept and helps bring to light rather than perpetuate any misconceptions.

How should I record my observations?

Recorded observations should be brief and to the point to avoid suffocating in a welter of paper. These records can be kept in a variety of ways. Here are some suggestions:

File cards
Cards may be kept in a box. Regular dated entries should be made. Cards may be added as required.

Record Book
A 3-ring binder or an exercise book clipped at the edge for easy indexing may be used. Allow 2 or 3 pages per child. Observations should be added regularly and dated.

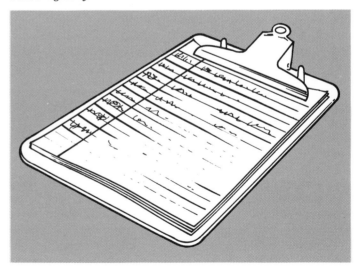

Clipboard and Pad
A chart may be placed on a clipboard and used to record observations as you circulate and interact with the children. Observations may later be transferred to permanent records.

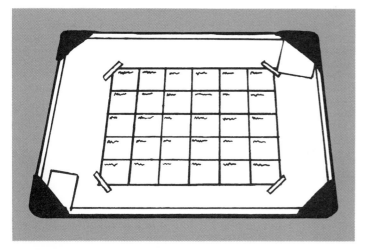

Desk Pad
Put the children's name on a chart on your desk, leaving space to jot observations. This will allow you to see at a glance who has not been observed recently.

Observations may be rewritten in permanent records, or cut and pasted. Blank peel-off stickers are a convenient way to transfer records from the chart to your record book.

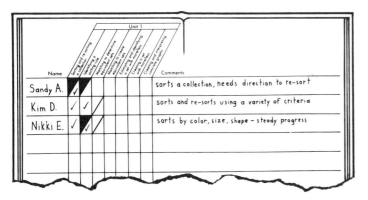

Name										Comments
Sandy A.	◣	◣								sorts a collection, needs direction to re-sort
Kim D.	✓	✓								sorts and re-sorts using a variety of criteria
Nikki E.	✓	◣								sorts by color, size, shape – steady progress

Line Masters
Line Masters 99 to 104 are provided to assist in recording a child's progress. Line Masters 99 and 100 can be used as an individual profile sheet. Line Masters 101 to 104 can be cut and affixed to the top of a class list. For convenience, symbols may be used to indicate the level of mastery. For example:

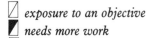

◹ *exposure to an objective*

◤ *needs more work*

✓ *objective met*

How can I modify the program to meet the children's needs?

Teacher observations and informal evaluation tasks will provide information which should form the basis of further action. In determining future appropriate programming, it is important to consider whether the child should be working at the concrete, pictorial, or symbolic levels. As you observed the child, did he or she display a solid grasp of the concept while working with concrete materials? When asked key questions, did the child respond appropriately with little hesitation and minimal need for prompting? If that was the case, you might decide to involve the child in activities more abstract in nature at the pictorial or symbolic level. Observe the child closely during this period to ensure that it was an appropriately-timed transition.

If a child is experiencing difficulty completing an activity, consider adjusting the quantity of materials or the number of examples to be completed. A child may be overwhelmed by a large collection of materials to sort. Reducing the number of items could make the task more appropriate for that child. If a child is demonstrating a solid grasp of the concept, it is also important to consider whether the child should begin to use less familiar materials for the activities. When the child has sorted and re-sorted plastic fruit successfully, he or she can apply those experiences to sorting a less familiar material such as a collection of odds and ends, a variety of buttons, or sea shells. Also, by varying materials, a different level of complexity can be introduced to a task. If a child has created interesting patterns with buttons focussing on the attributes of color or size, he or she can be challenged to create a pattern where position varies using toothpicks or tiles of one color. The suggestions offered for adapting specific activities under Meeting Individual Needs, as well as the activities suggested in Across the Curriculum and the Extension Projects for each unit provide ideas for meeting a child's learning needs.

It is also important to keep in mind the open-ended nature of many of the activities. Children working at different levels can work side by side at the same activity. As children sort materials or create patterns, it is their individual abilities and imagination which helps to determine the complexity and creativity of their activity. Different children can work with the same materials at number centers as each explores arrangements of a different number. Similarly, each can develop number concepts for the range of numbers he or she is working on while playing the same manipulating game as a child exploring different numbers. In addition, the recording sheets for these games have been designed to accommodate children working at the concrete, pictorial, and symbolic levels.

What materials do I need?

A comprehensive list of suggested materials is provided on pages xxiv-xxvii. However, do not feel that you must collect each and every item listed. You should feel free to substitute materials with those available to you. Generally, it is not the particular material which is essential, but that children have the opportunity to manipulate concrete objects. For example, children can sort or pattern with buttons, shells, keys, bottle caps, lids or any other set of objects with distinguishing characteristics, as long as they have many opportunities to sort and pattern. Similarly, it is not the type of small object — plastic animal, toy car, counter, or finger puppet — which is important when children act out number stories, but that they use the objects to create and show their stories.

How can I obtain the materials?

The materials listed on pages xxiv-xxvii fall into three categories: materials which can be collected, those which can be prepared, and those which are available commercially.

Collectables

Obtaining a sufficient quantity of collectable materials is a manageable task if you enlist the help of the children and their parents. As children contribute materials to a classroom, they develop an awareness that the classroom belongs to them and that they have responsibilities to it. Children also become aware of the mathematics surrounding them as they search their environment for appropriate materials. As the materials are collected, you may wish to record the type of materials contributed by each child on a class graph. This acts as a check on the kinds of materials that still need to be collected, and acts as an ongoing motivator. You will find it helpful to distribute a letter to parents outlining your requirements several times throughout the year. Sample letters are provided on page 317 which you may wish to use as models.

Prepared Materials

Here too you should enlist the help of parent volunteers as well as older children. Many of these materials (numeral cards, story boards, etc.) can be made more durable by laminating them.

Commercially available materials

Your supply of these materials can be built up over a period of time. Many of the materials may already be available in your school. Make arrangements to borrow appropriate materials from other classrooms for specific time periods to augment your own classroom supply. You should also note that prepared materials can be substituted for some of the commercially available materials. Some teachers may wish to equip the classroom immediately with all of the items listed. To facilitate this, a comprehensive kit, Math Manipulatives Kit (A) is available from the publisher.

How should I store the materials?

Materials which are clearly labelled and stored openly allow children to proceed to activities independently. There are many different types of containers you can use to store materials. A variety are shown here. Covering containers with wrapping paper, wallpaper, shelving paper, construction paper, etc., helps brighten otherwise drab storage areas.

Children can file their work in an overturned sawhorse which accommodates large sheets or in file boxes with clearly labelled dividers.

Materials that everyone will be using can be stored conveniently in a hanging shoe bag.

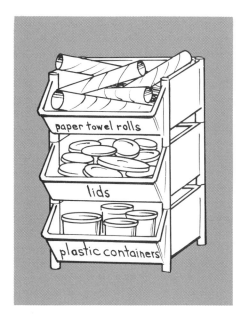

Stackable vegetable bins are convenient containers.

Pizza boxes stack nicely in a larger box.

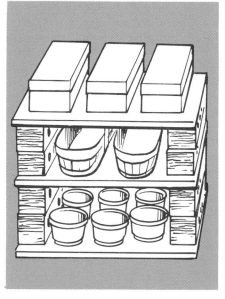

Many shoe boxes, baskets, or plastic food tubs fit on a shelf.

Milk cartons can be cut down and stored in a larger box; the small individual cartons are easily removed and replaced.

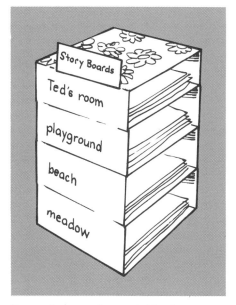

Large detergent boxes (with the tops removed) can be stacked and taped to store papers.

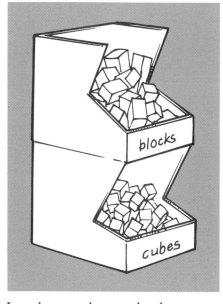

Large boxes can be cut so that they are easy to grip, carry, and stack.

Materials which are not going to be used can be placed out of sight in a cupboard or filing cabinet. However, it is beneficial to display many materials as children will naturally discover numerous valuable uses for them and will often think of ways to use them in their activities.

Before placing materials on shelves, you should label not only the container but also its storage place. Large containers should be labelled with a list of all the materials contained. These procedures enable children to develop an awareness of where materials belong. Children are then able to take responsibility for the orderliness of their classroom. Encourage children to participate in planning new organizations for centers, and to suggest improvements on the existing plan.

Suggested Materials

Collectables

- *Egg cartons, plastic food containers, boxes, cans, paper rolls*

- *Old magazines and catalogues*

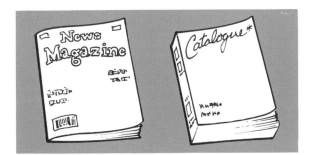

- *Toothpicks, popsicle sticks and/or tongue depressors*

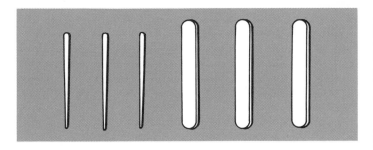

- *Containers for sorting mats*

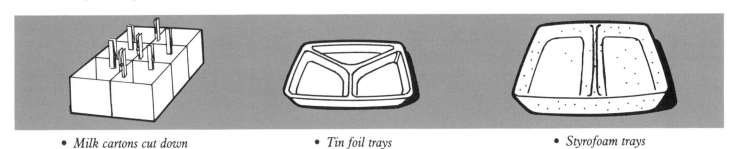

- *Milk cartons cut down*
- *Tin foil trays*
- *Styrofoam trays*

- *A variety of materials to use for sorting, patterning, and as counters*

Prepared Materials

- *Beansticks: made by squeezing white liquid glue along tongue depressor, placing 10 dried kidney beans or navy beans in place, then squeezing glue over beans*

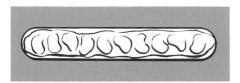

- *Sorting mats made on large sheets and laminated*

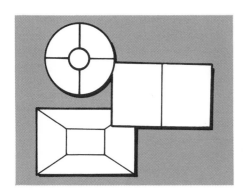

- *Large 100 square and 100 chart or 100 board*

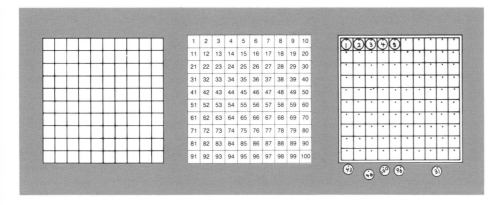

- *Variety of spinners: to operate hold a paper clip in place at center with a pencil and flick paper clip with index finger*

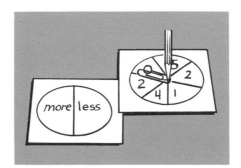

- *Balances*

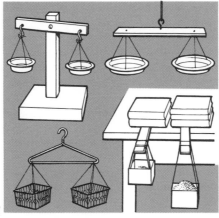

- *Numeral cards*

- *Expression cards*

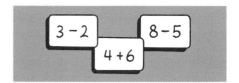

- *Timers*

- *Large and small graphing mats drawn on large sheets of mural paper or a plastic sheet sectioned off with masking tape*

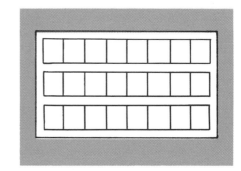

- *Line masters to consider laminating*

Numeral cards
Line Masters 8 to 10

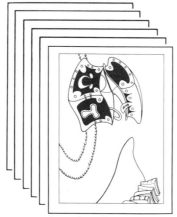

Story boards
Line Masters 18 to 23

Picture and dot cards
Line Masters 36 to 40

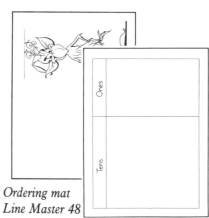

Ordering mat
Line Master 48

Place value mat
Line Master 88

Commercially Available

• *Counters and 2-sided counters*

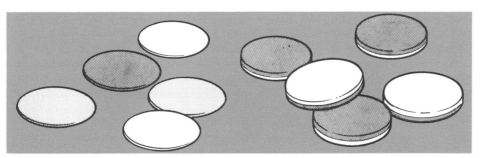

• *Blank playing cards, spinners, numbered cubes*

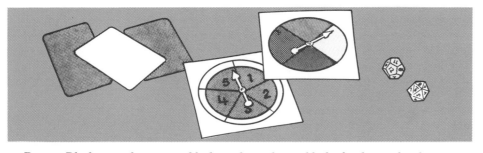

• *Pattern Blocks: wooden pattern blocks and translucent blocks for the overhead*

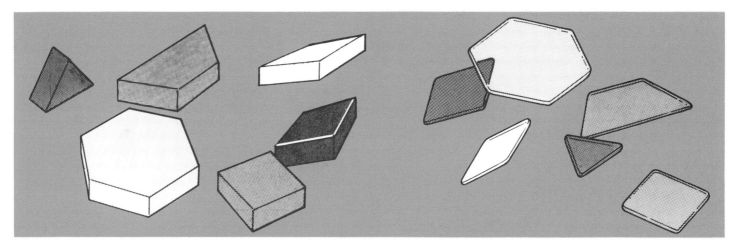

• *Materials for sorting and patterning: plastic animals, plastic fruit and vegetables, buttons, and vehicles*

• *Attribute Blocks*

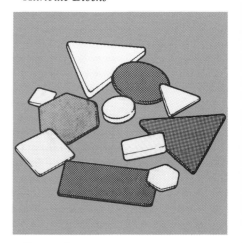

• *2 cm cubes*

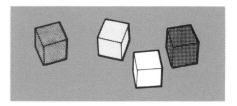

- *Geoboards*

- *Play money*

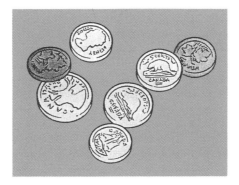

- *Clocks*

- *Primary Balance*

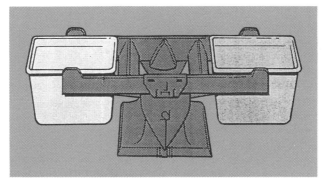

- *Litre cup*

- *3-dimensional geometric models: cube, cylinder, triangular prism, sphere, cone, rectangular prism*

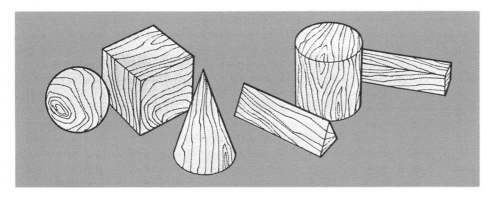

- *Interlocking cubes*

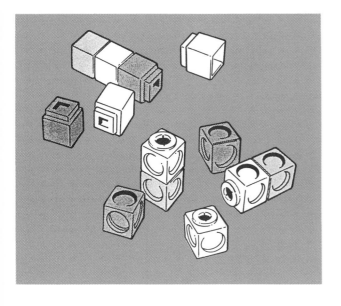

- *Thermometer*

- *Fraction set*

The Role of Language in *Explorations*

Throughout *Explorations* there is a strong emphasis on encouraging children to verbalize their ideas and discoveries. Ideas and discoveries are passed on, developed, and clarified through discussion. As children express themselves, the teacher is able to develop a clearer picture of the children's thought processes, and may become aware of confused perceptions which, if not explored further, can contribute to misunderstanding. Research on children's use of language indicates that it is important for them to verbalize what they are doing in order to internalize concepts.

A supportive, receptive atmosphere facilitates discussion. Acknowledge and explore all children's responses. Often an answer may not be the one expected or even perhaps considered appropriate. Further investigation of the child's unusual answer will often reveal an interesting, creative response, and may initiate further discussion and investigation. When a response is acknowledged and discussed, children receive the message that their ideas and discoveries are valued. This perception promotes an enthusiastic attitude toward learning and develops self-esteem. Many children will think of new ideas and questions which will result in self-motivated activity as they listen to peers explain their discoveries.

As children listen to you and to their peers, they hear many different ways to express an idea. It is important that the children be exposed to a variety of language patterns to express a mathematical operation or describe the result of an activity. The variety of language patterns enables the children to see concepts in a broader scope. For example, rather than relying on the crutch of listening for a key word, they begin to understand that "added to", "and one more", "joined", and "altogether" are all phrases which express the addition process. Gradually they become conversant in the language of mathematics — a rich and expressive language which can bring clarity to their thoughts.

Introducing the Story Characters

As you leaf through *Explorations 1*, you will note that stories and poems have been integrated into the instructional framework of the program. Although these stories and poems are optional, they serve several purposes:

- They are highly motivating.
- They informally introduce mathematics concepts and vocabulary.
- They serve as a vehicle to link mathematics to both the real world and the imaginative play world of the young child.

These stories and poems revolve around Ted, a troll-like character, his pet Troll-teddy, and a cast of imps led by Ari who, unbeknown to Ted, inhabit his house and delight in playing tricks on him.

The motivational impact of the stories and poems will be greatly enhanced if the characters are familiar and "alive" to the children. The introductory story on page 2 in conjunction with any of the activities described here, will help to accomplish this.

Pages 1–6 of *Ted is my Friend: Mathematics Activity Book* can also be used at this time to familiarize the children with the story characters.

Using Line Masters 2 to 7, children make puppets of the characters. These puppets can be used in ensuing units to act out number stories.

Children create masks of Ted. These masks can be used as props for plays or as attractive bulletin board displays.

Children enjoy acting out the unit stories as well as stories they themselves create.

Children listen to a taped story of Who Stole the Cookies? *as they illustrate personal story books.*

Who Stole the Cookies?

Deep in the darkest part of the forest stands a little white cabin. In the cabin lives a small blue troll with spongy pink hair. His name is Ted and he is usually a very happy troll. In his cabin, Ted keeps all of his favorite things: his piggy bank, a treasure chest full of his specially collections, his furry slip-on slippers, his cookie jar and his little troll teddy bear. Ted is happiest at bedtime when he can have his favorite honey drop cookies for a snack to help him go to sleep.

But on one particular evening, Ted was not very happy at all. He couldn't find his honey drop cookies! Ted looked everywhere for them. He looked on the highest shelf. He looked on the lowest shelf. He looked on all the shelves in-between, but he couldn't find a single cookie. Even his cookie jar was gone!

Ted sat down with a thump, wiggled his toes, and thought very hard. He looked at Troll-teddy curled up on the floor beside him.

"Oh, Troll-teddy," he said, "how can we have our bedtime snack if there are no honey drop cookies? How will we ever get to sleep? Someone must have *stolen* the cookies and eaten them all up, but who could it be? Whoever it was must have eaten my cookie jar too!"

Ted thought some more.

"Maybe it was mice that took them, Troll-teddy," he said. "Or . . . it could have been . . . ghosts!"

The thought of ghosts sent shivers all down Ted's back, and Troll-teddy's too. They looked at each other, ran into the bedroom, and hid under the blankets.

"Sometimes, when you can't figure something out," Ted told Troll-teddy, "it helps to sleep on it." Ted and Troll-teddy went right to sleep.

Hardly a minute later, many chattering little imps crawled out from a crack in the floor. They were whispering, giggling, and eating honey drop cookie crumbs.

"Tee hee," laughed the first imp, whose name was Ari. "Ted thinks we ate the cookie jar!"

"He thinks we're mice!" said the second imp, Slider.

"Or ghosts!" said the third imp, Rumple. The littlest imp, Kalaloo just giggled.

"Let's hide his piggy bank in the treasure chest!" said Rumple.

"Let's put honey on our feet and run on the ceiling!" said Slider.

"Let's tie Ted's hair into little bows," squeaked Kalaloo, "and borrow his slip-on slippers!"

"Let's do all those things! Let's find a new hiding place for Ted's cookie jar too!" said Ari. "But be quiet — we don't want Ted to find out about us!"

Rumple began climbing the shelves to reach Ted's piggy bank. Slider ran off to the kitchen to find the honey. Kalaloo climbed up the bedposts and made her way towards Ted's hair. Four more imps began a tug of war with Ted's slip-on slippers. And Ari pulled Ted's cookie jar out from its hiding place on the bookshelf.

"I know a better place to hide it," she said.

Suddenly Ted rolled over and began to mumble. In a flash, the imps disappeared through their favorite crack in the floor.

"Oohh, I dreamed this pillow had gone hard," said Ted as he sat up. He patted his pillow. He patted it again. "My pillow *did* get hard! It feels all knobby and bumpy!" Ted peeked into his pillow case and almost dropped it in surprise. There was his cookie jar, with two honey drop cookies left: one for Ted and one for Troll-teddy!

"Well," said Ted to Troll-teddy, "it's a good thing we slept on it!"

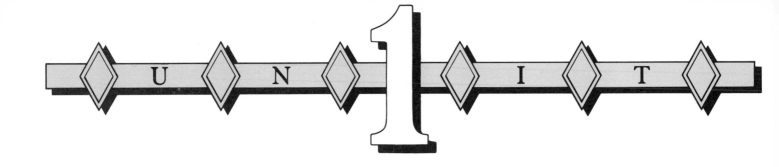

Sorting and One-to-one Correspondence

Unit Objectives

Section 1

A Sorting and Re-sorting a Collection
B Identifying a Sorting Rule

Section 2

C Matching to Determine Equivalent Sets
D Matching to Create Equivalent Sets
E Estimating and Identifying a Set with More/Less
F Creating a Set with More/Less

Section 3

G Creating and Interpreting Concrete Graphs

About this Unit

Sorting

Sorting is a basic thinking skill, one which children and adults constantly use to help them organize and understand their surroundings. At the most basic level, infants are sorting when they differentiate between mother and others. By providing appropriate materials and guided activities, the teacher can stimulate children to develop and refine their sorting skills. These skills will be applied in a variety of situations throughout this program, e.g., patterning, graphing, and sorting geometric objects.

In sorting, children must focus on a specific property or attribute which is the defining characteristic of their set. Initially, these attributes are very concrete and easily distinguishable. For example, the child forms a set of blocks. At the next level, the child can sort the set into subsets, e.g., red blocks and blue blocks. As the child gains more experiences, he or she begins to sort based on more abstract attributes, e.g., things that are soft or things that are used in the kitchen. Also, the child realizes that a collection of objects can be sorted in more than one way. By encouraging the child to explain her or his sorting rule, and to re-sort the collection in as many ways as possible, the teacher can stimulate logical, analytical thinking.

Section 1 offers a variety of activities to meet each of the sorting objectives. You may select some or all of the activities depending upon the needs of your children. It is suggested that you continue sorting activities over the course of the year. Varying the materials will encourage new ways of sorting and maintain the children's interest. Additional suggestions for sorting activities are interwoven throughout the program as well as in Sorting Across the Curriculum, pages 38–39.

One-to-one Correspondence

One-to-one correspondence is an essential prerequisite to the understanding of number. A young child who can recite number names in sequence will still be unable to count the number of objects in a set until he or she recognizes that there must be a one-to-one correspondence between each number name spoken and an object in the set.

The concept of one-to-one correspondence is established concretely by physically matching the objects in two sets. Comparisons between the sets can then be made without the use of numbers in response to questions such as, **Is there an egg for each egg cup? Are there as many forks as spoons? Are there enough paint smocks for each child? Are there more crayons or more pencils?** In this way, the children acquire the concepts and vocabulary that form the necessary groundwork for a true understanding of number.

Graphing

Graphing is a useful recording device frequently used in problem-solving situations as a means of organizing information. As a direct extension of the classifying and comparing skills, graphing presents and clarifies the relationship between groups through a visual display.

The prerequisite skills of classifying objects and comparing sets have been addressed in Sections 1 and 2 and will receive further application through the children's graphing experiences.

This unit provides an introduction to graphing. The children are involved in creating and interpreting concrete graphs. Graphing activities should result from spontaneous situations asked in the classroom. Meaningful experiences should occur frequently to provide the children with a realistic impression of the purpose and usefulness of graphing as a recording and organizational tool. Children will be involved in creating pictographs and bar graphs in later units.

Problem Solving

As children participate in the sorting activities of Section 1, they develop problem-solving skills. The children compare objects and identify likenesses and differences, as well as express the thinking that went into their choices and decisions.

Suggestions are also provided in Five Minute Math, pages 8–9, for further developing observation and listening skills, skills of identifying likenesses and differences, and using trial and error. Although the problems can be easily stated and defined in five minutes, the solutions should be discussed only after the children have had time to carefully think them through. Consider setting aside time daily to add to any lists or present additional solutions. As children talk to their parents, observe their environment, and participate in activities, they often think of additional ideas. By providing the children with an ongoing opportunity to contribute ideas, you send a clear message that their ideas are valued and foster the "back burner" approach to problem solving.

Vocabulary

- As Many As
- Collection
- Column
- Equal
- Graph
- Group
- Least
- Less*
- Match
- Member
- More
- Most
- Row
- Set
- Sort

* To be grammatically correct, one should use fewer when comparing sets, e.g., 3 apples are fewer than 5 apples. However, since less is the term we want children to use when comparing numbers (3 is less than 5), we suggest using less even when comparing sets.

Ongoing Objectives

- Reading the calendar and recording the weather
- Counting
- Recognizing numerals
- Printing numerals
- Problem solving
  - Identifying likenesses and differences
  - Developing observation and listening skills

Five Minute Math

Calendar Activities

- Invite the children to gather around the calendar board and begin the outlined activities.

1. Invite a child to turn the day card (Friday) face up in the sequenced cards.
2. Ask another child to find the matching day card for today (in the scattered cards on the right). Post it above.
3. Invite a child to take the date card off the calendar. Post it above.
4. Read the date aloud for and with the children.

5. Discuss the weather. Invite a child to record the weather on the calendar.

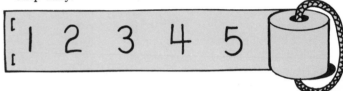

6. Discuss and record special events, e.g., Cara goes to a baseball game or Adam's birthday.

When the month is over, hang the completed calendar in a convenient place. These calendars form the basis of the Five Minute Math activities in the other units.

- Make a cumulative record of the number of days the children have been in school. This can be done by tacking a roll of adding machine tape so that it can easily be seen by the children. Knot a piece of heavy string through the roll and staple or tack it to the wall or chalk board. Print the numeral 1 on this tape on the first day of school, and add a numeral to the strip daily.

- Record the first day of autumn on the September calendar. This day may be celebrated in a special way, e.g., collecting leaves on a nature walk.

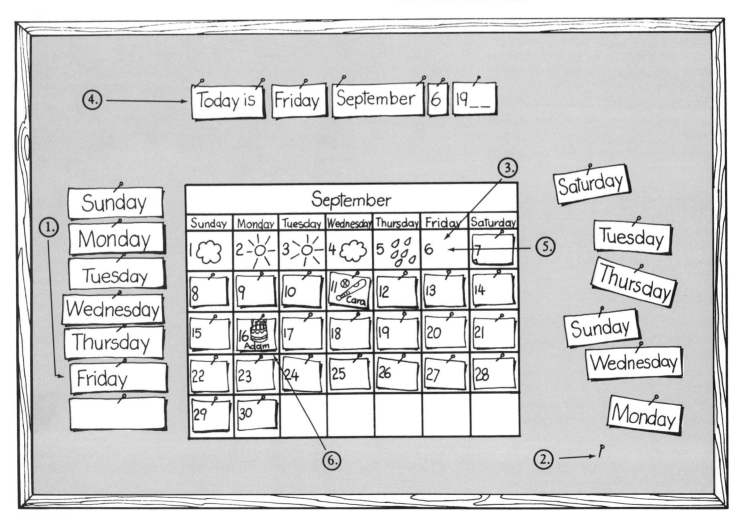

Counting Activities

Have the children count aloud to 4 over and over again to ensure that the sequence is well established:

- as they do exercises; up, down; up, down; up, down
- as they clap, pat their knees; clap, pat their knees
- as they stand up, sit down; stand up, sit down
- as they march on the spot
- as they pat their knees, shoulders, head, and extend their arms
- as they bend from side to side
- as they hop forward, stop on four, then hop backward for the second count to four

Extend the counting sequence after children are comfortable counting to 4.

Numeral Recognition Activities

- Play Who Stole the Cookies? This game requires numeral cards (an equal number of cards for 1 and 2) and 1 cookie card (Line Master 8). You will need a card for each child, as well as a 1 and 2 card for yourself. Once the children are seated in a circle, show them the cards with the numerals 1 and 2. Hold up the card that has a cookie on it. Engage the children's interest by telling them that this is *the* cookie from Ted's cookie jar! (See Who Stole the Cookies?, page 2.) The object of the game is to find the child who ends up with Ted's cookie. Shuffle the cookie card in with the numeral cards and place a card face down in front of each child with instructions not to peek. Demonstrate how the children are to pass the cards by sliding them along the floor to the next child. Establish a signal for passing the cards such as a tone, a pencil tap, or a word. The children pass the cards each time you give the signal. **Pass, pass, pass, . . . stop.** After you have given the signal to stop, tell the children to look very secretly at the card they are holding. Then chant, **Who stole the cookie from the cookie jar? Was it you number 1?**

Hold up the sample numeral 1. The children who have a numeral 1 will hold it up in the air.

Children holding 1:	**Who me?**
Other children:	**Yes you!**
Children holding 1:	**Couldn't be!**
Other children:	**Then, who stole the cookie from the cookie jar?**
	Was it you, number 2?

Hold up the sample numeral 2. The children who have the numeral 2 will hold it up in the air and say,

Children holding 2:	**Who me?**
Other children:	**Yes you!**
Children holding 2:	**Couldn't be!**
Other children:	**Then who?**

The child who has the cookie card then calls out,
I stole the cookie from the cookie jar!
The game continues by signalling the children to begin the passing again. Introduce other numerals as the children appear ready.

- Use sandpaper, cardboard or cloth to make numerals and glue each one on a card. Have the children close their eyes, choose a card, feel the numeral, and state which numeral they are touching.

- Print the numerals from 0 to 5 on sheets of paper. Scatter and tape these sheets (no more than half a metre apart) on the floor. The children direct a volunteer to place body parts on different numerals. For example: **Put your left foot on 2. Put your right hand on 5. Put your nose on 1.** When it becomes physically impossible to carry out directions, select another volunteer.

Numeral Printing Activities

Set up numeral printing centers as described. Direct children to these centers throughout the day. Have the children form numerals:

- with finger paint
- in trays of sand or salt or at the sand table
- out of Plasticine or play dough
- on the chalk board with paint brushes and water
- on the chalk board with chalk
- on large sheets of paper with markers

Demonstrate how to print the numerals one at a time and invite the children to print the numerals in the air and on their palms. Always display models of the numerals introduced. You may also provide models of the numerals at the different work areas. Introduce other numerals as the children appear ready.

The printing activities suggested here provide the children with opportunities to further develop their fine motor skills. Some children may require experiences tracing and copying numerals using a variety of media before they form the numerals freely. It is important that the children have these experiences forming numerals before approaching the task with paper and pencil.

Problem Solving Activities

Identifying Likenesses and Differences

- Display a concrete object such as a pencil, lunch box, or a book and ask the children to describe it. Encourage them to give a detailed description. If necessary, draw their attention to various attributes of the object through questioning.

- **What color is it?**
- **How does it feel?**
- **What shape is it?**
- **What do we use it for?**
- **What is it made of?**
- **Where can you find it?**
- **Is it bigger (smaller) than a _____ ?**
- **What is it like inside?**
- **Does it roll?**

You may wish to record the description as it unfolds.

When the children have completed the description, begin a new line of questioning. Focus on one or several of the details in the description and ask, **What other things are red? Smooth? Long and thin?**

- After the children are comfortable describing a number of concrete objects, introduce the comparison of 2 objects. Begin by displaying 2 similar concrete objects such as a crayon and a pencil, a hardcover book and a paperback book, or a plant and a flower. Ask, **How are these 2 things alike?** You may wish to list each detail as it is mentioned.

A pencil ⬡➔ and crayon ⬡⬡⬡ are alike.

They are:
- long and thin ⬡➔
- used for drawing ⬡
- in our class ⬡ ⬡
- pointed at one end ⬡ ⬡

When children can no longer name similarities ask, **How are these 2 things different?** Again, you may wish to list each detail as it is mentioned. Keep the lists posted so that children can add to them as they think of other similarities or differences.

When children are able to describe how 2 similar objects are alike and different, introduce comparisons of objects which are not as similar such as a ruler and a chalk eraser, a plant and an apple, or a jar and a tissue box.

Developing Observation and Listening Skills

- Have 3 children line up on one side of the room and another 3 children stand opposite them. Ask the remaining children to look at these children carefully and then tell them to close their eyes. Have 2 children switch places in the lines so that they are in new lines. Have the children open their eyes and say, **Have the lines changed? How?** When you repeat the activity, have different children form the lines. Interest remains high if you vary the number of children who switch lines. It is always fun to have no children switch.
- Display at least 4 items. Have the children look at them carefully. Ask them to close their eyes as you remove one of the items. Invite them to identify which item you removed. To maintain a high level of interest, increase the number of items.

Using the Story

The Specialmas Day story introduces the notion of sorting through a familiar situation. All children engage in incidental sorting activities when they are asked to put the dishes away, clean up their toys, or put their clothes into drawers. They may be familiar with the term "to sort," as it is frequently used in everyday experiences. Children may have heard: **Please sort your clothes so that I can put the laundry away. What sort of day is it? The postal worker had to sort the letters for our house.**

In the story Specialmas Day, Ted engages in a sorting activity as he searches for his missing slipper. This situation forms the basis for the activity Put It In This Hoop, pages 18-19. You may wish to use the story as a springboard for discussion of sorting activities the children do every day.

Ted has created a special day for himself. Purple Pasta, page 19, is an activity that relates to Ted's special lunch on this special day. You may wish to discuss special days that are celebrated by countries, large groups, families, schools, classes, and individuals. Use the calendar to record individual children's special days, e.g., birthdays or special class days, e.g., class trips to illustrate the use of a calendar and to initiate discussion related to the passage of time.

Put It In This Hoop

Put it in this hoop, If it's in my group.

If you have a green shoe, Put it in this hoop.

Supplementary Material

Ted is my Friend: Mathematics Activity Book, pages 7-13; sorting mat, pages 44 and 49; and story boards, pages 39-42 and 51-54.

Specialmas Day

"Troll-teddy, I wish today were Christmas. Christmas is so much fun and fun is what we need! But it won't be Christmas for such a long, long, lo-o-ong time." Ted sighed as he looked at the treasure chest in the corner of his bedroom. Troll-teddy sighed too.

"I know!" said Ted. "If today can't be Christmas, let's make it our own special day. Specialmas Day! Just think, Troll-teddy, we can empty the treasure chest and play with my special collection of very special foods, like . . . purple pasta! We can have plates and plates of purple pasta for lunch!"

The thought of eating purple pasta made Troll-teddy's tummy feel strange. She didn't like purple pasta as much as Ted did!

"Nothing yucky for us on Specialmas Day; just lots and lots of purple pasta," said Ted. Troll-teddy crawled under the bed. Happily, Ted poked his head under to talk to her. "It's just special stuff on Specialmas Day for you and me, Troll-teddy. I'll even wear my special pajamas and my furry slip-on slippers!"

Ted hopped over to his dresser and quickly put on his favorite blue pajamas with the bobbles on the sleeves. Then he looked for his slippers. Way down at the very bottom of the very last drawer, Ted found one of his slippers, but only one.

"Where did my other special slip-on slipper go? We can't start Specialmas Day without it. I wonder if it's in the cupboard?"

Ted opened the cupboard and peeked inside, but he could not see his slip-on slipper. No wonder! Ted's cupboard was stuffed with piles and piles of things!

So Ted began to empty the cupboard onto the bedroom floor. Printed pixie papers, boxes, toys, old socks, even a big hoop — *everything* went flying from the cupboard, but still Ted could see no slipper.

"Troll-teddy," he said, "we'll have to sort all this to find my slipper. Let's start with the printed pixie papers and sort in a special way." Then Ted began to sing:

> "Put it in the hoop,
> If it's in my group!
> If it's a printed pixie paper,
> Put it in the hoop!"

Troll-teddy nuzzled her way under a deep pile of paper and bounced up with a squeak. Papers and other things flew everywhere! Some printed pixie papers landed in Ted's hoop, and so did something else!

"This isn't a printed pixie paper," Ted said as he grabbed a furry thing from the hoop. "This doesn't belong in the hoop. It belongs on my foot!"

With a big smile, Ted slipped on his slipper and turned to Troll-teddy. "Now we can really start Specialmas Day!" he said. "Let's go fix the purple pasta."

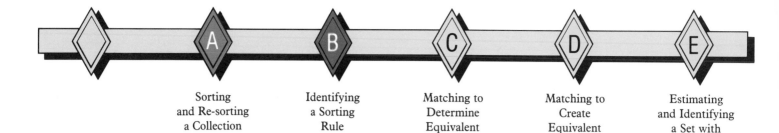

Section 1

Planning the Section

Objective	Level	Activity	Grouping	Program *or* Management Suggestions
	Concrete	1. Exploring the Materials	♦♦♦♦	Children should have many opportunities to freely explore materials. Place bins of materials in different areas of your room and direct children to these centers frequently.
A Sorting and Re-sorting a Collection	Concrete	2. Use Your Eyes	♦♦♦♦♦♦♦♦	In Activities 2 and 3 only one set is created. In all other activities 2 sets are created. There is the potential for the creation of more than 2 sets in many of these activities. While you are introducing Activities 5 through 7 to small groups, other children can be directed to Activity 8 to pursue independent sorting. Children who need many experiences at the concrete level should be directed to Activities 5, 6, 7, and 8 frequently. Vary the materials to maintain a high level of interest and motivation. Many of the activities are suggested for small groups or individuals. It is recommended that you refer to pages xviii–xix for record keeping and group rotation suggestions.
		3. Record a Set	♦	
		4. Put It In This Hoop	♦♦♦♦♦♦♦♦	
		5. Color, Shape, Size	♦♦♦♦	
		6. Purple Pasta	♦♦♦♦	
		7. Ted Could	♦♦♦♦	
		8. The Sorting Center	♦♦♦♦	
	Pictorial	9. Sort the Pictures	♦♦♦♦	
		10. The Photo Album	♦	
B Identifying a Sorting Rule	Concrete	11. What's My Secret Rule?	♦♦♦♦♦♦♦♦	In Activities 11 and 12 the children are asked to guess someone else's sorting rule. It is important that the children have sorted and re-sorted numerous collections according to their criteria before analysing a set created by another.
		12. Now Tell Me	♦♦♦♦♦♦♦♦	

About this Section

Throughout this section there are many suggestions for possible sorting criteria. There are numerous other possible sorting criteria the children may discover or you may wish to suggest.

All activities in this section involve 1 or 2 sorting groups. Children may create more sorting groups spontaneously as they define their own sorting criteria. Be prepared to recognize and discuss their different ideas.

Encourage the children to describe and name their sets. Children may present sets that appear unusual. It is important to take the time to discuss their sets in order to understand the thinking that went into creating them. Accept all reasonable responses.

Note that each set should have a clearly defined boundary. A sorting area can be defined by a chalked circle, hula hoop, or piece of yarn. Sorting mats also provide a boundary for the set.

When sorting, a child may discover an object that could fit into more than 1 set. This object would have the attributes of both sets. In this situation, encourage the child to suggest ways to solve the problem. In this discussion, you may wish to introduce the intersection of sets. By overlapping 2 hoops, you create a region which is part of both sets.

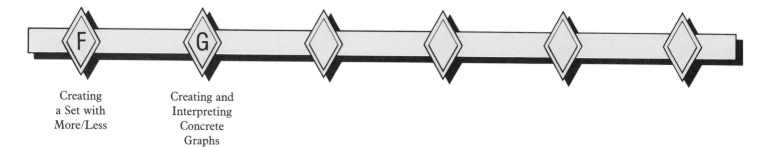

F — Creating a Set with More/Less

G — Creating and Interpreting Concrete Graphs

Observations and Evaluation

While children are exploring materials, you have an excellent opportunity to make observations. Some questions to keep in mind while observing the children are suggested here.

- Is the child able to follow directions?
- Does the child stay on task?
- Does the child initiate activities? Ask questions? Seek answers?
- Does the child keep her or his materials tidy?
- Does the child willingly use a variety of materials?
- Does the child talk about what he or she is doing with peers? With adults?
- What is the quality of the child's language?
- Does the child cooperate with others?
- Are there children who work particularly well together? Who distract each other?

As you circulate among the children, these key questions can form the basis of your discussion.

- **How are these the same?**
- **How are these different?**
- **Why does this belong in the set?**
- **Should this object be a member of your set? Why?**
- **Does anything in this set not belong?**
- **Which set does this object belong in? Why?**
- **What is your sorting rule?**
- **Can you please show me another way to sort these materials?**
- **What can you name this set?**

It is important to observe and record the various criteria a child uses for sorting. Circulate among the children so that you are able to discuss with each child her or his sorting criterion as frequently as possible. The children have numerous other opportunities to develop their sorting skills in the sorting activities which are interspersed throughout the program. The chart on page 14 offers some additional suggestions for direction.

A	B	C	D	E
Sorting and Re-sorting a Collection	Identifying a Sorting Rule	Matching to Determine Equivalent Sets	Matching to Create Equivalent Sets	Estimating and Identifying a Set with More/Less

Observations	Teacher Direction
The child persists in sorting according to one criterion, e.g., color.	Begin by commenting on how well the child has sorted collections by color. Place a collection so that all members are within the child's visual field. Start to sort the collection according to a criterion other than color. Verbalize your decisions as you place each object, e.g., **I'm placing this button here because it is big. I'm placing this button here because it is small.** When you have placed at least 3 objects in each set, invite the child to help you decide where a button should go and why it goes there. Discuss an appropriate label with the child. In the same sitting, try to re-sort the collection a few times. It is important that the child see many sorting possibilities for one material.
The child creates sets with members that do not belong.	Consider whether the child has had enough opportunities to explore the materials freely. A child may be choosing an item because it is appealing. Place 3 objects that are alike in some way and one that is different on a display area. Ask, **Which one does not belong?** Discuss why the item is not a member of the set. Gradually increase the number of objects that are alike.
The child cannot keep sorting criteria discrete, e.g., starts to sort by size; switches to color.	Have the child identify the sets he or she has sorted by size, e.g., a big set, a medium set, a small set. Pick up one of the objects he or she has sorted by color and ask, **Does this belong in the big, medium, or small set?** When the child has correctly placed it, pick up a few more one at a time, and repeat the question. Encourage the child to continue sorting the collection by size. When the child has finished, you may wish to have her or him re-sort the collection by color.
The child sorts and re-sorts with ease and appears to have benefited from previous experiences.	Engage the child in the Extension Project suggested on page 39 and/or any of the ideas offered in the Across the Curriculum, pages 38–39. Consider introducing this child to sorting along 2 criteria using a cross-classification chart as an organizer.

	White	Blue
Big		
Small		

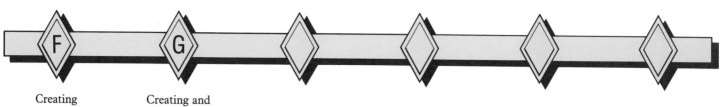

F — Creating a Set with More/Less

G — Creating and Interpreting Concrete Graphs

Suggested Materials

- 4 to 6 bins of varied materials such as twist ties, bread tags, lids, coffee sticks, stamps, cotton balls, textured cloth, Styrofoam chips, puzzle pieces, gum wrappers, pine cones, shells, bottle caps, seeds, plastic animals, old keys, or old nuts and bolts [Activities 1, 3, and 8]
- 6 bins of sorting materials: see page 16 [Activities 1, 7, 8, 11, and 12]
- A quantity of Attribute Blocks [Activities 1 and 5]
- 2 large hula hoops or long pieces of yarn [Activities 2, 4, 11, and 12]
- A variety of sorting mats such as pizza boxes, Styrofoam trays, egg carton lids, shoe box lids, paper plates, cardboard box dividers, floor tiles, clear plastic bags, large pieces of paper, or file folders [Activities 3, 7, 8, and 9]
- A quantity of pasta in 2 sizes and shapes, and in 2 colors for each child (See recipe for Purple Pasta on this page.) [Activity 6]
- An assortment of pictures from magazines [Activity 9]

MAKING PURPLE PASTA

Put half the rigatoni and elbow pasta in a plastic bag. Add several drops of purple (or blue and red) food coloring and about 15 mL of rubbing alcohol. Shake gently. Check that all pieces are colored. Add more food coloring and alcohol, if necessary. Spread on newspaper to dry.

Line Masters

Line Master **11**
Activity 8
A few copies

Line Master **12**
Activity 8
A few copies

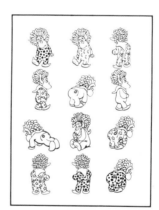

Line Master **13**
Activities 9 and 10
A large quantity

Line Master **14**
Activities 9 and 10
A large quantity

Line Master **15**
Activity 9
A few copies

Line Master **16**
Activity 9
A few copies

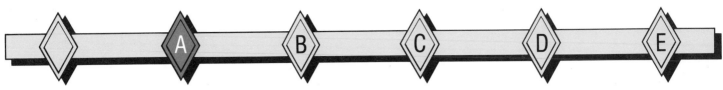

	A	B	C	D	E
	Sorting and Re-sorting a Collection	Identifying a Sorting Rule	Matching to Determine Equivalent Sets	Matching to Create Equivalent Sets	Estimating and Identifying a Set with More/Less

Suggested Bins

Box Bin	• A collection of boxes: food, candy, soap, china, jewellery, office supplies, fast food, shoe, . . . any box will do!	
Lid Bin	• A collection of lids: toothpaste, shaving soap, shampoo, flavoring, spices, jars, containers, perfume, or hand lotion	
Nature Bin	• A collection of nature materials: acorns chestnuts, pine cones, twigs, pebbles, seeds, shells, leaves, or pods	
Paper Bin	• A collection of paper: cups, napkins, tissues, towelling, paper plates, finger paint paper, sandpaper, lined paper, newsprint, newspaper, construction paper, glossy pages from magazines, comic book pages, photographs, wrapping paper, tissue paper, crepe paper, filing cards, folders, or corrugated paper	
Toy Bin	• A collection of toys: small cars, animals, trucks, boats, airplanes, figures, blocks, cubes, building toys, balls, costume jewellery, or hockey cards	
Odds and Ends Bin	• A collection of odds and ends: pencils, chalk, paper clips, brushes, Styrofoam chips and cups, erasers, straws, bottle caps, popsicle sticks, toothpicks, stones, plastic lids, interlocking cubes, or corks	

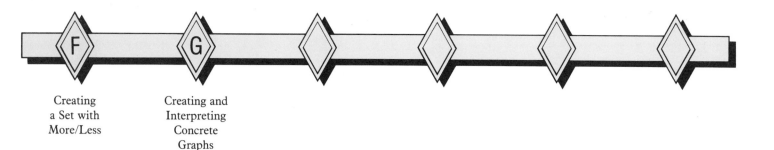

Creating
a Set with
More/Less

Creating and
Interpreting
Concrete
Graphs

Activities

1. Exploring the Materials

Invite the children to sit in a circle. Place all the bins of collected materials and the bins of Attribute Blocks (if available) in the center of the group. You may spread some of the items out on the floor and engage the children in a discussion about the materials. Discuss the types of materials, which materials they like, which materials they brought in, the purpose of the bins, etc.

Tell the children that they will have a chance to play with the things in the bins. Review your established routines with the children. Introduce and discuss any new rules. See page xix for suggestions on appropriate routines and ways to implement them.

Direct groups of children to select a bin of materials. Guide them to a work area and invite them to explore the materials from the bin.

These types of questions may be asked as the children explore the materials.

- **What have you been doing?**
- **What did you build? How?**
- **Why did you use these for the base of your tower?**
- **Could you have used these to build the tower?**
- **Why did you choose these materials? What else could you do with them?**
- **It looks as though you have a rule for putting these things together. What is it?**
- **Why does this belong? Why didn't you use it?**
- **This is interesting. What did you do first? Next? And after that?**
- **What other things would you like to have in these bins to explore?**

While the children are playing with the materials, circulate from group to group. The activities the children create while working with the materials will spark comments and sharing. Listen to what they are saying and pursue their ideas and knowledge through questioning. Observe what the children elect to do with the materials and encourage them to verbalize what they are doing and, possibly why they are doing it that way.

While exploring the materials, a child may spontaneously sort the objects. Encourage the child to describe the sets created and verbalize the decisions he or she made in sorting the materials.

The work areas should be large enough to spread out the materials, but not infringe on another group's working space.

2. Use Your Eyes   PS

Make a large circle with yarn or chalk and have the children sit in a semicircle facing this area. Sit or stand beside the loop and chant this rhyme:

"Use your eyes,
  Use your eyes.
  You can look and see.
  If you're (wearing a sweater),
  Come and sit (stand) by me."

Children wearing sweaters should sit in the looped area. After the children have settled in the loop, ask, **Why are these children in the loop? Does anyone else belong in the set?** If there is a child wearing a sweater who has not joined the group, invite her or him to do so now. Name the set (a set of children wearing sweaters). Have the children return to the semicircle.

Chant the rhyme again but substitute a different sorting criterion such as children wearing watches, glasses, or jeans.

As the children become more familiar with the rhyme, ask them to suggest different criteria.

Variation

Play Use Your Eyes with the bin materials. The children close their eyes and pick an object from the bin and hold it in their hand. Observe what the children have picked so that you can select a defining criterion that will ensure that a set of at least 3 members will be created. Chant the rhyme Use Your Eyes.

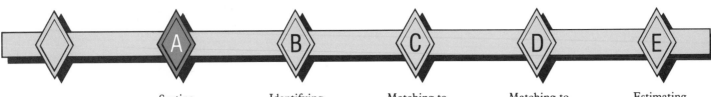

3. Record a Set   PS   A

Place the bins of varied gluable materials such as twist ties, bread tags, lids, coffee sticks, stamps, cotton balls, and the glue in the work areas. Invite the children to select a sorting mat from the collection before they go to the work areas. Ask the children to make a set of objects that belong together on their sorting mats.

Encourage the children to describe their sets to the other children. Circulate and ask,

- **Why do these things belong together?**
- **Does this belong too? Why?**
- **What could you name this set?**
- **What is another way to sort the materials? Show me. And another way?**

After the children have had the opportunity to create a number of different sets, tell them that there is a way to record their sets so that they can be shown to people outside the classroom. Have the children make a set of objects on their sorting mats and glue them down. Discuss their sets and with whom they will be shared.

The children work in very small groups with no more than 4 to 6 children per bin to facilitate the sharing of materials.

Meeting Individual Needs

- To help the child who is having trouble deciding on a sorting criterion, it is suggested that you choose a more obvious criterion such as color or size. Model an organized approach to the activity. Have the child select one item at a time, consider it, and place it in the set if appropriate or to the side if it is not to be included.
- The child who approaches this task with ease may be ready for more abstract sorting criteria such as material, use, places found, or texture.

4. Put It In This Hoop   PS   A

The children sit in a circle, take off one of their shoes and place it on the floor in front of them. Place 2 large hoops or circles of yarn in the center. Define and state the sorting criterion by singing or chanting Put It In This Hoop.

"Put it in this hoop
 If it's in my group.
 If you have a shoe (with buckles),
 Put it in this hoop."

Invite the children who indicate that they have shoes with buckles to put one shoe in the hoop. Ask, **What could we name this set?** (a set of shoes with buckles). Tell the children that they are going to make another set of shoes in the other hoop. Sing,

"Put it in this hoop
 If it's in my group.
 If you have a shoe (without buckles),
 Put it in this hoop."

Invite the rest of the children to place a shoe in the hoop. Ask, **What could we name this set?** (a set of shoes without buckles). Have the children name both sets. Have each child take back her or his shoe. Ask, **What is another way we could sort your shoes? What type of shoe would go in this hoop? And in this hoop?** Repeat the song with the new sorting criterion.

Keep in mind the language level of your children while playing this game. If necessary, take the time to develop the vocabulary used to define the sorting criteria by showing examples.

By placing only one shoe in the hoop, a child may use matching, if necessary, to retrieve her or his shoe from the group. Invite children who are able to tie their own shoes to assist those who are just learning.

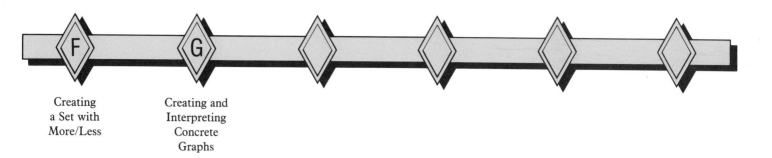

F — Creating a Set with More/Less

G — Creating and Interpreting Concrete Graphs

Put It In This Hoop

Put it in this hoop, If it's in my group.

If you have a green shoe, Put it in this hoop.

Variation

Play Put It In This Hoop with bin materials. Invite the children to close their eyes and pick one box from the box bin. Sing the song, Put It In This Hoop to define the sorting criteria for the boxes, e.g., boxes with/without lids. Name the sets and return the materials to the bin before re-sorting.

5. Color, Shape, Size   PS   A

Gather a small group of children around a flat surface where you can display Attribute Blocks. Place 2 large sheets of paper on the display area. On one sheet, place 3 blue blocks; on the other sheet, place 3 red blocks. Hold up a blue block and ask, **If I want to place all the blue blocks together, where should I put this?** Encourage the children to explain their answers. For example: **Put it on this sheet because all the blocks here are blue. The other sheet has only red blocks.** Hold up a red block and ask, **Should I place this here? Why not?** Continue to have the children explain where the blocks belong until they are expressing themselves clearly and without hesitation. Repeat this process, creating sets of different colors. On following days, have the children participate in a similar activity, however, change the sorting criteria to size and/or shape. For example: **I want to put all the circles together in one set and all the squares together in another set.** Or, **I want to put all the large figures together in a set and all the small figures together in another set.**

Note that you may substitute different materials for Attribute Blocks, e.g., felt figures on a flannel board, figures cut from colored acetate on an overhead, or figures cut from stiff cardboard of different colors.

6. Purple Pasta   PS   A

Engage the children's interest by telling them that on very special days Ted likes to make his favorite lunch of purple pasta. Display some of this colored pasta as well as the yellow pasta that Ted doesn't like.

Give each child an assortment of pasta in 2 sizes, 2 shapes, and 2 colors (including purple), and 2 pieces of colored construction paper for sorting mats. Have the children sort the pasta according to color on their sorting mats. Discuss the different possible labels for these sets. For example:

- purple pasta — yellow pasta
- pasta Ted likes — pasta Ted doesn't like
- dyed pasta — ordinary pasta
- pasta I wouldn't eat — pasta I would eat
- something you couldn't order in a restaurant — something you could order in a restaurant

Have the children clear their mats. Then, ask if they can think of another way to sort the pasta. Re-sort according to the new criterion and have the children label the sets created. Repeat this process a number of times.

When the children have explored numerous ways of sorting the pasta, ask them to choose a way of sorting which they would like to take home. Have the children make the sets and glue them on their sorting mats.

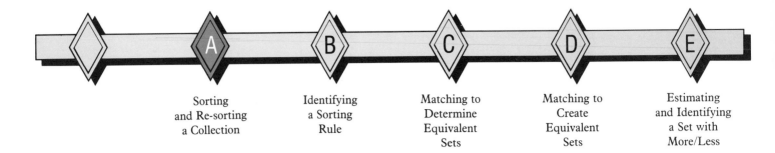

	A	B	C	D	E
	Sorting and Re-sorting a Collection	Identifying a Sorting Rule	Matching to Determine Equivalent Sets	Matching to Create Equivalent Sets	Estimating and Identifying a Set with More/Less

7. Ted Could   PS — A

Ted was left with a terrible mess after he emptied his cupboard. There are many ways that we can show Ted how to organize his things so that he can find them easily.

Invite the children to sit in a circle around 2 clear plastic bags and a pile of materials from the nature bin. Explain that Ted could put all the things that roll in this bag and all the things that don't roll in the other bag. That way when he wanted to play a rolling game, he could!

The children take turns picking an object from the pile, testing it, and placing it in the appropriate bag. Name the sets again when the sorting is finished. Empty the bags and invite the children to identify another way Ted could sort the nature things, e.g., by color, texture, or size.

Decide on a different sorting criterion and repeat the process of having the children select an object, testing it, and placing it in the appropriate set. Repeat this process until the children appear ready and motivated to sort these objects independently.

Place bins of collected materials and various sorting mats at different work areas. Guide the children to these areas to sort and re-sort the materials. Encourage them to describe their sets to others working with the same bin of materials. Circulate and ask questions to initiate discussion when necessary.

- **How did you sort these?**
- **Why does this belong?**
- **Why doesn't this belong?**
- **What could you name the sets?**
- **What other ways have you sorted? Show me another way. And another way.**

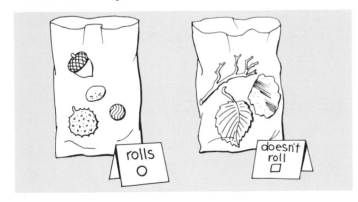

Meeting Individual Needs

If a child is ready for a further challenge, you might consider guiding her or him to a sorting situation which would involve the intersection of sets. For example, suggest sorting the lids into sets of lids with print and lids with pictures. Lids with both print and pictures require special treatment. Encourage the child to suggest solutions to this problem. A child may decide to move hoops to create a section that overlaps or may create a third set.

Variations

- Play Ted Could with the paper bin. You may wish to use file folders as sorting mats. There are many ways that the paper things can be sorted.

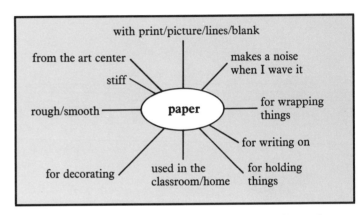

- Play Ted Could with the box bin. Long strips of mural paper can be used to represent Ted's shelves. These strips can also act as sorting areas.

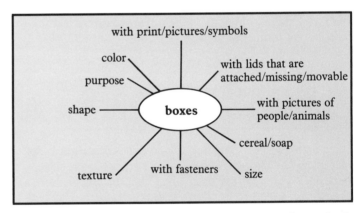

- Play Ted Could with the lid bin. Children can use large plastic food containers to hold their sets.

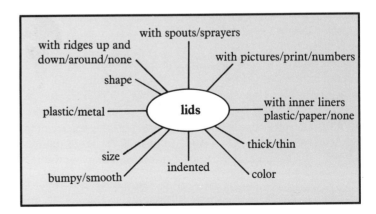

- Bins of Pattern Blocks, odds and ends, and toys can also be placed at different areas for the children to sort.

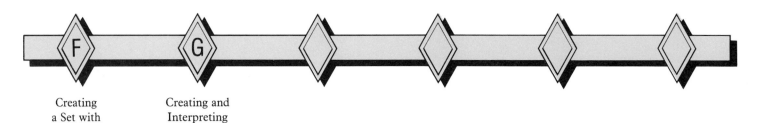

Creating
a Set with
More/Less

Creating and
Interpreting
Concrete
Graphs

8. The Sorting Center   PS   A

At a center, place a variety of materials for children to sort. On one shelf, place the bins of materials described on page 16. Place sorting labels cut from Line Masters 11 and 12 in the bin so that: the big/little labels are in the box bin; the metal/plastic labels are in the lid bin; the rough/smooth labels are in the nature bin; the like/dislike labels are in the toy bin; and the float/sink labels are in the odds and ends bin.

On another shelf, place collections in labelled containers (a shoe box is a good size), along with a variety of sorting mats such as the ones shown here.

Direct the children to this center to sort and re-sort different collections. Explain and/or discuss the use of sorting labels with the children. Circulate among them to observe the sorting in which they engage. See pages xx–xxi for ideas on how to note your observations.

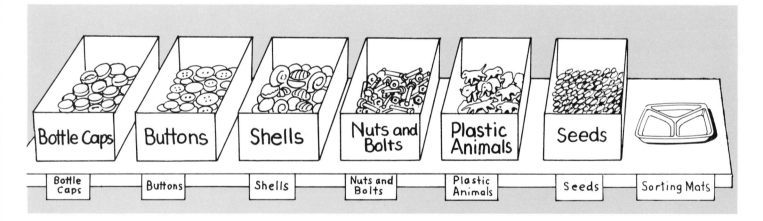

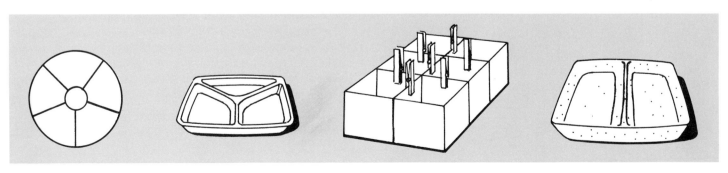

A large circular piece of paper marked off in sections

A tin foil tray

Milk cartons clipped together

Styrofoam tray divided into sections

A	B	C	D	E
Sorting and Re-sorting a Collection	Identifying a Sorting Rule	Matching to Determine Equivalent Sets	Matching to Create Equivalent Sets	Estimating and Identifying a Set with More/Less

9. Sort the Pictures   PS   A

Invite the children to sit in a circle around a bin containing a large number of pictures of Ted and the imps (Line Masters 13 and 14), animals (Line Masters 15 and 16), or pictures from magazines.

Select a handful of pictures, spread them out so that the children can see them, and ask them to suggest a way of sorting the pictures. The children place the pictures on the mats one by one according to the suggested criterion. Ask the children to name the sets, before returning the pictures to the bin. Repeat, using another handful of pictures.

Meeting Individual Needs

- If a child is having difficulty moving to the pictorial level, consider directing her or his attention to an obvious attribute. For example, creating a set of imps and a set of Teds is a simpler beginning. It may also be beneficial to use pictures with less detail initially.
- A child who is ready for a further challenge could broaden the sorting possibilities by coloring the figures or the decorations on the clothing.
- Provide a child ready for a further challenge with picture collections, greeting cards, post cards, or old photographs to sort.

10. The Photo Album   PS   A

Set up bins containing many pictures of Ted and the imps (Line Masters 13 and 14) in work areas with sufficient sheets of paper to use as sorting mats. Invite the children to go to a workspace, take a handful of pictures and a number of pieces of paper, and sort the pictures in any way they choose. The number of sets the children make may vary considerably. Encourage the children to name their sets. Ask the children to find a different way to sort their pictures. They may continue to re-sort as long as they can find a different way of sorting and interest is maintained. Encourage the children who have trouble thinking of new ways to sort by asking key questions and giving suggestions.

Tell the children that they are going to make a class photo album of Ted and the imps. Ask them to sort the pictures in the way they like best and then glue them onto the paper. The children can color the pictures to make their album pages more interesting. Discuss each child's pages, printing a title on each, e.g., All these imps have moons on their clothes. Have the child print her or his name on each page. Staple the pages together with a suitable cover and title and place the album in the classroom library.

If you keep the format of the titles constant, e.g., All these _____, some children may learn to recognize the repeated words.

You may wish to have a child decorate the cover. This album may be sent home each night with a different child so that the parents can see the result of a class activity. Having a comment page on the back cover allows the child and parent to indicate that they have looked through the album together.

Variation

Have the children paste a picture set on a sheet of paper. Post these sets under the title Mystery Sets. Set aside time each day for the children to suggest labels for each other's sets.

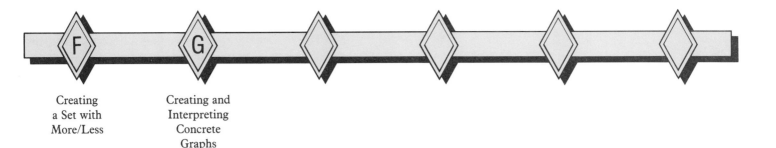

Creating
a Set with
More/Less

Creating and
Interpreting
Concrete
Graphs

11. What's My Secret Rule? PS B

Invite the children to sit in a circle with you. Place a bin of materials and a hoop or a circle of yarn in front of you. Engage the children's interest by telling them that you have a secret in mind. The secret has to do with how you could sort the materials. You won't tell them your secret, but you will give them some clues. Invite the children to watch carefully as you select objects from the bin. Hold up each item as you examine it and decide whether it goes in the hoop. Once a reasonable number of objects has been placed in the set, ask, **What's my secret rule?** Allow each volunteer an opportunity to guess your secret rule. If no one guesses correctly, place at least 3 more items in the hoop before you invite the children to guess your secret rule again. Once a child has guessed the sorting criterion, have the children name the set, e.g., a set of things that makes noise. Replace the objects in the container. Choose a new sorting rule and play again.

Children may guess a rule that differs from your original idea, but is appropriate for the set created. Accept any viable response. You may wish to explore their suggestions through more examples or discussion.

You may wish to have individual children decide on a secret sorting rule and present a secret set to other children. Once children are familiar with the game, they can play with partners or in small groups.

Variation

Play What's My Secret Rule? at the pictorial level. You could use the cutouts of Ted and the imps (Line Masters 13 and 14), animal cutouts (Line Masters 15 and 16), or an assortment of magazine pictures.

12. Now Tell Me PS B

Invite the children to sit in a circle around 2 large hoops or circles of yarn and a bin of materials. Engage the children's interest by telling them that they will have to guess the sorting rule for 2 secret sets. They will have to watch very carefully to find out what is the same about all of the objects in each set. Sort some of the materials into the hoops, e.g., toys with 2 wheels or toys with 4 wheels. Chant or sing,

''**Look at my groups, look at my groups,**
 Look and see, look and see.
 What's my rule for sorting? What's my rule for sorting?
 Now tell me. Now tell me.''

Now Tell Me

(tune: Frère Jacques)

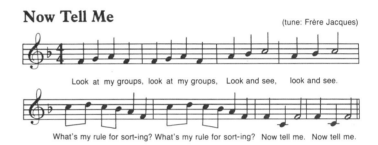

Look at my groups, look at my groups, Look and see, look and see.

What's my rule for sort-ing? What's my rule for sort-ing? Now tell me. Now tell me.

When a child identifies the rule for sorting, invite her or him to replace the materials and make 2 new sets. The child may wish to sing the song, Now Tell Me, or ask the class to sing along.

Some children may wish to make more than 2 secret sets. Extra hoops should be available if you wish the children to extend the game beyond 2 secret sets.

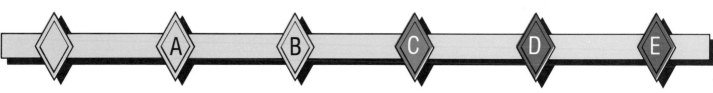

A — Sorting and Re-sorting a Collection

B — Identifying a Sorting Rule

C — Matching to Determine Equivalent Sets

D — Matching to Create Equivalent Sets

E — Estimating and Identifying a Set with More/Less

Section 2

Planning the Section

Objective	Level	Activity	Grouping	Program *or* Management Suggestions
C Matching to Determine Equivalent Sets	Concrete	1. Our Favorite Things 2. Find Out 3. Collection Match-up	♦♦♦♦♦♦♦ ♦♦♦♦♦♦♦ ♦♦♦♦	Activity 3 suggests a variety of materials for the children to match. Collect as many of these materials as possible. They will be used to reinforce the concepts of more and less. While a small group is involved matching these collections, direct other children to continue sorting materials from Section 1.
D Matching to Create Equivalent Sets	Concrete Pictorial	4. All Aboard 5. Make a Set 6. As Many Stories 7. One for Each	♦♦♦♦♦♦♦ ♦♦♦♦ ♦♦♦♦ ♦	Activity 4 introduces the children to the idea of increasing or decreasing the members in one set to make it equivalent to another set. As you work with a small group of children telling stories in Activity 6, the other children can be participating in Activities 3 or 5.
E Estimating and Identifying a Set with More/Less	Concrete	8. What Do You Think? 9. Look, Guess, Check	♦♦♦♦♦♦♦ ♦♦♦♦♦♦♦	In addition to these activities, have the children match the collections in Activity 3 and label the sets with the more, less, and same cards cut from Line Master 17. Reinforce the concept of more and less daily by asking questions such as the ones suggested in Activity 8.
F Creating a Set with More/Less	Concrete	10. Make Another Set 11. More or Less Stories	♦♦♦♦ ♦♦♦♦	Direct small groups of children to the collections described in Activity 3 as you engage the other children in Activities 10 or 11. Consider directing other children to sort materials suggested in Activity 8 of Section 1. Encourage them to describe the sets using the words as many as, more, or less.

About this Section

Many opportunities arise in daily classroom routines, e.g., handing out work, supplies, or notes which lead naturally into a discussion of whether there is enough/not enough, as many/not as many, etc. Try to involve the children in these discussions as often as possible.

Almost all of the activities of the previous section can be extended to include a comparison of the quantities of the 2 sets created. As children continue to engage in sorting activities, encourage them to consider whether the sets created have an equal number of members, or whether one set has more or less members than the other.

F

Creating
a Set with
More/Less

G

Creating and
Interpreting
Concrete
Graphs

Observations and Evaluation

As you circulate among the children, these key questions can form the basis of your discussion.

- **Are there as many _____ as _____?**
- **Are there enough _____?**
- **Show me another set with as many as this set. And another set.**
- **Do you think there are more (less) _____ than _____?** **How could you find out? Show me.**
- **Show me a set with more (less) than the set you just made.**

Observe the children as they participate in the matching activities to gain insight into their level of thinking. It is important to ascertain whether children are conserving number. To do so, ask a child to create a set equivalent to the one given. Ask, **Are there as many white counters as there are blue counters?** If the child responds, **Yes,** continue the task by spreading out a row of counters.

The non-conserver will see one row as longer and then conclude it has more. The child considers the length of the row as an indicator of number. The conserver knows the number has remained constant even though the arrangement of objects has changed.

One-to-one correspondence forms the foundation for later number concepts. Children who are not yet conserving number should be assessed again before beginning Unit 3, the first number unit. If their level of thinking has not developed further, engage them in further matching activities. Number will have limited meaning for the non-conserver.

Suggested Materials

- A variety of different collections for matching such as cups and saucers, juice cans and straws, toy cars and small people figures, toy baby and adult animals, toy cars and garages (cut off milk cartons), jars/containers and lids, envelopes and greeting cards, plastic flowers and vases (cans), egg cups and Plasticine eggs, or candles and candle holders (inverted Dixie cups) [Activity 3]
- A variety of bin materials such as popsicle sticks, coffee stirrers, Pattern Blocks, cubes, lids, beads, counters, or bread tags for each pair of children [Activities 5 and 10]
- Several pieces of string, wool, or pipe cleaners for each pair of children [Activity 5]
- A collection of magazines or catalogues [Activity 7]
- 2 clear plastic bags or containers [Activity 9]
- A large quantity of counters in 2 colors [Activity 9]

Ask, *Are there as many white counters as blue counters? Tell me why you think that.*

A	B	C	D	E
Sorting and Re-sorting a Collection	Identifying a Sorting Rule	Matching to Determine Equivalent Sets	Matching to Create Equivalent Sets	Estimating and Identifying a Set with More/Less

Line Masters

Any of Line Masters **18 to 23**
Activities 6 and 11
A large quantity

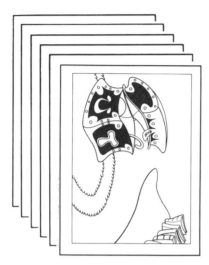

Any of Line Masters **14 to 16**
Activities 6 and 11
1 per child

Activities

1. Our Favorite Things

Gather the children together. Invite a small group of children (approximately 6) to each bring a favorite book in the classroom to this gathering. Have them display these books on a chalk board ledge. The small group stands facing the larger group. Ask each child to tell about the book he or she chose. As a group, state which book each child chose. **Marie is matched with (book title). Joshua is matched with (book title).** Have the children who shared their favorite books stand as a group and ask, **Has each child standing shared a book? Are there as many books as children?**

Ask the children to return the books, and repeat the activity with a different small group of children. You may have them choose a favorite toy, puppet, record, etc.

Variation

Display art work, books, coats from the cloakroom, lunch boxes, etc. Hold up one item at a time and ask, **Who owns this?** Each time an owner is identified, have her or him stand with the item. Encourage the children to describe what has been discovered. **This painting belongs to Tina.** Continue matching item with owner until all items are claimed. Point to the children standing and ask, **Is there an owner for each object?**

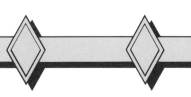
2. Find Out

Gather the children together and ask the ones wearing striped shirts to stand as a group in one spot. Identify them as the set of children wearing striped shirts. Next, ask the children wearing plain shirts to stand. Group these children and identify them as a set of children wearing plain shirts. Ask, **Do you think there are as many children wearing striped shirts as there are wearing plain shirts? How can we find out?** Discuss and try the methods suggested. If necessary, suggest that all children wearing striped shirts stand in a line facing children wearing plain shirts. You may have the pairs join hands to emphasize the matching process, sit down and touch feet, or have the children repeat, **one striped shirt for one plain shirt** every time there is a match. When the sets of children are matched, ask, **Are there as many children wearing plain shirts as children wearing striped shirts? How can you tell if there are as many?** Lead a discussion to ensure that the children understand that there are as many members in one set as the other set, if all members are matched.

Repeat, using other clothing sets such as the set of children wearing t-shirts/not wearing t-shirts, the set of children wearing white running shoes/colored running shoes, or the set of children wearing jeans/corduroy pants.

3. Collection Match-up

At different work areas, place containers (a shoe box is a good size) of items to be matched. These items should be ones that naturally go together, e.g., cups and saucers.

Gather the children together to explain that there are a number of collections of 2 sets for them to match. As they match the sets, they will discover if there are as many/not as many members in each. Guide the children to the different work areas. Encourage them to describe the results of their matching to the other children at the center. As you circulate among the groups, ask,

- **Do you think there are as many _____ as _____?**
- **How are you going to find out?**
- **What have you discovered?**
- **How do you know there are as many/not as many _____ as _____?**

The items can be matched in a variety of ways such as placing one object beside the other, placing each collection in a line and matching the members with string, or placing the collections in lines on paper and drawing lines between items in each set. These should be discussed and demonstrated before the children begin to match the materials.

Variation

The children match collections at the pictorial level using pictures found in magazines, catalogues, or calendars. These picture collections can be stored in large envelopes or file folders. You may wish to include picture files of cars and drivers, children and toys, dogs and bones (cut from cardboard), cats and little balls of wool, imps (Line Master 14) and feathers, or animals (Line Masters 15 or 16) and appropriate foods.

A	B	C	D	E
Sorting and Re-sorting a Collection	Identifying a Sorting Rule	Matching to Determine Equivalent Sets	Matching to Create Equivalent Sets	Estimating and Identifying a Set with More/Less

4. All Aboard

Invite the children to sit as a group. Place a row of at least 6 chairs in front of them and say, **These chairs are seats on an imaginary airplane.** Discuss possible destinations and choose one. Announce, **Children wearing striped shirts, all aboard for (destination).** Have the children wearing striped shirts stand in a group beside the airplane seats. Ask, **Do you think there are enough (not enough) seats for the children in this group?** Discuss ways to establish whether there is a seat for each child without counting. Try the methods suggested and have the children summarize the findings. **There are as many (not as many) seats as children.** Have volunteers remove any extra chairs or provide more chairs to accommodate the children who remain standing. After all children wearing striped shirts have been seated on the plane, announce their arrival. They then return to the larger group.

Have the children choose a new destination and repeat the activity using a different group.

Variation

Distribute tickets (different colored pieces of paper) to the children. Have all children with red tickets board the plane and discuss the seating.

5. Make a Set

Have the children work in pairs with bin materials. Provide them with several pieces of string, wool, or pipe cleaners to use to match their sets. Each child, in turn, will make a set with one material (popsicle sticks) and say, **Make a set that is equal to mine.** The other child makes an equivalent set with another material (coffee stirrers). The child who created the initial set then checks to see if the sets are equivalent by matching a member of one set to a member of the second set with the strings. The children return the materials to the bin and repeat the process, alternating roles as long as interest is sustained.

You may limit the number of available objects in the bins so that the children do not create sets that are too large.

Variations

- Have the children make muffins out of edible muffin dough. Give the children muffin liners or waxed paper circles. Have them make very small, imp-sized muffins and match them to their liners to make equal sets. You may wish to serve these muffins at a class tea party.

EDIBLE MUFFIN DOUGH

- 1 part corn syrup
- 1 part peanut butter
- 1 part powdered skim milk

- Provide Plasticine and egg cups and have the children make a Plasticine egg for each egg cup.
- Provide Plasticine and candles and have the children make a Plasticine candle holder for each candle.

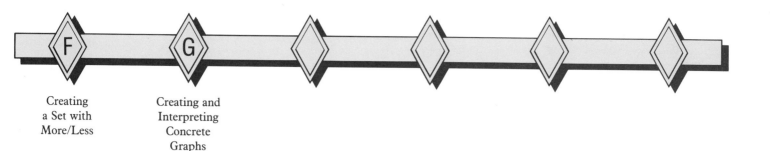

F

G

Creating
a Set with
More/Less

Creating and
Interpreting
Concrete
Graphs

6. As Many Stories

Gather a small group of children together. Provide each child with a story board (Line Master 18) and story characters cut from Line Master 14 or small objects to represent characters. Explain that you are going to tell stories for the children to act out with the story characters on the story boards. Each story should have an incident which requires the child to make a set equivalent to the one they have already created. For example, using Ted's room as a story board and the imp characters, a story such as this would be appropriate. **One night while Ted was asleep some imps crawled out of a crack in the floor and ran to play with his treasure chest.** (Children place some imps near the treasure chest.) **They were having so much fun that other imps decided to come out to play on Ted's shelves. There were as many imps playing on Ted's shelves as there were at Ted's treasure chest.** (Children place as many imps on the shelves as they placed at the treasure chest.) **Suddenly the imps heard a noise! They quickly disappeared into the crack in the floor.** (Children clear their story boards.)

Before you ask the children to clear their boards, invite volunteers to tell you a story, in their own words, about the scene they have created. Encourage them to use the phrase, **as many as**, in their description. Have the children demonstrate the various ways they went about creating an equivalent set. Lead a discussion to examine the ways they could use to check their story boards to ensure that the sets are equal. Continue to tell stories for the children to act out on their story boards.

Keep the children's interest high by keeping a quick pace to your stories. Varying the boards and the story characters also helps to maintain interest. After you have modelled a number of stories, you may wish to invite the children to tell stories for others to act out on the boards. On following days, divide the children into pairs. In turn, the children can tell stories for their partners to act out on the board.

7. One for Each

Provide a magazine or catalogue for each child. The children cut out a set of pictures, e.g., people, cars, or furniture and glue their sets on one half of a large piece of newsprint. Ask them to draw an equal set of objects to go with the magazine set on the other half of the paper. For example, a child who has cut out a set of people could draw a hat, dog, car, or toy for each person. The children draw lines to match and check the equivalent sets.

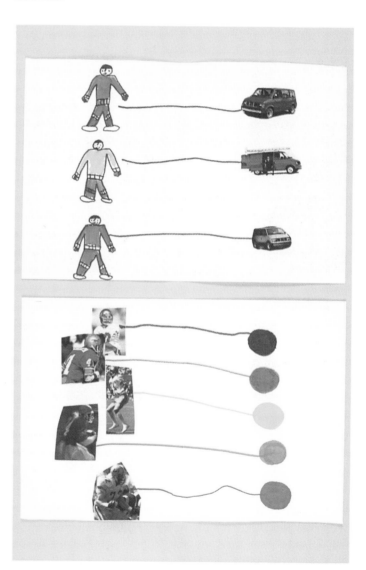

Variation

Conduct this activity in pairs. Each child draws or cuts and pastes a set. Tell the children to switch papers with their partners. They then draw an equivalent set to match the set their partners created.

A	B	C	D	E
Sorting and Re-sorting a Collection	Identifying a Sorting Rule	Matching to Determine Equivalent Sets	Matching to Create Equivalent Sets	Estimating and Identifying a Set with More/Less

8. What Do You Think?

Invite the children to sit in a circle. Ask, **Do you think there are more children wearing blue shirts today or more children wearing striped shirts? How can we find out?** Accept and try out all reasonable responses. Discuss your findings as a group. Ensure that the children give complete answers. **There are more children wearing blue shirts. There are less children wearing striped shirts.**

Continue to pose a variety of questions which require the children to compare 2 sets of objects. Types of questions you may wish to ask are:

- **Do you think there are more (less) children wearing buckled shoes than laced shoes?**
- **Do you think there is a pair of scissors for each child?**
- **Do you think there are less (more) records than cassettes in the listening center?**
- **Do you think there are as many right-handed as left-handed children in our class?**

Get a consensus of what the children think before you actually compare the different sets. Discuss ways to determine an answer to the questions and try as many of the methods suggested as possible.
Always have the children verbalize the answer they discover.

Variation

This activity can be done using pictures. Display a large picture such as those found on calendars, posters, or 2-page magazine spreads. Identify 2 sets and ask, **Do you think there are more _____ than _____?** The sets can be matched using a pencil to draw lines or by laying pieces of string from object to object.

9. Look, Guess, Check

You will need 2 clear plastic bags or containers and a number of counters in 2 colors (red and green). Place red counters in one bag and green counters in the other bag. Have the children sit in a circle, and give each one a red and green counter. Display the bags of counters so that all children can see them clearly. Ask, **Which bag do you think has more (less) counters?** The children indicate their response by holding up the corresponding counter. Invite a volunteer to empty the bags and match the counters. When all the counters are matched, ask, **Which bag had more?** The children indicate their response by holding up the corresponding counter. Check to see that all children are holding up the appropriate color. Encourage the children to verbalize their discovery. **There are more red counters than green counters.** Change the number of counters in each bag and repeat the activity as long as interest is maintained.

Variation

- Have the children play Look, Guess, Check in pairs or small groups. The children should take turns filling the bags and posing the questions.
- Play Look, Guess, Check using opaque plastic containers. Paste a different colored piece of paper on each lid. Shake each container then have the children indicate which has more (less) counters by holding up the counter which matches the color of the container's lid.

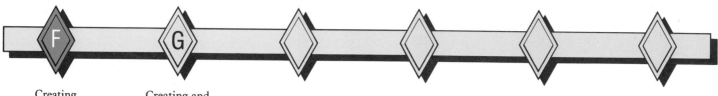

Creating
a Set with
More/Less

Creating and
Interpreting
Concrete
Graphs

10. Make Another Set

Gather a small group of children. Ensure that each child has a workspace and 2 kinds of bin materials such as blocks, Pattern Blocks, or beads in 2 colors. Invite the children to make a set using one material. When they have made a set, say, **Show me another set with more members than the one you just made. Use different materials.** Ask the children to describe the 2 sets using the words "more" and "less". After each child has had this opportunity, have them clear their area. Repeat the activity a number of times. Vary your requests so that the children are creating sets with more and less.

As children become familiar with the procedure, you may divide them into pairs to play this game.

Variation

You may repeat this activity using the more and less cards cut from Line Master 17 instead of giving verbal directions.

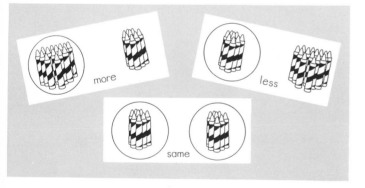

11. More or Less Stories

This is a story board activity. Follow the procedure outlined in Activity 6. In this story-telling session, each story should ask the children to create a set with more or less members than the set already formed. For example, using the forest (Line Master 19) as a story board and the animals cut from Line Master 15, or small objects to represent characters, these stories are representative of the type you could tell.

- **There was a group of squirrels playing in the leaves.** (Children place squirrels on the leaves.) **There were less squirrels playing on the branch.** (Children place an appropriate set of squirrels on the branch.) **When it started to get dark, all the squirrels left.** (Children clear their boards.)
- **There were black rabbits running under the tree.** (Children place black rabbits by the tree.) **There were more white rabbits than black rabbits running under the tree.** (Children place an appropriate set of white rabbits.) **When the rabbits were tired, they ran home.** (Children clear their boards.)

Before you ask the children to clear their boards, invite volunteers to tell you a story in their own words about the scene they have created. Encourage the children to use the words, "more" and "less" in their stories.

You may have the children create a pictorial record of these more and less stories or create ones of their own. The children draw or paste story characters on a story board. Encourage them to describe the pictures they create. These pictures could be displayed on a bulletin board or assembled into a book entitled More or Less.

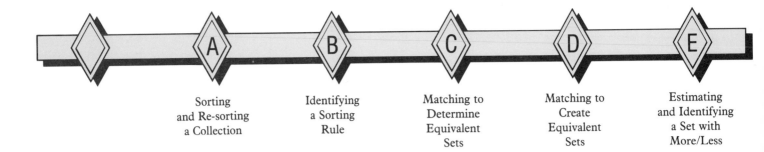

Sorting
and Re-sorting
a Collection

Identifying
a Sorting
Rule

Matching to
Determine
Equivalent
Sets

Matching to
Create
Equivalent
Sets

Estimating
and Identifying
a Set with
More/Less

Section 3

Planning the Section

Objective	Level	Activity	Grouping	Program *or* Management Suggestions
G Creating and Interpreting Concrete Graphs	Concrete	1. Let's Graph! 2. People Graphs 3. My Own Graph	ꙭꙭꙭꙭꙭꙭ ꙭꙭꙭꙭꙭꙭ ꙭꙭꙭꙭ	Each activity illustrates a variety of concrete graphs. It is not intended that these graphing activities form the basis of your program for a block of time. Rather, it is recommended that you involve the children in a graphing activity on an average of once a week.

About this Section

This section offers many suggestions for concrete graphing activities. The concrete graph forms the foundation for later graphing experiences at the pictorial and symbolic (bar graph) levels. As children create and interpret concrete graphs, they apply their sorting and classifying skills and compare groups using the vocabulary as many as, more, most, less, and least.

It is recommended that topics and questions for graphing activities be related directly to the ideas and experiences of the children. Emphasis should be placed on graphing as a problem-solving tool, that is, a way to clearly display and then interpret information. Try to begin each graphing activity with an interesting question that will immediately involve all the children. Encourage the children to estimate which groups have more or less before the materials are actually displayed on the graph.

Encourage the children to ask questions for which the answers may be discovered and displayed through graphing. Knowing the right question to ask is also an important problem-solving skill.

Initially, confine the graphing activities to 2 columns. When children are comfortable interpreting 2-column graphs, introduce 3-column graphs. Each column of the graph should have a label. Ensure that children place objects on the graph sequentially, working up (or across) from the label. You may wish to use actual objects, pictures, words, or a combination of all 3 as labels. It is recommended that you make many group graphs to firmly establish the purpose and procedures before directing children to create individual graphs.

Observations and Evaluation

These key questions can form the basis of a discussion on the concrete graphs created in this section.

- **Do you think there are more (less) _____ than _____?** (Ask this before you begin to create a graph.)
- **Which column has more (less, most, least)?**
- **Are any columns the same? What does this mean?**
- **Are there more (less) _____ or _____?**
- **What does this graph tell us?** (This last question should be asked after the children have interpreted a few concrete graphs.)

Number is not a focus of these activities but will form the core of graphing activities later in the program. However, some children may spontaneously discuss the graph in terms of number. For example, **There are 5 pencils that need sharpening.**

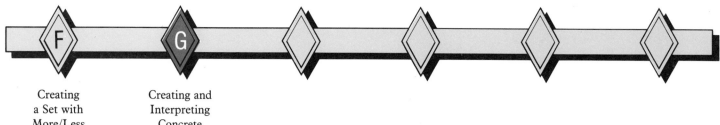

Creating
a Set with
More/Less

Creating and
Interpreting
Concrete
Graphs

Suggested Materials

- A variety of graphing mats such as large divided plastic sheets of mural paper, egg cartons, or a region of floor divided into sections. [Activities 1, 2, and 3]
- 2 pieces of apple and orange for each child [Activity 1]
- A variety of labels such as [Activity 3]

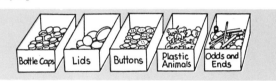

- A magnet [Activity 3]
- Collections of buttons, lids, bottle caps, toy plastic animals, etc. [Activity 3]

Graphing Mats

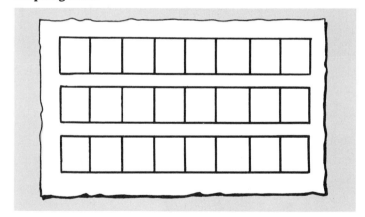

A large sheet of plastic marked into sections with masking tape

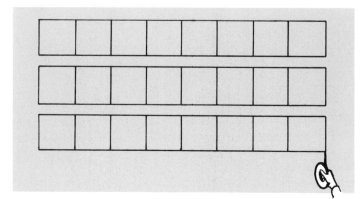

Masking tape or chalked lines on the floor or pavement

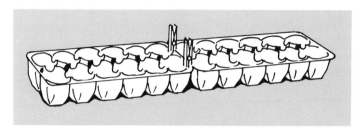

Egg cartons clipped together with clothespins

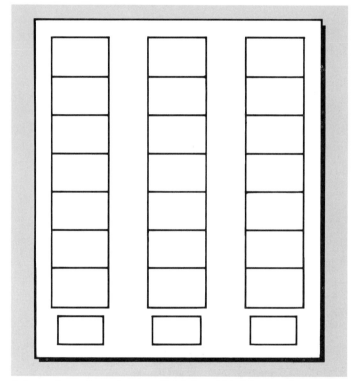

A large sheet of mural paper divided or folded into sections

Line Masters

Labels cut from Line Masters **11** and **12**
Activities 1 and 3
1 copy of each

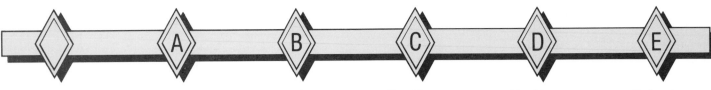

A	B	C	D	E
Sorting and Re-sorting a Collection	Identifying a Sorting Rule	Matching to Determine Equivalent Sets	Matching to Create Equivalent Sets	Estimating and Identifying a Set with More/Less

Activities

1. Let's Graph!   PS G

Invite the children to sit in front of a large graphing mat. Ask the children to take off one of their shoes and place it in front of them. Explain that today they are going to learn a new way to compare things.

Place the rough and smooth labels cut from Line Master 12 at the end of 2 columns on the graphing mat. Ask the children to examine the sole of their shoe to decide whether it is rough or smooth. Ask, **Do you think there are more (less) children whose shoes have rough soles or more (less) children whose shoes have smooth soles?** After the children have responded, invite all children who have shoes with rough soles to place a shoe (sole side showing) on the mat in the appropriate column. Then ask all those children having smooth soles to place a shoe on the mat. These questions can form the basis of your discussion of the graph.

- **Point to the column that has more.**
- **Point to the column that has less.**
- **Do the columns have the same number of shoes?**
- **Are there more shoes with rough soles or smooth soles?**

When interpreting a graph comparing 3 groups, these directions can also be considered.

- **Point to the column that has the most.**
- **Point to the column that has the least.**
- **Point to the columns that have the same.**

Are there more children who want a piece of apple or more who want a piece of orange for a snack?

Are there more sharp pencils or more dull pencils?

Do most children want to use crayon, pastel, or chalk to draw their picture?

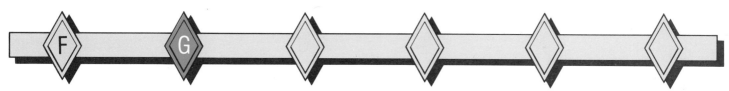

Creating
a Set with
More/Less

Creating and
Interpreting
Concrete
Graphs

2. People Graphs PS G

The children, themselves, form the graphs in these activities. Note that the children participating in the graph should not be expected to answer questions as they cannot see clearly the information presented.

Are there more children wearing jeans than there are wearing corduroy pants?

Which book do most children want me to read (display 2 or 3 books as labels)?

Are there more children wearing blue shirts than there are wearing red shirts?

There are an unlimited number of questions you can ask to initiate a people graph. For example:

- **Are there more children with blue eyes than there are with green eyes?**
- **Are there less children wearing skirts than there are wearing dresses?**
- **Are there less children with red hair than there are with blond hair?**
- **Do more children walk or ride a bike to school?**
- **Do most children prefer the color blue, red, or yellow?**

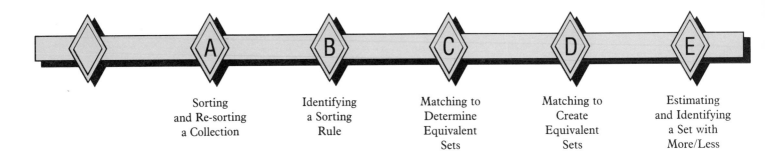

PS G

3. My Own Graph

Direct small groups of children to a work area where collections of buttons, lids, bottle caps, plastic animals, etc., and a variety of graphing mats have been placed for individual graphing. Place labels as shown with each collection so that the child can start to graph independently. Encourage the children to ask each other questions about their graphs. They should now be familiar with the different kinds of questions.

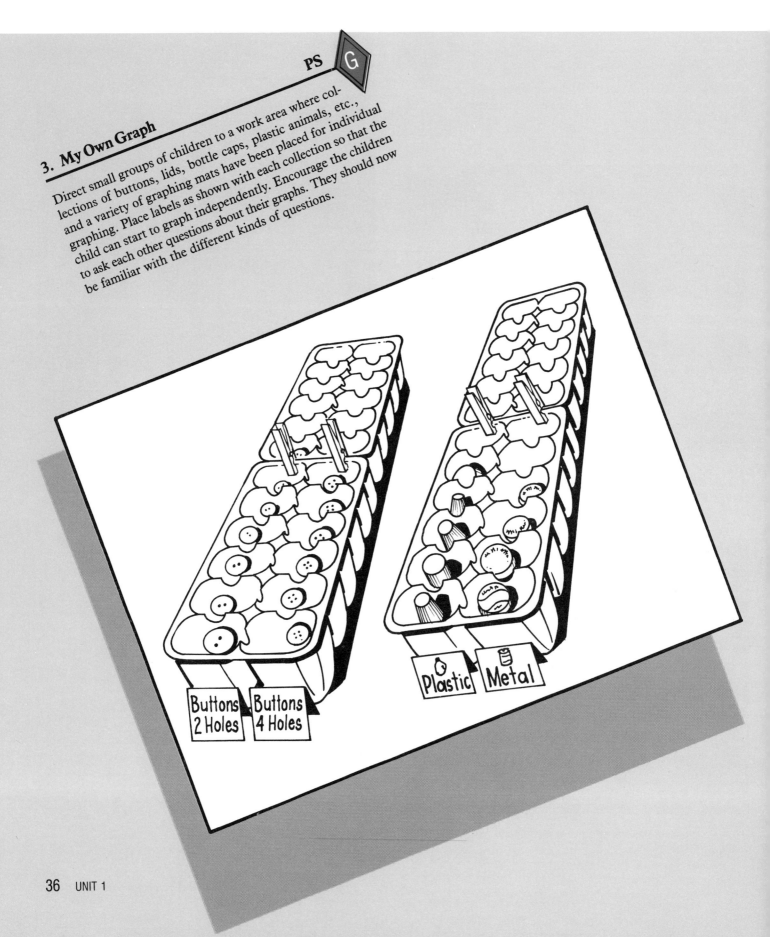

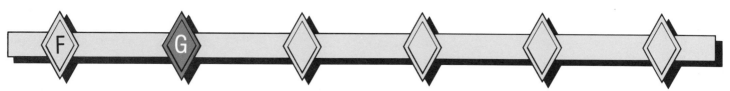

Creating
a Set with
More/Less

Creating and
Interpreting
Concrete
Graphs

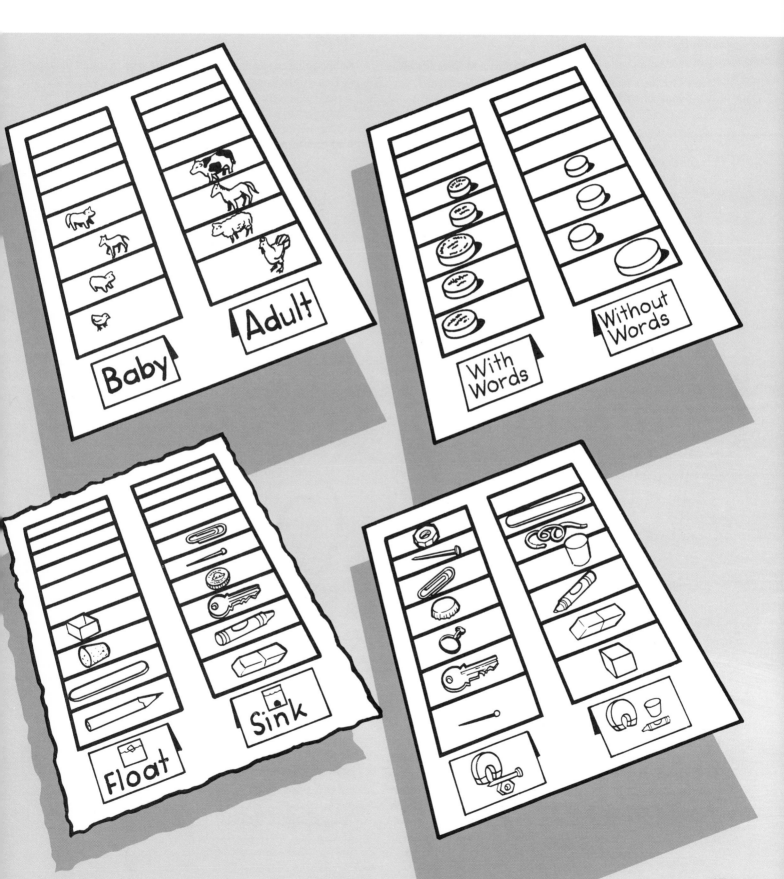

Sorting Across the Curriculum

Language Arts

- Print the children's names on cardboard and have the children sort their names by first or last letter.
- Visit your school library. Ask the librarian to explain why and how the books are sorted. Identify different book sections with the children.
- Display and discuss a picture dictionary. Have the children begin to make picture dictionaries as a class or individually. On each new page the child prints a letter and draws pictures of things which begin with that letter.

- In conjunction with this unit, you may wish to read any of these stories (see page 318, for an annotated bibliography):
  - *The Baby's Catalogue* by Janet and Allan Ahlberg
  - *Each Peach Pear Plum* by Janet and Allan Ahlberg
  - *Is it Red? It is Yellow? Is it Blue?* by Tana Hoban
  - *A House is a House For Me* by Mary Ann Hoberman

Art

Provide the children with a variety of materials such as pieces of fabric, wallpaper scraps, popsicles sticks, toothpicks, tissue paper, wool, or cotton balls. Invite the children to decide what set of materials they would like to use to make a picture. For example, they may choose to use items that are red, wooden, soft, or rough. Have the children select items according to their chosen criterion and begin to create a picture. Children who decide to sort by texture may enjoy selecting items with their eyes closed.

Music

- The children sort instruments by the type of sound they make
- The children sort and re-sort objects by the sound that they make when they are dropped, tapped with a pencil, shaken, etc.
- Discuss loud and soft sounds with the children. Keep a list of the sounds the children identify.

Science

- Place a variety of objects and a magnet at a center. Invite the children to use the magnet to sort the objects.

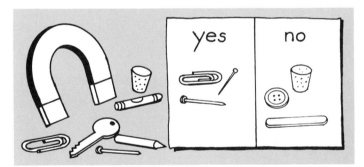

- The children collect and sort leaves by kind, color, size, etc.

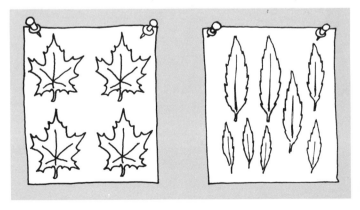

- Dip cotton balls into a variety of different smelling liquids such as vanilla, perfume, lemon juice, or tobasco. Place each cotton ball in a container. There should be at least 3 containers with the same smell. Have the children sort the containers using their sense of smell.

Social Studies

- The children sort toy animals or pictures of animals by kind, habitat, body covering, color, etc.

- Go for a walk in the neighborhood or on the playground to collect interesting things. The children can sort these collections in the classroom. If children combine their collections, the potential scope of the sets expands.
- Explore the school to identify how the people in school have been sorted into various rooms. Record these decisions on a map of the school.
- Take a trip to your neighborhood post office to see how the mail is sorted.
- Take a trip to a neighborhood supermarket. Discuss where the different items are displayed. Identify the various aisles, shelves, freezers, etc., with the children and brainstorm the different sorting rules used.

Physical Education

In the gym, have children demonstrate how they can move in a low, middle, and high body position. Mark off 3 areas of the gym and identify each one as low, middle, or high. Once the children decide how they are going to move, ask them to go to the appropriate area to explore ways to move in the chosen body position. Each group demonstrates to the other groups.

Establish a book making center in your classroom. The children choose a title for their book which is, in fact, a sorting criterion. Display a variety of book jackets as illustrated to motivate the children. Cut sheets of paper and construction paper covers into different sizes and place them in labelled folders. Create a library for the books out of a shoe box or any other appropriate size box.

You may wish to provide magazines and catalogues for the children to use in their book making. Ensure that the children have the opportunity to read their books to you, other children, and/or other adults. You might consider placing library cards in these books so that children can borrow them overnight and share each other's books with their families.

Patterning

Unit Objectives

Section 1

A Identifying Patterns
B Extending Patterns

Section 2

C Creating Patterns

About this Unit

Patterning

Patterning, the repetition of a sequence, is a skill which touches virtually every aspect of a child's life. When infants recognize the human face as a regular arrangement of eyes, nose, and mouth, they are beginning to see pattern. The toddler who automatically brings a storybook at bedtime has recognized (or is seeking to establish) a pattern.

Recognition of pattern will continue to be a requisite skill throughout a child's academic life. Mathematics, literature, the arts, and the sciences all demand the recognition and creation of patterns.

This unit leads children through a sequence of activities which allows them to experience patterns visually, auditorially and kinesthetically. Exploring the materials gives children the opportunity to focus on interesting characteristics of the materials provided. Some children may pattern spontaneously in the course of their exploration. The activities begin by having the children identify and then extend a simple pattern using concrete materials such as block, bead, block, bead, block, bead. They progress to extending more complex patterns, first with concrete materials and sounds, then with pictures. The second section of the unit gives children opportunities to create patterns with many different materials at both the concrete and pictorial levels. The patterns created may be as simple or as sophisticated as the child's abilities and imagination dictate.

Throughout the unit it is emphasized that children should have opportunities to read and read again in other ways the patterns they extend and create. Reading patterns aloud helps children focus their attention on the pattern, provides a way of checking the pattern, and is especially beneficial for auditory learners.

Problem Solving

As the children participate in the activities of this unit, they develop problem-solving skills. In each activity, the children

- identify, extend, and/or create patterns.

They always have the opportunity to "read" their pattern aloud. The children are also encouraged to think of different possible ways to read these patterns. These patterning activities provide the children with opportunities to apply their sorting skills. In addition, activities provided in Five Minute Math, pages 44-45 develop the following problem-solving skills:

- sorting
- identifying likenesses and differences
- developing observation and listening skills
- creating stories

Vocabulary

- Next
- Pattern

Planning Ahead

The next unit focusses on number to 10. It is suggested that you assess the children's understanding of number while you progress through the current unit so that you will have the information you need to provide an appropriate program when you are ready to begin the number work. See page 71 for a suggested assessment technique.

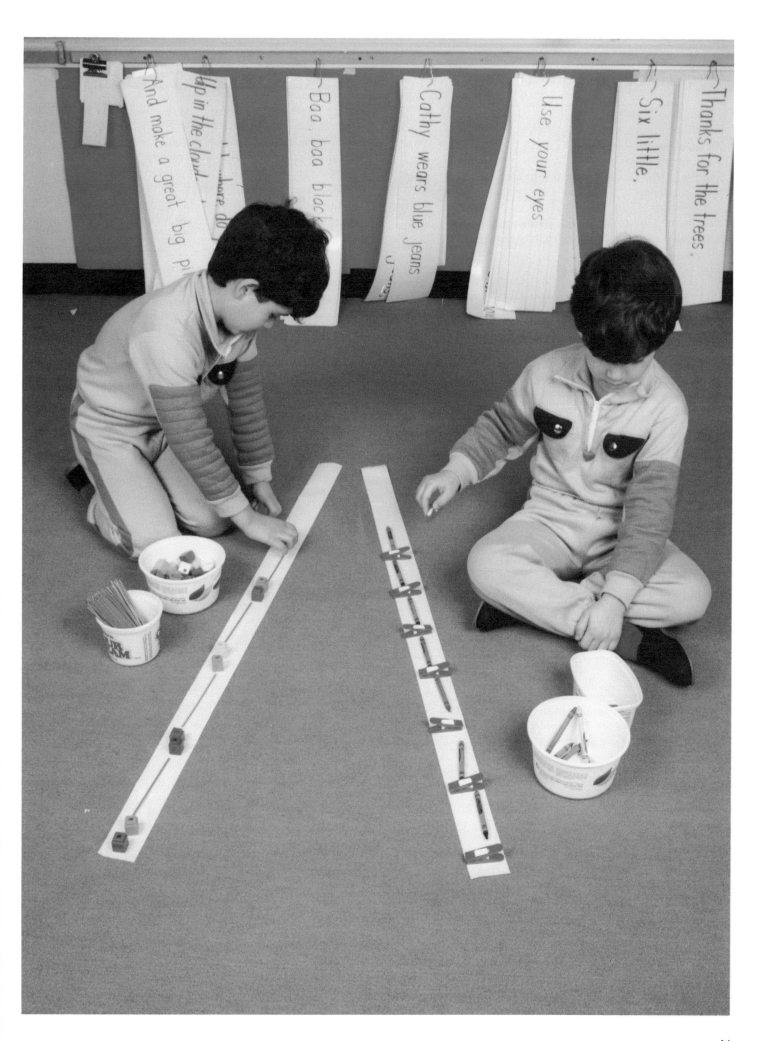

Ongoing Objectives

- Reading the calendar
- Counting and counting back
- Recognizing numerals
- Printing numerals
- Identifying the set with more/less/as many as
- Problem solving
  - Sorting
  - Identifying likenesses and differences
  - Developing observation and listening skills
  - Creating stories

Five Minute Math

Calendar Activities

- Extend the calendar routines to include discussion and activities about yesterday and tomorrow.

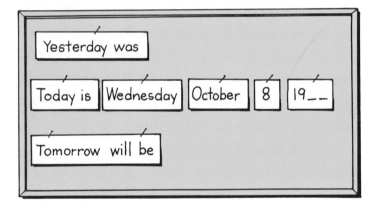

1. Post the [Yesterday was] strip. Start the Calendar Activities by pointing to the date posted the previous day and asking, **Is today Wednesday?** The children respond, **No.** Remove the [Wednesday] card and ask, **When was Wednesday?** After a correct response is given, post the [Wednesday] card to complete the [Yesterday was] strip. Say, **Yesterday was Wednesday.**

2. Post the [Tomorrow will be] strip when children have responded well to the questioning about yesterday. After the date is posted, ask, **Who knows what day tomorrow will be?** Invite a volunteer to find the card on the board and post it to complete the [Tomorrow will be] strip.

- Questions such as these could be included in your calendar time:

  - **Is Kim's birthday this month? Show us when. What day was it?**
  - **Are we going on a trip this week? Show us where it is recorded.**
  - **Did it rain yesterday? The day before? What day was that?**

Counting Activities

- Have the children count to 10 and back from 10 as they engage in the counting activities introduced previously. Depending on the ability of your children, you may introduce these counting back activities by starting from 4. Gradually add numbers to the sequence as children appear ready.
- Play a piano key, xylophone, rhythm band instrument, etc. as the children count to and/or back from a designated number.
- In the gym or on the playground have the children count as they walk to a specific number; change directions; and walk and count to the number again, etc. You may wish to have the children switch from counting to 4 (or 10) to counting back from 4 (or 10) each time they change directions.
- Have the children count to themselves as you tap a pencil. Have them say the last number following the tap out loud.

Numeral Recognition Activities

- Give each child a set of numeral cards from 0 to 10. Call out numbers for the children to hold up.
- Tape a number line (with the numerals 0 to 10) on the floor, or draw a number line with chalk on the playground. Ask children to follow directions such as these:

  - **Stand on 4. Move to 1. Did you move forwards or backwards?**
  - **Stand on 3. Take 1 step. What number are you standing on now?**

- Hang number necklaces from 0 to 10 on 11 volunteers. Have the children stand at the front of the room and ask the audience group questions such as the ones listed.

  - **Who is wearing necklace number 4?**
  - **Give number 5 a pencil. Who did you give the pencil to?**

- Distribute a numeral card to each child. Guide the children to different areas of the room using these directions:

  - **All children with a 3 line up at the door.**
  - **All children with a 5 go sit at a table.**
  - **All children with a 9 go to the clothes closet and stand on one foot.**

After the children have followed each direction, ask them to hold up their card to check their position. Have the children switch cards after a few directions.

- On large sheets of paper, print the numerals 0 to 10. Tape these sheets on the floor at least a metre apart. Give directions such as these:

  - **All children wearing red walk to 5.**
  - **All children with brown hair hop to 3.**
  - **All children with a name that starts with B slide to 8.**
  - **All children with a birthday in August jump to 9.**

Numeral Printing Activities

- Have the children try to guess the mystery numeral their friends trace on their backs.

- Print numerals large enough for a child to trace on a sheet of paper. Slide the paper into a clear plastic folder. The child traces over the numeral on the plastic sheet with water soluble markers or crayons.
- When children are ready for paper and pencil printing practice, provide them with a model of the numeral and lined or blank paper. Some children may benefit from additional guidance as illustrated.

Number Activities

- Any of these games: Our Favorite Things, page 26, All Aboard, page 28, and Look, Guess, Check, page 30 can easily be played in 5 minutes to further reinforce and review the skill of identifying a set with more, less, or equal amounts.
- Have the children continue to compare groups by matching one-to-one. Encourage them to use the vocabulary more, less, as many as, or equal, in their description of the quantities of the 2 sets.

These questions are representative of an unlimited number you can ask to initiate matching activities.

- Are there less children with blond hair than there are with brown hair?
- Are there as many children who eat at school as there are who eat at home?
- Do I have enough pencils for everyone?
- Are there more red chairs than there are blue chairs?
- Do we need more glue bottles, or do we have one for each work area?

Problem Solving Activities

Sorting

- Any of these games: Use Your Eyes, page 17, Put It In This Hoop, pages 18–19; What's My Secret Rule? or Now Tell Me, page 23 can easily be played in 5 minutes to reinforce and review sorting skills.
- Have the children sort the clothes or objects in the lost and found. Lead a discussion on the type of sets formed, when they think items were lost (season), clues as to the owners, etc.
- Have the children sit in a circle so that they can see each other easily. Decide on a sorting rule, e.g., children wearing short sleeves, blue jeans, or watches. Name the children who are members of the set and ask them to stand. Invite the children to guess your sorting rule. If the children guess incorrectly, discuss why their choice is an inappropriate sorting rule, e.g., **Jane would also be standing**, or **Craig is standing and he isn't wearing . . . .**

- Before going to the library, discuss the books the children are returning. Encourage the children to think of ways to sort these books.

Identifying Likenesses and Differences

- Encourage the children to select 2 concrete items for their classmates to compare. Explain that if a child wants to present 2 objects, he or she must know at least one way in which the items are alike and one way in which they are different. Encourage the children to select items from the class or from home. You might consider sending a letter home to explain why children may want to bring items to school for the day. Post a sign-up sheet for children to sign when they have objects they would like to present. Each day inform the child who will be presenting the next day to allow her or him time to prepare.
- Ask the children to identify a child who is like them in one way. Have the child identify the person and explain how that person and he or she are alike. You may wish to keep a record of the children's explanations.

Janine and Carol have brown hair.

Barry and Tommy are wearing red shirts.

Sara and Nicole live on the same street.

Maria and David like chocolate ice cream best.

Alex and Jennifer are wearing watches.

Sita and Mary are wearing short sleeves.

Michael and Tony ride their bikes to school.

Eric and Josh have freckles.

Developing Observation and Listening Skills

- Tell the children that you have selected a mystery object in the classroom. They are to be detectives and try to figure out what the mystery object is after you give clues. Say, **The mystery object is orange.** Print orange on the chalk board. If a child guesses an object that is orange, give another clue. **The mystery object is made of plastic and metal.** Add plastic and metal to the list on the chalk board. Give another clue only after the children have identified an item (if not the mystery object) that is orange and made of plastic and metal. **The mystery object is something you sit on.** When the children identify the mystery object, check it to each clue given before another object is selected.

- Have the children sit in a circle. Ask a volunteer to leave the room. While this child is out of the room, choose a leader. The leader begins a motion such as clapping, tapping knees, patting shoulders, or shaking her or his head. All children copy the motion the leader performs. The leader should change the motion at frequent intervals and the other children should follow. Call the volunteer back into the room when all children are participating. Encourage the volunteer to try and determine who the leader is by carefully observing the group. The volunteer should watch for a change in the performed action as well as to which child the group directs its attention.

Creating Stories

Tell more/less stories such as these and have the children suggest what could have happened.

There were many tomatoes growing in the garden. The next day there were less tomatoes growing in the garden. What could have happened?

The children might respond:
- **Someone picked some tomatoes.**
- **Some tomatoes fell to the ground.**
- **A squirrel ate some of the tomatoes.**
- **A strong wind blew over the tomato plant.**

Or,

There were a few leaves on the front lawn. The next day there were many more leaves on the front lawn. What could have happened?

The children might respond:
- **More leaves fell from the tree.**
- **A wind blew leaves onto the lawn.**
- **The children raked the leaves from the back yard into the front yard.**
- **The neighbor's lawn mower blew the leaves onto the lawn.**

Using the Story

In the story Plip, Plip, Plop! the imps create a pattern through their mischief and fun. As the imps land on Ted's tube of toothpaste, their step by step motion causes the toothpaste to squirt out; creating a sound pattern. Sound patterns form the basis for the activity Plip, Plip, Plop, page 52. This sound pattern has been represented visually in the picture.

You may wish to have children identify and act out other patterns that would have happened in the story:

- The imps mischief – climb, jump, land; climb, jump, land;...
- A sequence of imps jumping – Kalaloo, Slider; Kalaloo, Slider;...
- The action of the toothpaste – squished, spurted; squished, spurted;...

Toward the end of the unit, children have the opportunity to create their own textured patterns on a line master of Ted's sink as they engage in the activity Toothpaste Patterns on Ted's Sink!, page 60.

Supplementary Material

Ted is my Friend: Mathematics Activity Book, pages 7-10 and 14-19.

Plip, Plip, Plop!

"Kalaloo, where are you?" whispered Ari as she peered from imp to imp. "Kalaloo, where are you?" she repeated in a worried voice.

From the top of the mirror, a tiny face looked down and smiled. "I'm up here! Look, Ari, I'm way up here," squeaked Kalaloo.

"Shh!" said Ari, "I see you. Now shh, you'll wake Ted up. Come down now so that we can play. But be careful, Kalaloo!"

"Watch me Ari! Watch me! I can jump right onto Ted's toothpaste tube!" Kalaloo swung her arms and jumped into the air. "Watch out be-e-low!" she sang out as quietly as she could.

Down came Kalaloo, down and down and down right on top of Ted's toothpaste tube. Plip! went one foot, and out came a splotch of toothpaste. Plip! went the other foot, and out came a second splotch of toothpaste. Plop! went another lovely splotch of gooey blue toothpaste as Kalaloo flopped back onto the tube.

"Kalaloo, be careful!" said Ari and Rumple together.

"It's all right. I *always* clean my teeth at night," said Kalaloo as she dipped her finger into the toothpaste and put it in her mouth. "Besides," she giggled, "it's fun!"

Kalaloo adjusted the toothpaste tube and scampered to the top of the mirror. "Watch out be-e-low!" she sang out again. Plip! went one foot. Plip! went the other foot. Plop! went another splotch of toothpaste.

"Watch out be-e-low!" Kalaloo quickly looked up. There was Slider ready to jump! "It looks like fun, Kalaloo. I want to do it too!"

Plip, plip, plop! Slider landed on the tube. "That *is* fun, Kalaloo! Come on, imps, follow me!"

Imp after imp followed Slider and jumped onto the tube. Plip, plip, plop! Plip, plip, plop! Plip, plip, plop! On and on it went.

Ari and Rumple could not believe their eyes. The imps were squirting toothpaste all over Ted's sink! They looked at each other and smiled. Then they looked up at Kalaloo. "Be careful!" they called.

Kalaloo's little face peered down from the pixie light hanging above the mirror. "Watch the toothpaste squirt, Ari! Watch the splotches make a picture when we go plip, plip, plop!"

Ari and Rumple watched the splotches of toothpaste land on the sink. "You've made a pattern!" exclaimed Ari.

"Won't Ted be surprised!" chuckled Rumple.

Kalaloo clapped her hands, "Come on, let's make it all around the sink. Come and help, you two!"

Ari and Rumple looked at each other, then ran giggling to join the others. Plip, plip, plop went the pattern; Plip, plip, plop; Plip, plip, plop; . . .

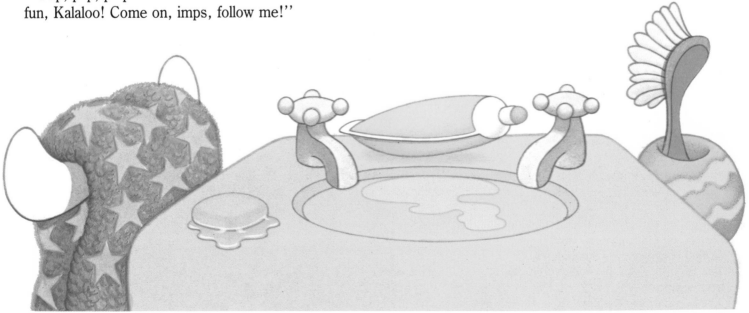

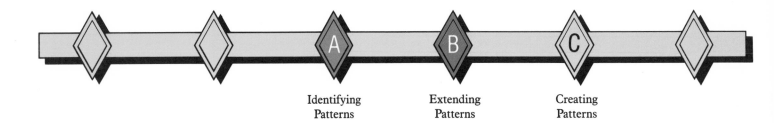

Identifying
Patterns

Extending
Patterns

Creating
Patterns

Section 1

Planning the Section

Objective	Level	Activity	Grouping	Program *or* Management Suggestions
	Concrete	1. Exploring the Materials	♦♦♦♦	Children should be given many opportunities to explore the materials they will be using later in this unit. Circulate among the children to observe the activities they engage in. These observations will help you determine appropriate programming. Try to set aside time each day for children to share their discoveries about the materials.
A Identifying Patterns	Concrete	2. Tap a Pattern	♦♦♦♦♦♦♦	While a small group is playing a game, other children can be directed to explore materials, to work at the patterning or sorting centers, to engage in familiar Five Minute Math activities, etc. Activities 2 and 3 introduce the concept and word "pattern." Children slow to grasp this concept will benefit from participating in both activities and/or several exposures to one activity with a variety of different materials.
		3. Read My Pattern	♦♦♦♦♦♦♦	
		4. Whisper a People Pattern	♦♦♦♦♦♦♦	
B Extending Patterns	Auditory	5. Plip, Plip, Plop!	♦♦♦♦♦♦♦	Activities 5, 6, and 7 initially require teacher direction. Here, the children are guided in extending patterns. Children who are able to approach tasks independently and appear to have a solid understanding of pattern as a repetitive sequence may be directed to the centers suggested in Activity 8. Materials for these activities can be set up at different work areas and children can rotate through centers. Refer to page xx for suggestions on how to keep track of the centers a child visits.
	Concrete	6. Magic Pattern Makers	♦♦♦♦	
		7. Make My Pattern	♦♦♦♦	
	Concrete and Pictorial	8. Let's Extend	♦♦♦♦	

About this Section

The children should experience different types of patterns. These
patterns are suggested in the activities of this unit:

ababab pattern

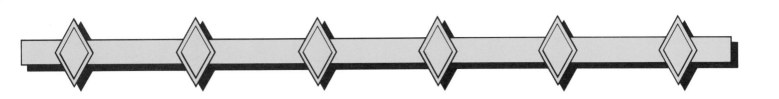

abbabbabb pattern

aabaabaab pattern

abcabcabc pattern

Develop one type of pattern at a time to avoid confusion. These are only a few of the patterns you may wish to explore with the children.

When presenting a pattern for the children to identify, it is important to show at least 3 repetitions.

This section presents only the first of the many patterning activities interspersed throughout the program. Remember that the children will have many more opportunities to explore patterns. It is not necessary for them to master all the skills developed in this unit.

Suggested Materials

- Several bins of assorted materials that lend themselves to sorting and patterning such as blocks, beads, straws, bottle caps, lids, chestnuts, acorns, popsicle sticks, toothpicks, paper clips, buttons, macaroni, or rigatoni [Activities 1 and 3].
- Plasticine or play dough, cookie cutters, and materials for making imprints such as shells, spools, old keys, bottle caps, or metal nuts [Activity 1].
- 3 items such as a block, card, and bean for each child [Activity 2].
- Several bins of sorted materials such as popsicle sticks, toothpicks, macaroni, rigatoni, or beads [Activities 6 and 7].
- A large quantity of paper strips (20 cm by 20 cm) in 2 colors [Activity 8].
- A variety of seeds such as navy beans, kidney beans, split peas, corn, or pearl barley [Activity 8].
- A quantity of colored drinking straws [Activity 8].
- 5 to 6 blunt tapestry needles [Activity 8].
- Teacher-prepared pattern cards [Activity 8].
- A large quantity of Pattern Blocks, interlocking cubes, or colored rods to copy prepared pattern cards [Activity 8].

Line Masters

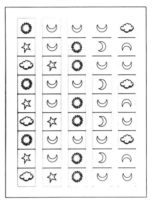

Line Master **24**
Activity 8
A large quantity

Line Master **25**
Activity 8
A large quantity

Observations and Evaluation

These key questions should be asked frequently as the children work with the materials.

- **How could you read this pattern?**
- **What is another way to read the pattern? Another way?**
- **What would you put next in this pattern? And after that?**
- **Show me more of this pattern.**

If you want to gather more information on how some children extend patterns, engage them (individually or as a small group) in this simple task. Begin a pattern using materials the children have worked with previously.

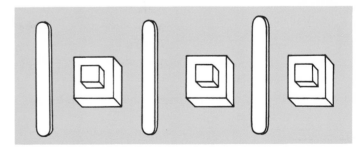

Ask, **What have I made? Let's read the pattern aloud.** Have the children chant the pattern as they copy it. After each child has copied the pattern, say, **Continue the pattern**. If necessary, repeat the task with a different pattern.

Many of the activities in this section are open-ended and therefore accommodate a wide range of abilities. This chart describes some observations and offers suggestions for teacher direction.

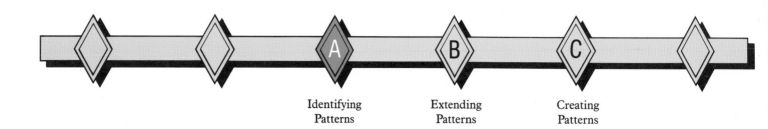

Identifying
Patterns

Extending
Patterns

Creating
Patterns

Observations	Teacher Direction
The child extends the pattern by randomly placing objects.	It may not be a random placement. Establish through questioning whether or not the child has attempted to create/begin a new pattern.
The child is trying to extend the pattern but has difficulty.	Make pattern cards by tracing concrete objects (at least 3 repetitions). Have the child place concrete objects directly on top of the tracings. Invite the child to read the pattern. Place another card with the same pattern to the right of the first one and invite the child to place objects on top of the tracings. Continue with other cards. Have the child read each pattern aloud. Ask, **What comes next? And next? And after that? And after that?**
The child appears comfortable placing objects and reading the pattern cards.	Invite the child to continue the pattern off the card. Encourage the child to say the pattern aloud while placing the objects. Ask, **What comes next?** 
The child extends the pattern one repetition and claims that he or she is finished.	The child may not have grasped pattern as a continuous repetitive sequence. Comment that it is a good beginning. Tell the child you want a longer pattern. Pose a gentle challenge. **Can you make the pattern as long as your arm/the table/ this piece of string?** Return after a few minutes and have the child read the pattern aloud. Be sure to comment on how long the pattern has become. Ask the child to make the pattern 2 (or 3, or 4) objects longer.
The child chooses to extend only one type of pattern, e.g., ababab.	The child may have generalized the ab abab sequence as a definition of pattern. Begin a pattern other than an ababab one and ask, **What do you think should be next?** (The child identifies and places it.) **And next?** (The child places it.) **And next?** Have the child read the newly created pattern aloud. Comment on how interesting this pattern is too.
The child extends patterns without hesitation and appears ready for a further challenge.	Engage the child in the Extension Project suggested on page 63.

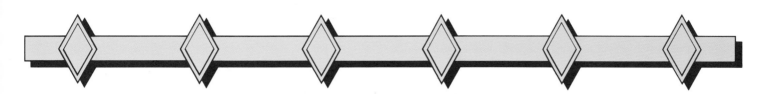

Activities

1. Exploring the Materials

In a work area, place Plasticine, cookie cutters, and materials with which the children can make imprints. Fill 3 bins with a variety of seeds. Fill at least 3 other bins with materials the children will be using for patterning.

Invite the children to sit in a circle and place the bins in the center. You may wish to spread some of the items out on the floor. Engage the children in a discussion about the materials. Discuss the type of materials, which materials they like, which materials they brought in, the purpose of the bin, etc.

Tell the children that they will have a chance to play with some of the materials you have presented today. Explain that over the next few days they will have a chance to play with all of the different things you have shown them. Review your established routines with the children and discuss any new rules. Direct groups to the Plasticine center or to the bins of materials.

While exploring the materials, children may spontaneously create patterns. These children may be ready for more challenging patterns. Observe them to determine how comfortable they are creating patterns. This information will help you determine an appropriate entry level to this unit. For example, if a child is creating linear patterns with confidence, it would be appropriate to involve her or him in activities of Section 2 at the outset.

Some children may continue to sort materials. It is suggested that you note any further progress to keep an up-to-date record.

2. Tap a Pattern PS

Invite the children to sit in a circle. Give each child 3 different objects, e.g., block, card, bean, which they place on their laps. Gently tap every other child on the head. Ask the children who were tapped to take a specified object, e.g., a block, and place it on the floor in front of them. Then ask the other children to place a different object, e.g., a card, on the floor. Say, **Look, we've made a pattern**. Chant the pattern with the children as you point to each object, e.g., **block, card, block, card, block, card**. Ask the children to return the objects to their laps; then tap out a new pattern. Invite the children to suggest ways of reading the new pattern before the group chants the pattern.

If there is an uneven number of children in the group, you should join the circle after the tapping is complete so that the pattern continues around the circle.

The children should experience different types of patterns in this game. Tap every third child to create an aabaabaab pattern. Use 3 different types of taps to form an abcabcabc pattern, e.g., tap on head, tap on knee, tap on shoulder.

Variation

Play Tap a Pattern with different materials. Provide the children with 2 or 3 new types of materials.

To increase the level of difficulty, provide one type of material with different attributes, e.g., rough paper, smooth paper.

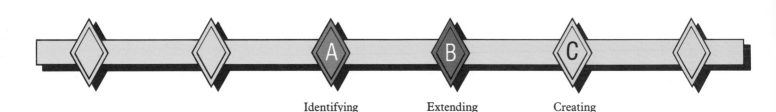

Identifying
Patterns

Extending
Patterns

Creating
Patterns

3. Read My Pattern   PS A

Invite the children to sit in a group around bins of sorted materials and a long strip of paper. Ask the children to watch closely. Make an ababab pattern on the long strip of paper. Say, **I've made a pattern!** Ask a volunteer to read the pattern, e.g., **bead, macaroni, bead, macaroni, bead, macaroni.** Once the child has read the pattern, have all the children chant the pattern. Challenge the children to think of a new way to read the pattern, e.g., **round, flat, round, flat, round, flat; plastic, food, plastic, food, plastic, food; short, long, short, long, short, long.** Return the materials to the bins. Make a new pattern and repeat the process several times.

Meeting Individual Needs

If the children read ababab patterns very easily, you may wish to try a variety of more complex patterns, e.g., abbabbabb aabaabaab, or abcabcabc.

4. Whisper a People Pattern   PS A

Divide the class into 2 groups: a pattern group and an audience group. Invite the pattern group to line up in front of the audience. Whisper directions to these children and guide them in forming a pattern, e.g., forward, backward, forward, backward, forward, backward. Invite the children in the audience group to guess the whispered people pattern. Once the whispered people pattern is identified, have the children chant the pattern as you point to each member of the group. Have the groups switch roles.

This game will generate discussion on the many ways one pattern can be described. It is extremely important that any reasonable suggestion for the pattern labels be acknowledged and reinforced.

5. Plip, Plip, Plop!   PS B

Invite the children to sit in a circle. Ask them if they remember the sound the toothpaste made as it hit Ted's sink. (See the story Plip, Plip, Plop! on page 46). If no one remembers, you may wish to read the story again or simply start to chant, **Plip, plip, plop; plip, plip, plop; plip, plip, plop.** As you say, **plip,** clap your hands; as you say **plop,** pat your knees. Invite the children to make this sound pattern with you. Once the children have mastered the **plip, plip, plop** pattern, you may wish to create other sound patterns for them to repeat and extend.

Possible sound patterns include:
- *snap, clap; snap, clap; snap, clap; (snap your fingers for "snap", clap hands for "clap").*
- *pat, thud, thud; pat, thud, thud; pat, thud, thud (pat your knees for "pat", stamp your feet for "thud").*
- *snap, clap, pat; snap, clap, pat; snap, clap, pat.*
You may wish to invite a volunteer to begin the pattern.

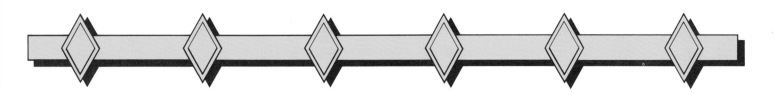

6. Make My Pattern PS B

Invite a small group of children to sit in a semicircle facing a long strip of paper and 2 bins of sorted materials. Give each child 2 plastic food containers and a strip of paper. Ask the children in turn to scoop some materials from each bin using their containers. Have the children place their materials on the floor in front of them. The children watch as you make a pattern on the paper strip with the bin materials, e.g., chestnuts and popsicle sticks. Ask the children to chant the pattern. Have them tell you what comes next.

Invite the children to reproduce the same pattern with their materials and extend it as far as space and materials allow. Have the children sort their materials back into their containers. Repeat, using a new pattern.

Be careful to make your pattern from your right to your left so that the children see the pattern formed from left to right.

Variation

Play Make My Pattern at the pictorial level using cutouts from Line Master 25 to extend strips cut from Line Master 24.

7. Magic Pattern Makers PS B

You will need 2 bins of sorted materials, e.g. rigatoni and macaroni, and a magic wand, e.g., a chalk board pointer. Direct 2 small groups to sit on either side of a long strip of paper. Place a bin of materials in front of each group.

Ask the children to name the set of materials in front of them. Then ask each child to take one object from the container in front of her or him. Explain that when you tap them on the head with the wand, they name their object, then lean forward, and place it after the last object on the strip to make a pattern. Tap children on opposite sides alternately, so that they form a pattern, e.g., rigatoni, macaroni, rigatoni, macaroni, rigatoni, macaroni. Give each child a chance to place her or his object in sequence on the strip. Invite one group of children to read the pattern together. Comment, **It's a pattern! What comes next?** Ask some children from each group to pick another object from the container. Guide them in extending the pattern and ask the other group to read the pattern. Encourage the children to think of other ways to read the pattern, e.g., long, short, long, short, . . . ; big, little, big, little, . . . ; straight, curly, straight, curly, ... Return the materials to the containers. Repeat the game using new patterns.

Identifying
Patterns

Extending
Patterns

Creating
Patterns

8. Let's Extend

PS B

These activities suggest a variety of
ways to further reinforce the concept
of extending patterns. In each case, begin a pattern which shows at least 3 repetitions. Place the patterns you have started
and the necessary materials at different
centers. Add newly started patterns to the
centers when necessary. If you have a limited number of certain materials, have the
children dismantle the pattern so that materials can be reused.

You may wish to display the completed
patterns on a bulletin board, or hang them
from the ceiling. Ensure that the children
have the opportunity to read their patterns aloud.

Meeting Individual Needs

- If a child has difficulty extending seed patterns, ask her or him to copy the strip you have created by laying seeds directly under those on the strip. Have the child read the starter strip.
- The child who is ready for a challenge may be interested in extending patterns that move in 2 directions as illustrated.
- The child who is ready for a more challenging activity might enjoy using a number of strips cut from Line Masters 24 and 25 to make a patterned quilt, wallpaper, wrapping paper, etc.

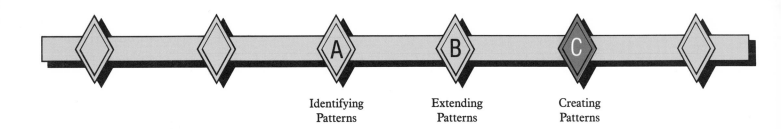
Section 2

Planning the Section

Objective	Level	Activity	Grouping	Program *or* Management Suggestions
C Creating Patterns	Concrete	1. Kernel Pop Pop	👤	You may have children working on the same activity at different work areas or set up a variety of different activities. Establish a rotation system. See page xxviii for suggestions.
		2. Can You Make My Pattern?	👤👤👤👤	Children who require many experiences at the concrete level before moving to the more abstract pictorial level should have ample opportunity to participate in Activities 1-4 with a variety of different materials.
		3. Cube Patterns	👤👤👤👤	
		4. Many Creations	👤👤👤👤	Activities involving pictures cut from line masters are considered the more basic of the pictorial level activities because the children are able to actually manipulate the pictures. Therefore the children can change order, and consider a variety of possibilities before creating a permanent record. When working with the finger paint or chalk, the child has the opportunity to "erase" the pattern. However, there is no opportunity to physically move things around.
	Pictorial	5. Laundry Patterns	👤👤👤👤	
		6. Toothpaste Patterns on Ted's Sink!	👤	
		7. Picture a Pattern	👤👤👤👤	When working with paint, stamps, or glue, the children create permanent records.

About this Section

Many children enjoy creating their own patterns. To ensure that they are not restricted in their pattern making, provide long strips of paper or demonstrate how strips can be joined together.

Encourage the children to describe (read) their patterns aloud and to their classmates.

Some children may create patterns that differ from the ones you have suggested and presented to date. For example, a child may choose to create a pattern that has 10 different items in each repetition. Always explore an unusual pattern with the child to determine whether a pattern is actually created and to gain further insight into the child's thinking.

Observations and Evaluation

These key questions should be asked frequently as the children work with the materials.

- **How could you read your pattern?**
- **What is another way to read your pattern?**
- **Show me a different pattern with these same materials.**

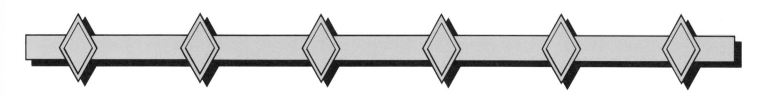

Observations	Teacher Direction
The child has chosen to create only ababab patterns.	Comment on how the child has made many interesting patterns with 2 kinds of objects. Invite her or him to make a pattern with 3 colors or 3 different items.
The child has extended many patterns but appears reluctant to initiate one on her or his own.	Ask the child what object he or she would like first in the pattern, next, next, and next, etc. Continue to question and guide the child until at least 3 repetitions have been created. Comment on the fact that he or she created a pattern of his or her own.
The child has extended and created most patterns with ease.	Invite the child to create more complex patterns such as: abacad, a pattern with 4 (or more) objects before a repetition, a pattern consisting of 2 lines, or a pattern that develops in 2 directions. Consider having the child make a pattern of textures using a variety of materials. Engage the child in the Extension Projects suggested on page 63.

Suggested Materials

- A large quantity of popped and unpopped kernel corn [Activity 1]
- 2 plastic food containers for each child [Activities 1 and 2]
- Bins of interlocking cubes [Activity 3]
- A large quantity of Plasticine in different colors [Activity 4]
- A variety of cookie cutters [Activity 4]
- Felt cutouts and a flannel board [Activity 4]
- Peg boards and pegs [Activity 4]
- A variety of imprinting materials such as keys, spools, blocks, bottle caps, metal nuts, macaroni, bread tags, shells, or caps [Activity 4]
- Clothespins [Activity 5]
- A clothesline or long piece of rope for each work area [Activity 5]
- A cotton swab for each child [Activity 6]
- Finger paints and finger paint paper [Activity 7]
- A variety of print-making objects such as vegetables, sponges, blocks, spools, or Styrofoam chips [Activity 7]
- A variety of brushes such as nail brush, glue brush, toothbrush, mascara brush, basting brush, or different paint brushes [Activity 7]

Line Masters

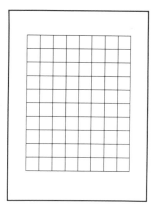

Line Master **26**
Activity 3
1 per child

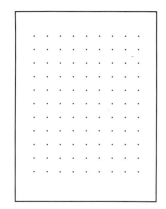

Line Master **27**
Activity 4
A large quantity

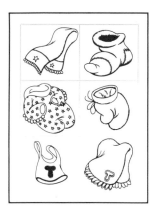

Line Master **28**
Activity 5
1 per child

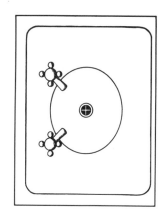

Line Master **29**
Activity 6
A large quantity

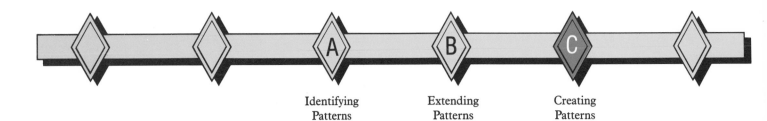

Identifying
Patterns

Extending
Patterns

Creating
Patterns

Activities

1. Kernel Pop Pop   PS C

Each child scoops some popped corn and some unpopped
corn from the bins with their plastic food containers. They
then take their containers to a work area where glue and long
paper strips have been placed. Instruct the children to make
several corn patterns. Have them record one of their patterns by
gluing it to a long strip of paper. The children put their names
on their papers and lay them in a designated place for drying.
Encourage the children to describe their patterns before taking
them home.

*Any easily-glued materials which you do not intend to use for another
activity may also be used.*

Meeting Individual Needs

Guide the child who needs additional support to create a pattern
through questioning such as: **What are you going to use to make
the pattern? Is it sorted and easy to use? What do you want to
place first? After that? And after that? What part repeats?**

2. Can You Make My Pattern?   PS C

Place several bins of materials in a central location along
with several long strips of paper. Provide each child with 2
plastic food containers and 2 paper strips. Invite the children to
scoop 2 different groups of materials from the bins with their
containers. Divide the children into partners and guide each pair
to a work area.

Invite the children to make patterns individually with the materials on their paper strips. When the children have completed
their patterns, have them change places with their partners. Each
child places her or his second paper strip at the end of the
partner's pattern. Each child now uses her or his partner's
materials to extend the partner's pattern to the end of the second
paper strip. The children then return to their places and check
each other's work before sorting the materials back into the containers. Repeat the game asking the children to make different
patterns.

*The complexity of the pattern may be increased by having children
scoop from a third group of materials.*

3. Cube Patterns   PS C

Place bins of interlocking cubes or blocks at different work
areas. Direct small groups of children to the work areas to
create patterns.

Children can record their patterns by gluing squares cut from
colored construction paper, using gummed stickers, or coloring
2 cm paper on Line Master 26.

4. Many Creations

These activities provide children with more opportunities to create concrete patterns. Set up all or any of the activities at a center. Rotate among the children and invite them to read their patterns. Encourage the children to describe their patterns to their classmates.

One child imprints a pattern in a slab of Plasticine while another child arranges cookies cut from Plasticine in a pattern.

The children use felt cutouts to create a pattern on a flannel board.

A child makes a pattern parade of animals.

Children create patterns on a peg board. These can be recorded on dot paper (Line Master 27). A child uses Pattern Blocks to create a pattern. These can be recorded using Line Masters 30 to 35.

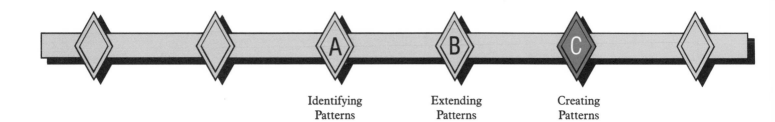

Identifying
Patterns

Extending
Patterns

Creating
Patterns

5. Laundry Patterns   PS

Hang clotheslines or long pieces of rope at different work areas. At each area, place many pieces of Ted's laundry cut from Line Master 28. Encourage the children to cooperate in hanging Ted's laundry in a pattern from the clothesline. Have them read the pattern aloud.

The children can then record their own laundry patterns by gluing the pictures on a long piece of ribbon. These patterns would make an attractive bulletin board display.

These cutouts hang best if there is a space left between the top of the clothesline and the picture.

6. Toothpaste Patterns on Ted's Sink!   PS

Mix a little blue paint into a container of white glue to create the appearance of toothpaste. Place some containers of the blue glue and cotton swabs at the work areas. Give each child a picture of Ted's sink (Line Master 29). Engage the children's interest by telling them that they are going to make a toothpaste pattern on Ted's sink, just like the imps did. Have them use cotton swabs to apply the glue mixture to their page. Have the children apply the glue mixture quite thickly so that a texture is created. Encourage the children to tell about their patterns.

Have the children touch these patterns when they are dry. It is interesting to ask the children to close their eyes, touch the glue, and describe the pattern as they trace over it with their fingers.

60   UNIT 2

7. Picture a Pattern
PS C

These activities provide children with opportunities to create pictorial patterns. Place the materials at different centers.

Encourage the children to experiment making prints with a variety of objects. After they are familiar with the printing process, have them create patterns. Provide a variety of brushes for children to use when painting a pattern. Encourage them to investigate the different brush strokes they can achieve before they begin.

Children use stamps to create a pattern.

If children are ready for a further challenge, you might consider inviting them to create circular patterns or patterns that extend in 2 directions.

Patterning Across the Curriculum

Language Arts

- Develop printing readiness by having children extend patterns such as this.

OOIIOOIIOOII

- Develop letter recognition and formation skills by having children read and reproduce or extend this kind of pattern. Use a variety of media: sand, salt trays, finger paint, as well as pencils.

abc abc abc

- Have the children use their ability to recognize their names to read a word pattern.

Julia Kim Julia Kim Julia Kim

- Children use letters or words cut from magazines, newspapers, or greeting cards to create patterns.
- In conjunction with this unit, you may wish to read any of these stories (see page 318 for an annotated bibliography):
  - *Drummer Hoff* by Barbara Emberley
  - *Bears* by Ruth Krauss
  - *Brown Bear* by Bill Martin, Jr.
  - *I Love the Morning* by Seiji Yabuki
  - *Bonnie McSmithers you're driving me dithers* by Sue Ann Alderson

Art

This unit provides opportunities to explore a variety of art materials. Be on the lookout for patterns occurring spontaneously in the children's art work. Invite the children to talk about these patterns.

- The children may wish to make a patterned frame or border for their favorite piece of artwork.

- Have the children make rubbings of different patterned surfaces such as leaves, corrugated cardboard, the soles of their shoes, brick walls, or imprints on cutlery. Note that the children should be shown how to hold (or tape) a sheet of paper over the surface. Encourage them to experiment rubbing the surface with the side of a crayon. Invite the children to do many rubbings. These can be cut out and used to create a picture or a pattern.

- Cut 2 colors of felt squares (an even number of each). Distribute a square to each child. Encourage the children to decorate their pieces by cutting and pasting scrap pieces of felt on them. When all the children have finished decorating their squares, gather them together. As a group, arrange the squares to form a patterned quilt. Post them in the pattern on a bulletin board with tacks. Note that you can substitute paper for felt.

Science

Have the children make patterns with natural objects such as pebbles, leaves, twigs, or seeds.

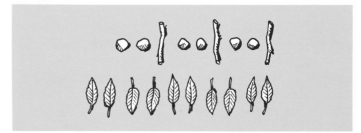

Extension Project

Social Studies

- Take the children on a pattern walk to find examples of patterns in the school or neighborhood. Draw their attention to the floor tiles, wallpaper, brick walls, fences, gardens, etc.
- Have the children bring in patterns they find on wrapping paper, ribbons, fabric scraps, wallpaper or floor tile samples, etc. These patterns can be collected into a class book, posted on a bulletin board, or the children may keep personal scrapbooks.

Music

- Prepare a tape of sound patterns. Leave space on the tape between patterns so that the children can extend the patterns.
- Have children create and tape record their own sound patterns.
- Have the children identify and extend rhythm patterns, such as snap, snap, – ; snap, snap, – ; snap, snap, – . After some experience with a variety of these, some children may wish to create rhythm patterns.
- Have pairs of small groups of children create sound patterns using musical instruments for other children to identify.
- In conjunction with this unit, you may wish to teach these songs:

    - Row, Row, Row Your Boat
    - The Hokey Pokey
    - Head and Shoulders
    - Frère Jacques
    - This Old Man
    - The Farmer in the Dell

Physical Education

- Groups of children make body patterns in the gym or other large areas. Encourage them to describe each pattern in a variety of ways.

Stretch	Bend	Stretch	Bend	Stretch	Bend
or
Pole	Bridge	Pole	Bridge	Pole	Bridge

- The children move around the gym using repetitive movements such as: hop, hop, step; hop, hop, step. Invite children to create their own sequence.

Identify different ways in which the children contribute patterns to decorate the classroom. For example, they could create:

- patterned strips for a bulletin board or large calendar trim
- patterned book covers for their personal notebooks or class library books
- patterns to cover a large surface such as the door, filing cabinet, or cupboard doors.

At a large center place long strips of paper, large sheets of newsprint, construction paper cut in different shapes, crayons, templates; and any other materials which the children could use to create these patterns. Have the children (the designers) sign their patterns.

Number to 10

Unit Objectives

Section 1

A Creating a Set of 1, 2, 3, 4, 5, and 0
B Labelling a Set of 1, 2, 3, 4, 5, and 0

Section 2

C Creating a Set of 6, 7, 8, 9, and 10
D Labelling a Set of 6, 7, 8, 9, and 10

Section 3

E Identifying Ordinal Position
F Identifying the Number Before/
   After/Between
G Identifying the Greater/Lesser
   Number
H Ordering Number to 10

About this Unit

Number

Many children enter grade 1 already "knowing their numbers." A closer analysis, however, often reveals that this knowledge is limited to reciting the number names in order. This rote counting, while it is a very satisfying achievement and one which will assist the child in acquiring an understanding of numbers, should never be mistaken for such understanding.

A child does not truly understand the number concept 3 until he or she understands these ideas about 3.

- There is a one-to-one correspondence between each number name and an object in the set being counted. That is, in counting a set of 3 toothpicks, the child points to toothpicks in turn as he or she says, **1, 2, 3**.
- The number name 3 applies not only to the last toothpick named, but also to the entire set of toothpicks.
- 3 toothpicks are 1 more than 2 toothpicks.
- There are the same number of toothpicks in a set of 3 toothpicks as in a set of 3 trees or any other 3 objects.
- The number of toothpicks does not change if we vary their arrangement. Although the sets may look very different, each has 3 toothpicks.

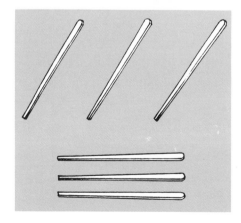

The activities in this unit are designed to develop a number concept one at a time by focussing on the relationship of this new number to the familiar numbers through the notion of one more. The children then explore the arrangements and combinations of this number by manipulating a variety of objects. The many familiar objects are arranged and rearranged so visual patterns and combinations of the number can be discovered and discussed. It is through this manipulation and discussion that the child's understanding that quantity does not change when the set takes on new configurations is heightened.

When the child has demonstrated an understanding of a number at the concrete level, he or she is encouraged to record how many are in the set pictorially and then symbolically. Children are asked to match numerals to sets before they are asked to print them. The skill of associating a symbol with a particular quantity is quite different from that of printing numerals.

When the concept of number is firmly established, children are ready to make comparisons between numbers, for example; **5 is greater than 3 but less than 8; 3 is less than 6, 4 is also less than 6; 4 is 2 greater than 2.** At this point, too, the concept of ordinal numbers can be introduced.

Problem Solving

While exploring the concept of number, the children are also presented with opportunities to develop, extend, and apply different problem-solving skills. They extend their sorting skills in the activities Sift and Sort, page 83 and Number Sort, page 100. They apply patterning skills in Set Patterns, page 89. The activity, Polka Dots, page 103, provides children with the opportunity to develop the strategy of planning ahead. In addition, activities provided in Five Minute Math, pages 66–67 develop these problem-solving skills:

- sorting
- identifying, extending, and creating patterns
- identifying likenesses and differences
- developing observation and listening skills

Vocabulary

- After
- Before
- Between
- First, Second, Third, Fourth, Fifth
- Greater
- Less
- More
- Number
- Order
- One, Two, Three, Four, Five, Six, Seven, Eight, Nine, Ten

Planning Ahead

The next unit deals with measurement and requires several special materials. It is recommended that you begin now to collect and prepare these materials. Non-standard timers are illustrated on page 113 and balances are shown on page 129. In addition to these homemade scales, borrow as many from other classrooms as possible. You might also consider arranging to borrow a water or sand table for the capacity activities.

Ongoing Objectives

- Reading the calendar
- Counting on and counting back
- Recognizing time names
- Discussing temperature
- Problem solving
  - Sorting
  - Identifying, extending, and creating patterns
  - Identifying likenesses and differences
  - Developing observation and listening skills

Five Minute Math

Calendar Activities

- Direct the children's attention to last month's calendar. These questions can form the basis of your discussion:

  - **Did it rain (snow) last month?**
  - **What day was Adam's birthday? What was the date?**
  - **How many birthdays were in (September)?**
  - **Did we go on a class trip in (September)? When? Where did we go?**
  - **Did we have a bake sale last month?**

- Create a monthly mural to record current events. Have each child who has an event to share record it on the mural.

Counting Activities

- Have the children count aloud as they bounce a ball to a partner or jump a skipping rope.
- Frequently draw the children's attention to the Cumulative Record of Days in School. Have them count aloud as you point to each numeral starting at 1. On another day, have them count back from 10 as you point to the corresponding numerals.
- On a signal, have the children count silently as they pat their knees 3 times and then count on aloud to 10. Have the children generate ideas for different actions to perform during the silent counts. Begin counting on from 3 and extend the number of silent counts as children feel more confident and comfortable. On another day, adapt this activity. Have the children count back silently from 10 as they pat their knees 3 times and then count back aloud to 0. For example, **Pat, pat, pat, 7, 6, 5, 4, 3, 2, 1, 0. (Blast off.)**
- Tap a pencil and ask the children to count to themselves a designated number of taps. At the designated number, have them all continue to count aloud.

Measurement Activities

- Make frequent, incidental references to time so that children become familiar with the time of the day's events. For example, these references are appropriate and help children develop a frame of reference for daily events.

  - **Let's start our school day. It's 9 o'clock.**
  - **Clean up, get ready for recess. It's almost 10:30.**
  - **12 o'clock, time for lunch!**
  - **Afternoon recess . . . yes, it's already 2:30.**
  - **Let's start to pack up. We go home at 3:30.**

- Place catalogues and old magazines at a center. Have the children cut out pictures showing hot and cold objects during their free time. After the children have had ample opportunity to search for pictures, have them compare the pictures according to temperature. Display some of the pictures. Hold up a picture, e.g., ice cream and ask, **Is there a picture of something that is warmer than this ice cream? Is there another picture of something warmer? Is there a picture of something that is colder?**

  On another day, you could post 3 to 5 of these pictures and ask the children to put them in order from coldest to hottest.

Problem Solving Activities

Sorting

Have the children sit in a circle so that they can see each other easily. Decide on a sorting rule which involves 2 criteria and state it aloud. For example, say, **If you are wearing running shoes and a short sleeve shirt, stand at the front of the room.** When everyone is assembled, say, **Does everyone standing here belong?** Choose a child who did not join the group and ask, **Should Leah be in this group? Why not?**

Identifying, Extending, and Creating Patterns

- Any of these games: Tap a Pattern, page 51; Whisper a People Pattern and Plip, Plip, Plop!, page 52; and Magic Pattern Makers, page 53 can easily be played in 5 minutes to reinforce and review patterning skills.
- Have the children identify those children wearing a patterned item of clothing such as shirts, socks, pants, or sweaters. Read the patterns aloud with the children, **Blue stripe, white stripe, blue stripe, white stripe.**

- Draw 3 repetitions of a pattern with different colored chalk on the chalk board. Have the children, in turn, select a piece of chalk and extend the pattern. Invite children to begin a chalk pattern for others to create.

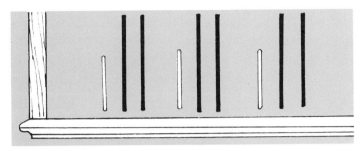

Identifying Likenesses and Differences

- Display 2 books which are familiar to the children. Ask, **How are these books the same?** After the children have described a number of similarities ask, **How are these books different?** Encourage the children to consider the size, color, thickness, titles, and number of pages. Children may suggest similarities and differences in content.
- Display a collection of Pattern Blocks, Parquetry Tiles, or Attribute Blocks. Hold up a block so that all children can see it and, say, **Find me a block from this collection that is the same color.** Invite several children to select a block in response to your statement. Display another block and, say, **Find me a block from this collection that has the same shape (size, or thickness).** If children respond comfortably to these directions, continue with statements such as these:
  - **Find me a block with the same shape and color.**
  - **Find me a block that is the same color but which has a different shape.**

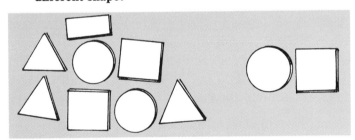

Developing Observation and Listening Skills

- Ask a volunteer to stand in front of a group of children. Tell the children to observe the child very carefully. After a few moments, ask the children to close their eyes. Change something about the child's appearance. (For example you could: untie a shoe, have the child roll up/down her or his sleeves, remove a cardigan, untuck a shirt, put her or his shoes on the wrong feet, etc.) Invite the children to open their eyes, and observe the child to determine what change took place.
- Display a concrete object such as a paintbrush and say, **I'm going to tell you about this paintbrush.** Make a number of statements about the paintbrush. Include 1 or 2 false statements and ask the children to identify them. For example, you could say, **This is a paintbrush. You use it to paint pictures. It is brown and black. You sharpen it when it is dull. It is long and thin.** Have the children identify the false statement and then ask, **What other correct details can you tell me about the paintbrush?**

Using the Story

The story With a Hum and a Hum and a Ho introduces creating sets through the action of adding one more. A practical situation of packing a bag is used. Ted is preparing for a picnic and is verbalizing the number of items he will need, **I'll pack one for me and one more for you.** These actions confirm through one-to-one correspondence that he will have enough for Troll-teddy and himself. This situation forms the basis of the activity Pack Your Bag, page 74.

The story also refers to Ted's practice of having a picnic in the meadow every Monday. You may wish to discuss weekly classroom or personal routines and post them on the calendar, e.g., gym is every Tuesday and Thursday, library is every Friday.

When discussing the story, you may wish to introduce the ordinal vocabulary stressed in this unit by using some of these questions.

- **What did Ted put is his bag first? Second? Third?**
- **What did Ted take out of his bag first? Second? Third?**
- **What was the first thing Ted did to get ready for the picnic?**

The children may enjoy drawing pictures of the events or of the series of objects and sequencing them according to the story.

With a Hum and a Hum and a Ho

Supplementary Material

Ted is my Friend: Mathematics Activity Book, pages 7-10 and 20-26; story boards, pages 39-42 and 51-54; and game boards; pages 45-48.

With a Hum and a Hum and a Ho

Ted's nose pressed up against the windowpane. The raindrops trickling down the glass matched the teardrops sliding down his face. "Monday," he sighed. "Monday means meadow day. A picnic in the meadow, with muffins and tea and toys and our song, and the grass and the birds and the flowers. But it's too wet and cold for a picnic in the meadow, Troll-teddy. It's just too wet today."

Troll-teddy's tail fell between her legs and she gave a heavy sigh. Ted looked down at his feet and sadly wiggled his toes. A tear slithered down his cheek and landed on the rug under his feet. The rug was green; green as the grass that grew in the meadow. "That's it, Troll-teddy! This rug could be the green grass of the meadow. We'll have our picnic right here, and we'll make it just like it is in the meadow!"

Troll-teddy's tail wagged with delight as she watched Ted start packing his picnic bag. "We'll need honey muffins," Ted said, reaching carefully for them, past the flower in the white vase on his kitchen table. "I'll pack one for me and one more for you, Troll-teddy." In went two muffins. "We'll need apples too. One apple for me and one more for you." In went two apples. "And we'll need a blanket too. But we need just one blanket to share, Troll-teddy." Then Ted raced from room to room, packing all the special things he always took on a Monday meadow picnic. Finally, the bag was stuffed full.

"Kites! We always take our kites to the meadow. Here, Troll-teddy, you take the kites." Ted tied two fluffy cloud kites to Troll-teddy's collar. "Are we ready?" Ted peered into the bag.

"We're ready for our picnic in the meadow," said Ted, smiling. "Let's go!" Ted and Troll-teddy began to march around the room, singing their picnic song:

> "Through the forest and meadow go we,
> With a hum and a hum and a ho—
> The grass and the birds and the flowers to see,
> With a hum and a hum and a ho.
> A picnic, a song, what fun there'll be,
> So pack your bag and come with me—
> We'll eat our muffins and sip our tea,
> With a hum and a hum and a ho.
> With a hum and a hum and a ho."

Happily, Ted made his way round and round the room. The kites fluttered and flew as Troll-teddy pranced along behind Ted.

"We're here," Ted decided as he came to a sudden stop. He rummaged in his bag. Out came the blanket. Out came the apples. Out came the muffins and tea.

Then, out came Ted's bubble pipe. Out came his jar of silver suds. Out came his lucky dragon's teeth and his favorite crystal. Ted peered deep into the bag. Then he turned it upside down and shook it. Out came a feather he'd found on the floor. "We'll pretend this is a bird," he said.

Carefully, Ted spread everything on the green rug-grass with the feather-bird, and stared at the meadow picnic he had made. Something was missing. Ted wiggled his toes and thought.

Suddenly, Ted said, "Stay here, Troll-teddy. I'll be right back!"

Ted ran round and round the room retracing their steps. He made his way in and out of the kitchen. Then round and round he went until he plopped himself beside Troll-teddy. "I had to go back to the house to get this," smiled Ted as he held up his flower in the white vase. "We can't have a Monday meadow picnic without a flower to look at!" And Ted hummed happily as he began to serve the muffins and pour the tea.

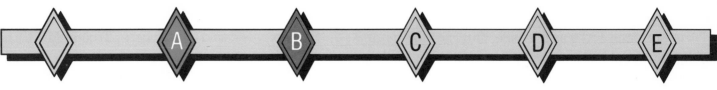

			A			B			C			D			E

| | Creating a Set of 1, 2, 3, 4, 5, and 0 | Labelling a Set of 1, 2, 3, 4, 5, and 0 | Creating a Set of 6, 7, 8, 9, and 10 | Labelling a Set of 6, 7, 8, 9, and 10 | Identifying Ordinal Position |

Section 1

Planning the Section

Objective	Level	Activity	Grouping	Program *or* Management Suggestions
A Creating a Set of 1, 2, 3, 4, 5, and 0	Concrete	1. Pack Your Bag 2. How Many Now? 3. And One More Imp 4. Making Number Arrangements Many Ways 5. Making Number Combinations Many Ways	♦♦♦♦ ♦♦♦♦ ♦♦♦♦ ♦♦♦♦ ♦♦♦♦	Activities 1 to 3 introduce each number by relating it as one more than the previous number taught. In Activities 4 and 5 the children explore number arrangements and combinations using a variety of concrete materials. These materials must be collected ahead of time. Place each material at a different center. Ensure that the children investigate number at these centers frequently.
B Labelling a Set of 1, 2, 3, 4, 5, and 0	Concrete Concrete, Pictorial, and Symbolic	6. Number Charts and Books 7. Show a Story 8. Record the Ways 9. Many Stories 10. Quick and Quiet 11. Make It True 12. Silly Sentences 13. Sift and Sort	♦♦♦♦♦♦♦ ♦♦♦♦ ♦ ♦ ♦♦♦♦♦♦♦ ♦♦♦♦ ♦♦♦♦♦♦♦ ♦♦♦♦♦♦♦	In Activity 6 children begin number books which they will add to on a continuing basis. Arrange a storage spot so that they are readily accessible. Children begin to record their investigations at the number centers only after they have had many opportunities to explore number with concrete materials. These recordings will be elaborated on in Unit 5. They should be filed for further use. Introduce Activities 10 to 13 with sets to 5 to further reinforce the concept of identifying and labelling sets.

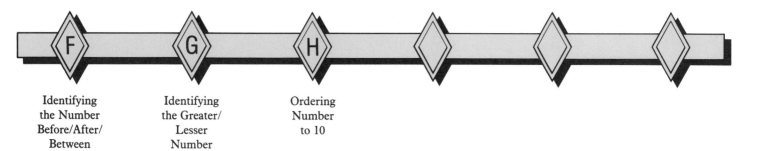

F
Identifying
the Number
Before/After/
Between

G
Identifying
the Greater/
Lesser
Number

H
Ordering
Number
to 10

About this Section

In this section children apply their counting and numeral recognition skills, developed in previous Five Minute Math activities, to concrete sets. It is recommended that you introduce and develop each number only after the child has a solid grasp of the number previously under consideration. That is after the children have demonstrated an understanding of 3, introduce them to the number concept of 4. Though activities often refer to a specific number, they can be extended to any number. Zero is an abstract number concept. Children often understand zero as simply meaning "nothing." In this section, zero is presented as a number representing an empty set. Creating and identifying empty sets is an enjoyable and worthwhile activity which can be interwoven throughout many activities. For example, after children are familiar with the procedures of Activities 1 to 3, include a situation which will initiate a discussion of zero.

- **You packed 0 umbrellas. Show me your bag. How many umbrellas are in your bag?**
- **0 imps were playing in Ted's room. How many imps are on your story board?**
- **There is 1 counter under the container. I slide it out. How many counters are under the container now?**

Number centers are established in Activities 4 and 5. It is important that all children have many opportunities to explore number through manipulating concrete materials at these centers. Each child will benefit from these experiences in a different way depending on the child's level of development. Some children may discover that the number of a set does not change as materials are rearranged. Other children may develop an appreciation of the patterns of number whereas yet another child may discover all the combinations of the number under consideration. These discoveries form the foundation for later number concepts.

Children should begin to keep records of their discoveries only after they have had many opportunities to explore number at the different centers. These records should be kept as they will be used in Unit 5 to develop the concepts of addition and subtraction.

Note that because most materials are already familiar to the children, there is no formal exploring materials activity built into this unit. However, if some of the materials at the number centers were not used in Units 1 and 2, you should provide many opportunities for free exploration of those materials at the outset of this section. In addition, those children who lose track of the number they are focussing on and begin instead to build random designs with the materials may be sending a signal that they need more time to explore materials.

Observations and Evaluation

Children enter grade 1 having had a variety of past experiences with number. In order to provide relevant programming for each child, you should assess each child's grasp of number concepts. This initial assessment should determine which sets a child can create, identify, and label. Though ideal, individual assessments often prove to be time consuming. The assessment techniques suggested here are easy to implement with an individual or in small groups of 2 to 6 children.

Creating sets

Provide each child with at least 6 objects (counters) and a piece of paper to act as a display board. Say, **Show me a set of 2 counters on your paper. How many counters on your paper? Show me a set of 3 counters.** Consider asking those children who are successful at this task to create sets to match a numeral you display.

Identifying and labelling sets

Provide each child with the numeral cards 0 to 5 cut from Line Masters 8 and 9. Display several sets of 0 to 5 numbers. Vary the arrangement of the objects as shown here.

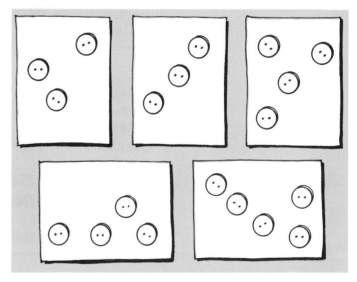

Each time you point to a set, say, **Hold up the number that tells about this set.**

In addition, as you rotate among the groups of children, keep these key questions in mind.

- **How many in this set? Show it to me another way. Another way.**
- **Show me a set of (4). Which number card tells me about this set?**
- **Show me a set with 1 more/1 less. How many in this new set?**

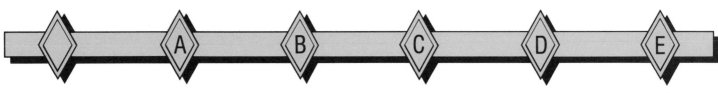

A
Creating a
Set of
1, 2, 3, 4, 5, and 0

B
Labelling a
Set of
1, 2, 3, 4, 5, and 0

C
Creating a
Set of
6, 7, 8, 9, and 10

D
Labelling a
Set of
6, 7, 8, 9, and 10

E
Identifying
Ordinal
Position

Observations	Teacher Direction
The child creates a set of a requested number and then must count to tell you how many are in the set.	The child may not have a solid understanding of number. Direct the child frequently to explore number with concrete materials at the number centers described on pages 76–77.
The child can verbalize the number of members in a set but often chooses the inappropriate numeral card.	Engage the child in the Numeral Recognition Activities described in Five Minute Math in Units 1 and 2.
The child creates and labels sets with confidence.	A child who successfully creates and labels sets will still benefit from exploring number at the number centers. As a child creates sets with a variety of materials in different arrangements, he or she will discover the many arrangements and patterns of each number. You may also wish to involve the child in the Extension Projection, page 105.

- Templates of Pattern Blocks [Activity 8]

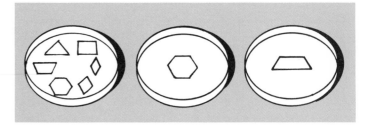

- A variety of dot cards for each number [Activity 10]

- A variety of containers with the numerals 0 to 5 printed on them [Activity 11]

Line Masters

Suggested Materials

- A small clear plastic bag for each child [Activity 1]
- Several small objects for each child such as beads, plastic toys, counters, or blocks [Activities 1, 2, 12, and 13]
- A container such as a plastic food tub, a Styrofoam cup, or a box [Activity 2]
- A large quantity of toothpicks [Activities 4 and 8]
- A large quantity of Pattern Blocks [Activities 4 and 8]
- A large quantity of bottle caps [Activities 4, 5, and 8]
- A large quantity of objects with 2 distinctly different sides such as bottle caps, lima beans spray painted on one side, or coins [Activities 5 and 8].
- A large quantity of interlocking cubes [Activities 4, 5, and 8]

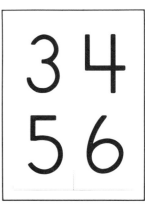

Line Masters **8** and **9**
Activities 7, 9, 10, 12, and 13
1 per child

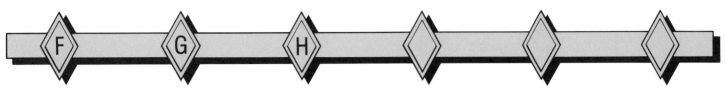

F — Identifying the Number Before/After/Between

G — Identifying the Greater/Lesser Number

H — Ordering Number to 10

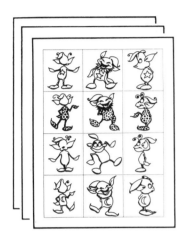

Any of Line Masters **14** to **16**
Activities 3, 4, 7, 8, and 9
A large quantity

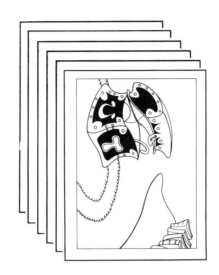

Any of Line Masters **18** to **23**
Activities 3, 7, and 9
A large quantity

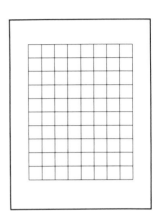

Line Master **26**
Activity 8
A large quantity

Line Masters **30** to **35**
Activity 8
A large quantity

Line Masters **36** and **37**
Activities 12 and 13
1 per child

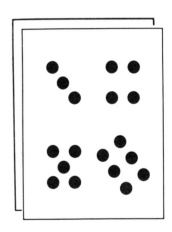

Line Masters **39** and **40**
Activity 13
1 per child

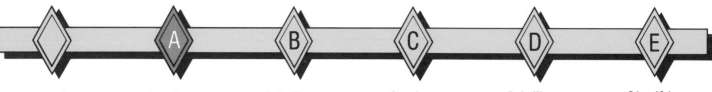

Activities

1. Pack Your Bag

A

Invite a small group of children to sit in a circle. Give each child a clear plastic bag and small objects such as beads, plastic toys, counters, or interlocking cubes to represent various items to be packed. Engage the children's interest by telling them that they are going on a trip; for example, to a playground with a friend, and have to pack their bags before they set out. Hold up a bag and say, **I haven't anything in my bag. At the playground I'll need 1 marble for me.** Place 1 bead to represent a marble in the bag as you say, **1.** Then say, **In my bag I have 1 marble for me but I also need 1 more for my friend.** Place another marble in the bag, as you say, **1 and 1 more is 2.** Ask the children to count with you to check how many marbles are in the bag, **1, 2.**

Invite the children to pack their own bags. After they place the first bead in the bag, ask everyone to count the contents aloud, **1.** As they place the second bead, model the phrase, **1 and 1 more is 2. 1, 2.** Have the children empty their bags.

Ask the children to suggest other places they might go with their bag and what they could pack. Have the children place an (object) in the bag. Ask, **How many (objects) are in your bag?** Encourage everyone to respond, **1.** Ask, **If you put 1 more in, how many will there be? Why?** Children should be encouraged to respond, **2, because 1 and 1 more is 2.** Have everyone count the (objects) together to check, **1, 2.** Extend this activity to the number under consideration.

Variation

Have the children add 1 more and count to check as they create a paper chain, string beads, snap interlocking cubes together, or place small objects in a container. You may wish to store the paper chains or bead necklaces after creating each number and then distribute them again as you introduce the next number.

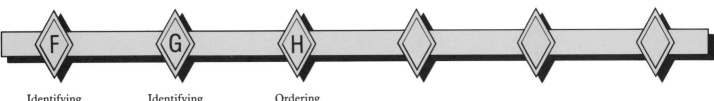

F	G	H			
Identifying the Number Before/After/ Between	Identifying the Greater/ Lesser Number	Ordering Number to 10			

2. How Many Now?

Invite the children to sit in a circle. You will need small objects such as counters, plastic toys, beads, or interlocking cubes, and a container (plastic food tubs, shoe boxes, or Styrofoam cups, work well). Take one object and place it in front of you. Ask, **How many?** Encourage all the children to respond, **1.** Cover the object with the container. Lift the container as little as possible and slide another object under the container as you say, **1 and 1 more. How many now?** Verify the child's response by lifting the container and counting the objects aloud with the children. Cover this set and continue to add objects one at a time until you reach the number you are developing. Repeat this activity with different initial sets.

Extend this activity to include a discussion of 1 less. Display a set of 3, ask, **How many?** and cover it with a container. Lift the container as little as possible and slide an object from under the container as you say, **1 less, how many now? Can you close your eyes and picture how many are still under the container?** Continue to remove one object at a time.

When the children are familiar with the procedures of this activity, provide similar materials at different work areas. Guide small groups of children to these areas to continue the activity. Have the children take turns manipulating the objects.

3. And One More Imp

Invite the children to sit in a circle. Place containers of imp pictures (Line Master 14) within reach of each child. Give each child a copy of the story board of Ted's room (Line Master 18). Tell the children a 1 more story involving imps. Each time another imp appears in the story, the children should add an imp to their story boards, describe that action, and the result. For example, say, **Late one night when Ted was asleep, an imp came out through a floorboard crack.** The children place an imp on the story board and say, **1.** Continue the story, **The imp had planned many fun things to do this night. 1 more imp crept out of the floor.** The children place another imp on the story board. Guide the children to say, **1 and 1 more is 2. 1, 2.** Continue, **Suddenly another imp jumped out of Ted's cupboard to join the others.** Again an imp is added and the children describe their boards, **2 and 1 more is 3. 1, 2, 3.** Continue the story, adding imps until you reach the number that you are introducing.

Have the children clear their story boards by removing 1 imp at a time. Tell a story for them to act out which will result in restoring a clear story board. **The 3 imps were having a terrific time but 1 became tired and went to sleep in the crack in the floor.** The children remove an imp and say, **2 is 1 less than 3. 3, 2.** Continue, **Another imp decided to go outside for fresh air.** The children remove an imp and say, **1 is 1 less than 2. 2, 1.** Continue the story until the story boards are clear. Begin again with a new story.

Variations

- Have the children play And One More Imp in pairs , making up stories in turn.
- Use a variety of story boards (Line Masters 19 to 23) and small objects or cutouts from Line Masters 15 and 16.

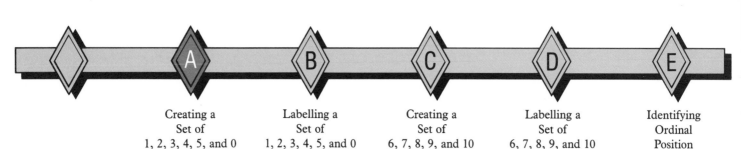

A	B	C	D	E
Creating a Set of 1, 2, 3, 4, 5, and 0	Labelling a Set of 1, 2, 3, 4, 5, and 0	Creating a Set of 6, 7, 8, 9, and 10	Labelling a Set of 6, 7, 8, 9, and 10	Identifying Ordinal Position

4. Making Number Arrangements Many Ways — A

Invite the children to sit around a workspace. Place a container of one of the materials from the number centers e.g., toothpicks. Take 3 toothpicks and place them in an interesting arrangement. Encourage the children to describe the arrangement a number of ways and then invite them to take 3 toothpicks and make their own design. Encourage each child to describe her or his arrangements. **I used 3 toothpicks to make a tepee. In my picture of 3, all the toothpicks touch.** Have the child count the number of toothpicks in each arrangement aloud as he or she points to each one. Invite the children to continue to make as many different arrangements of 3 as they can. It is important that the children begin to see that numerous arrangements are possible before they begin to work at the various number centers.

Give each child a numeral card for the number he or she will be exploring. Guide small groups to each number center where materials have been placed.

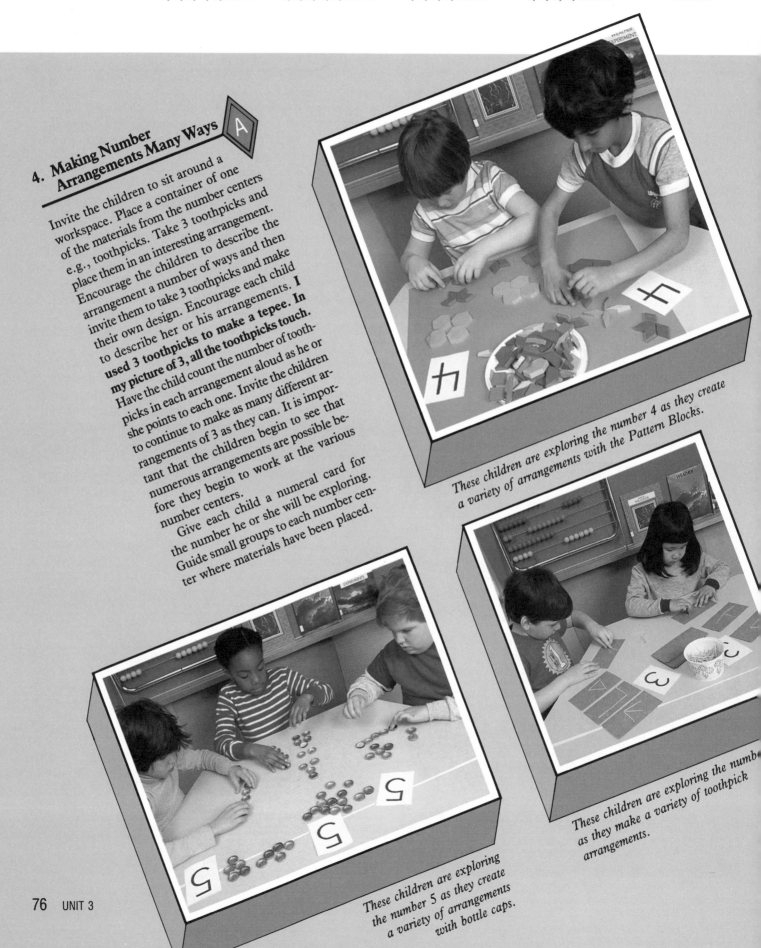

These children are exploring the number 4 as they create a variety of arrangements with the Pattern Blocks.

These children are exploring the number 5 as they create a variety of arrangements with bottle caps.

These children are exploring the numb⦁ as they make a variety of toothpick arrangements.

F G H

Identifying
the Number
Before/After/
Between

Identifying
the Greater/
Lesser
Number

Ordering
Number
to 10

These children are exploring the number 4
as they create a variety of arrangements
with interlocking cubes

These children are sorting junk into sets of 5.
The paper plates act as sorting mats.

These children are arranging pictures
cut from Line Masters 13 to 16
in a variety of arrangements.

Children must be given the opportunity
to explore number at these stations frequently. Initially you may wish to begin
with only one material such as toothpicks.
As the children become more familiar
with the routines and procedures of this
activity, place different materials at the
centers for them to explore.

You may wish to arrange that all children at each station are working on the
same number concept to avoid confusion.
When you have ensured that your record
keeping system works, you may consider
mixed groupings.

It is important that the children have
opportunities to explore number at different centers as each material presents
different arrangements and possibilities.

NUMBER TO 10   **77**

 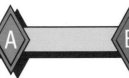 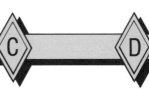

A	B	C	D	E
Creating a Set of 1, 2, 3, 4, 5, and 0	Labelling a Set of 1, 2, 3, 4, 5, and 0	Creating a Set of 6, 7, 8, 9, and 10	Labelling a Set of 6, 7, 8, 9, and 10	Identifying Ordinal Position

5. Making Number Combinations Many Ways **A**

Invite the children to sit around a workspace. Place a container of interlocking cubes in 2 colors within reach of each child. Ask them to make a train of 3 cubes using the 2 colors. Have each child describe her or his train. **My train has 3 cubes, 2 are blue and 1 is red.** Have the children make as many different combinations of 3 as they can. Encourage the children to describe these combinations as they create them.

On another day invite the children to sit around a workspace. Place a container of small objects with 2 distinctly different sides such as bottle caps, coins, or lima beans spray painted on one side within reach of each child. Ask each child to select 3 bottle caps and hold them a reasonable distance from the surface (floor or table). Have them drop the bottle caps. Ask each child to describe how their bottle caps landed: **I dropped 3 caps. 2 landed cork side up, 1 landed metal side up.** Have them place this set aside, select another 3 bottle caps, and repeat the process. Continue this as a group activity until you think that the children can work independently. Guide them to the number centers to explore number combinations.

Note that when children describe number combinations, they describe the quantities of 2 subsets. For example, a train of 3 interlocking cubes can be described as 2 blue and 1 red; 3 bottle caps can be described as 3 facing up, 0 facing down. Note that the focus is on the total set created. Children should have many opportunities to explore number combinations.

6. Number Charts and Books **B**

Invite the children to sit in a circle. Post a piece of chart paper with the title "One . . . 1" and have the children read the title aloud. Challenge the children to identify things that there is only 1 of in the classroom. Have a child bring the item to the circle or point it out for all to see. List and sketch each appropriate response under the phrase, "In our class we have:". Help the children read each phrase after it is recorded. Read the entire chart aloud with the children.

Have the children begin their number books. Provide each child with a large piece of construction paper to make a folder and a sheet of paper. Invite them to print "1" (and, if you wish, "one") on the top of their page. Have the children cut and paste a picture of one object from a magazine or draw a picture of an object. You may wish to have the children continue this book as numbers are introduced or make a book all about "one" Have the children add to these books on ensuing days.

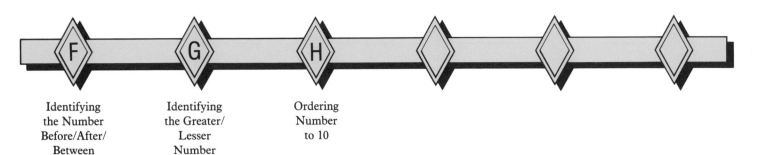

F	G	H			
Identifying the Number Before/After/ Between	Identifying the Greater/ Lesser Number	Ordering Number to 10			

On another day, list things that naturally appear in pairs on a "Two . . . 2" chart. After the charts 1 and 2 have been developed, begin a "Zero . . . 0" chart. This chart could list things which do not appear in the classroom. Help develop the children's understanding by asking, **How many elephants in our room?** The phrase, how many, focusses the children's attention on zero as a number rather than as another word for nothing.

Leave all the number charts posted and encourage the children to think of other items to add to the different lists. Each day set aside some time to record the children's observations. Continue to create charts for 3, 4, and 5 if interest remains high.

Note that to date children should have had many opportunities to practice forming numerals as suggested in the Five Minute Math activities of Units 1 and 2. In addition you may wish to duplicate copies of the charts omitting the numerals. The children can then record the numeral beside each object. These mini-charts may be read to a friend or family member.

Variation

Have the children create a display of labelled sets in any of the ways illustrated.

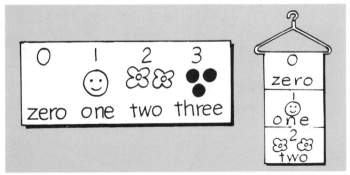

Meeting Individual Needs

Children who appear ready for a further challenge may enjoy the independent task of taking inventory at home. Have the children make lists of things they have one of at home, things they have 2 of, etc.

7. Show a Story

Provide each child with a story board selected from Line Masters 18 to 23, a set of numeral cards cut from Line Masters 8 and 9, a handful of small objects such as counters, interlocking cubes, plastic animals, figures, or story characters cut from Line Masters 14 to 16.

Tell a story involving number to 3 for the child to act out. For example, this story told for the forest story board is representative of an unlimited number of stories you can tell.

- **There were 2 white rabbits playing in the forest.** The children place 2 white rabbits on their boards. **1 black rabbit came to join them.** The children place 1 black rabbit. **How many rabbits were playing altogether?** The children respond, **There were 3 rabbits playing.** Continue, **Which number card tells us about this story. Place it beside your board.** The children select the numeral 3 card and place it by their story board.

  Check to see, that all children have selected an appropriate numeral card before you begin a new story.

- **A squirrel, a mouse, and a rabbit were playing a game of tag up and down the trees. Count the animals.**

Repeat the process as long as interest is maintained. Encourage the children to contribute stories for their classmates to act out on the story boards. Have the children work in pairs. In turn, the children tell stories for their partners to act out.

◇ — A — B — C — D — E

| Creating a Set of 1, 2, 3, 4, 5, and 0 | Labelling a Set of 1, 2, 3, 4, 5, and 0 | Creating a Set of 6, 7, 8, 9, and 10 | Labelling a Set of 6, 7, 8, 9, and 10 | Identifying Ordinal Position |

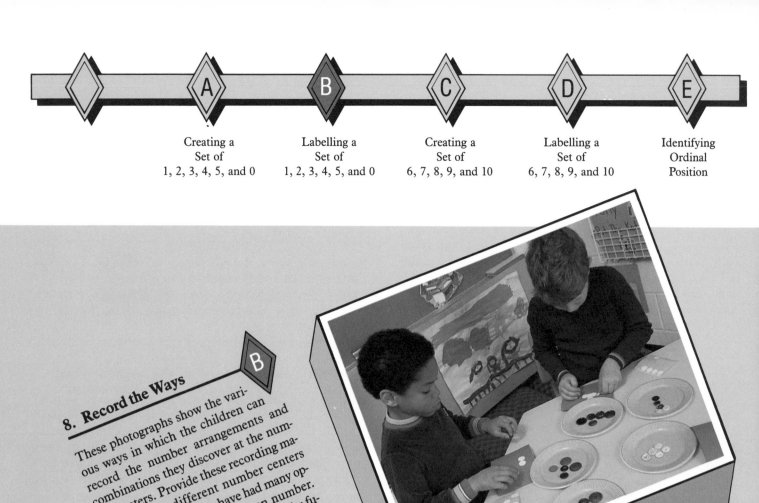

8. Record the Ways B

These photographs show the various ways in which the children can record the number arrangements and combinations they discover at the number centers. Provide these recording materials at the different number centers only after the children have had many opportunities to explore a given number. These recordings should be stored for future use as they form the basis of further number work in Units 5 and 7. These records can be stapled into books, posted on bulletin boards, or kept in a student file.

Children draw or trace the junk arrangements. Gummed stickers or pre-cut circles may also be used to represent the arrangements.

Children may record bottle cap arrangements by tracing the bottle caps, drawing dots to represent them, or pasting gummed stickers or pre-cut circles. Records of the combinations of bottle caps can be recorded by drawing them using 2 colors.

Pictures are glued down on pieces of newsprint.

Children may record the interlocking cube arrangements by tracing the cubes, drawing squares to represent them, or pasting gummed stickers or pre-cut squares. Records of the combinations of interlocking cubes can be recorded by coloring Line Master 26 with 2 colors. This line master should be cut to the number the child is working on.

Toothpicks are glued on colored construction paper.

Pattern Block arrangements can be recorded by using templates, gluing down pre-cut shapes from Line Masters 30 to 35, or tracing around the blocks.

NUMBER TO 10   81

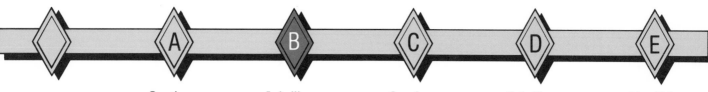

A	B	C	D	E
Creating a Set of 1, 2, 3, 4, 5, and 0	Labelling a Set of 1, 2, 3, 4, 5, and 0	Creating a Set of 6, 7, 8, 9, and 10	Labelling a Set of 6, 7, 8, 9, and 10	Identifying Ordinal Position

9. Many Stories

B

Place story boards (Line Masters 18 to 23), characters cut from Line Masters 14 to 16, and/or small objects to represent the items in the stories such as counters, interlocking cubes, plastic toys, or figures at different work areas. Give each child at least 6 to 8 numeral cards cut from Line Masters 8 and 9 of the number he or she is working on and direct the child to a work area. Invite the children to select story boards, act out stories for the number they are developing on a board, and label each with a numeral card. Encourage the children to tell their stories to you and/or other children at their work area.

10. Quick and Quiet

B

For this activity, you will need to make a variety of dot cards for each number. These are for display purposes and therefore should be on large cards.

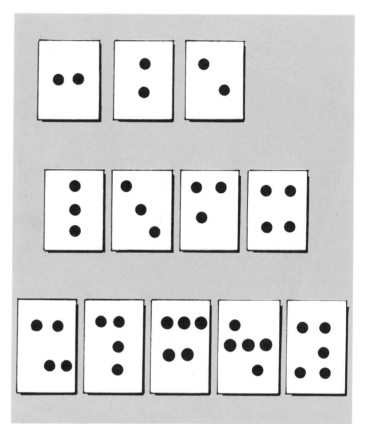

Distribute a set of 1 to 5 numeral cards cut from Line Masters 8 and 9 to each child. Have the children place the cards face up in front of them so that they can see the numerals at a glance. Display a dot card and invite the children to identify the set by holding up the appropriate numeral card. Have the children replace the numeral card. Hold up another dot card for them to identify.

Children should be recognizing the sets visually. This is not intended to be a counting activity. Keep a quick pace to encourage visual recognition.

Gummed sitckers may be used to make these cards.

Meeting Individual Needs

Some children may benefit from a tactile approach to this activity. Make a set of dot cards for children to identify by touch. You may make these cards by gluing circles or simple shapes cut from sandpaper, cloth, heavy cardboard, etc. Place the cards at a center. Have the children close their eyes while they pick out a card and feel it to discover the number.

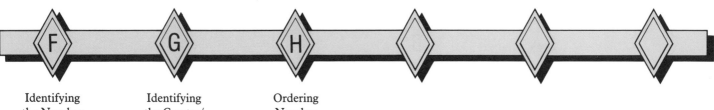

F G H

Identifying
the Number
Before/After/
Between

Identifying
the Greater/
Lesser
Number

Ordering
Number
to 10

11. Make It True

At different work areas, place 6 empty containers with the numerals 0 to 5 printed on them and a container of small objects. Direct small groups of children to the work areas. Tell the children that they are to place the appropriate number of objects in each container.

You may wish to provide different types of number containers and objects at each work area. This will add interest as well as provide the children with a variety of situations to describe.

Variation

Divide the children into pairs. Give each child at least 20 small objects and at least 2 cards for numerals 0 to 5 cut from Line Masters 8 and 9. Ask each child to make sets of 1 to 5 members so that all her or his objects are used. Have the children label their partner's sets with the numeral cards.

Meeting Individual Needs

Children who require more guidance in creating and labelling sets will benefit from using a structured container. These containers can be made from egg cartons or boards with affixed dowels.

12. Silly Sentences

Gather the children around a surface where you can post cards. A bulletin board, chalk board, or an easel would do nicely. You will need 2 sets of numeral cards and picture cards for numbers 0 to 5 (Line Masters 8, 9, 36 and 37). Post a numeral 2 card. Leave a space as big as the card, print the word "hug" and post a numeral 3 card to the right of it. This should create the following: 2 _____ hug 3 _____ . Display the 2 sets of picture cards. Invite the children to select 2 picture cards to complete the sentence. Have a volunteer post these cards in the spaces.

Guide the children to read the sentence aloud, **2 birds hug 3 turtles.** Continue to make silly sentences so that all numeral and picture cards are used. Change the verb in each sentence.

13. Sift and Sort   PS

For this activity, each child will need a set of numeral cards, a set of picture cards, a set of dot cards for 0 to 5 (Line Masters 8, 9, 36 to 39 and several small objects such as beans, buttons, pebbles, or counters.

Ensure that each child has an adequate workspace. Ask the children to show you the items from their collections that mean 1. Give the children time to sort their collections. Discuss their representations of 1 and then repeat the same process for numbers 0, 2, 3, 4, and 5. Encourage the children to describe the sets they create.

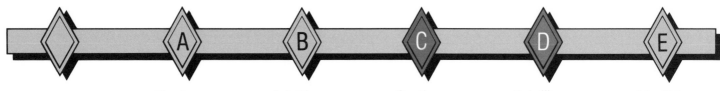

Section 2

Planning the Section

Objective	Level	Activity	Grouping	Program *or* Management Suggestions
C Creating a Set of 6, 7, 8, 9, and 10	Concrete	1. One More Honey Drop 2. One More Penny		Activities 1 and 2 introduce each number by relating it as one more than the previous number taught. In addition, you may wish to extend the activities: Pack Your Bag, page 74; and How Many Now and And One More Imp; page 75 to 6, 7, 8, 9, and 10. While you are introducing these activities to small groups, direct the other children to the number centers set up in Section 1 to explore the patterns and arrangements of 6.
D Labelling a Set of 6, 7, 8, 9, and 10	Concrete Pictorial Concrete and Pictorial	3. Penny Sale 4. I Wrote Six Letters 5. The Treasure Hunt 6. Shopping List 7. Sets of the Sky 8. Set Patterns 9. A Number of Ideas		While you are involved in introducing Activity 3 to a small group, you can direct other children to add to their number books, or record the arrangements and combinations they discovered at the number centers. While children are involved in Activities 7 or 8, gather a small group of children together to create stories involving sets to 6, 7, 8, 9, and 10 on story boards, as described in Show a Story, page 79 and Many Stories, page 82. Activity 9 suggests a variety of games to review and reinforce number concepts to 9. Some of the materials must be prepared ahead of time.

About this Section

This section introduces the number concepts for 6 to 10 inclusive. All activities reference the number 6. It is intended that you introduce the activities of this section, first to develop the concept of 6, then 7, 8, 9, and finally 10. You may wish to introduce Activity 9 only after you have developed the number concepts to 10.

The activities of Section 1 are easily adapted and extended to develop the number concepts for 6 to 10. It is important that the children have many opportunities to explore the patterns and arrangements of these numbers at the number centers. Follow the same procedures as in Section 1. After the children have had many opportunities to manipulate the concrete materials at the number center, encourage them to record their discoveries. Remember to file these records, as they will form the basis of an activity in Unit 7, Addition and Subtraction to 10.

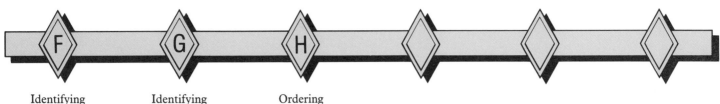

Observations and Evaluation

The tasks described on page 71 can be extended to assess the child's understanding of numbers through 10. As it is difficult to see at a glance how many are in a set greater than 5, you might consider providing each child with a strip of paper divided into 10 sections shown here.

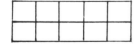

Have the children place 1 counter only in a section. The observations noted on page 72 are also relevant for this section.

As children work through these activities and explore number at different number centers, these key questions can form the basis of discussion.

- **How many are in your set?**
- **How could you label this set?**
- **If you add 1 more (or remove 1) from your set, how many will you have? Show me.**
- **Show me 5 and 1 more (or less).**
- **Show me this number another way. And another way.**
- **Have you made all the combinations for 6?**

Suggested Materials

- A small lump of Plasticine for each child [Activity 1]
- A large collection of pennies or play money [Activities 2, 3, 5, and 9]
- A plastic container with a slit in its lid for each child [Activity 2]
- A collection of old envelopes, post cards, greeting cards [Activity 4]
- Small items priced 1¢ to 10¢ [Activities 3 and 9]
- A collection of magazines and catalogues [Activity 6]
- A large quantity of interlocking cubes [Activity 8]
- An inkpad [Activity 9]
- Containers labelled with numerals 1 to 10 [Activity 9]
- Commercial beads or Cheerios, pieces of straw, or paper squares for stringing necklaces [Activity 9]

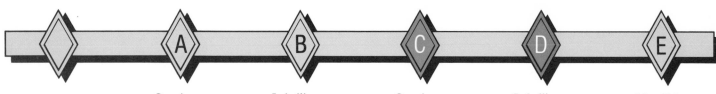

A	B	C	D	E
Creating a Set of 1, 2, 3, 4, 5, and 0	Labelling a Set of 1, 2, 3, 4, 5, and 0	Creating a Set of 6, 7, 8, 9, and 10	Labelling a Set of 6, 7, 8, 9, and 10	Identifying Ordinal Position

Line Masters

Line Masters 8 to 10
Activities 1, 4, and 9
A large quantity

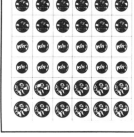

Line Master 41
Activity 5
1 per child

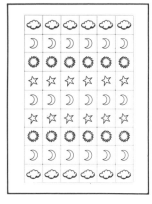

Line Master 25
Activity 7
A large quantity

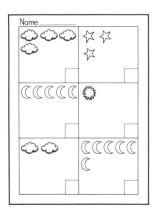

Line Master 42
Activity 7
A large quantity

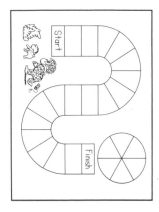

Line Master 43
Activity 9
1 copy

Activities

1. One More Honey Drop

Invite the children to sit in a circle. Provide each child with a paper circle and some Plasticine. Hold up a picture of Ted's honey drop cookie cut from Line Master 8. Tell the children that they are going to make a pretend honey drop cookie for Ted using the paper circle and Plasticine.

Hold up a paper circle (cookie) and ask, **How many honey drops are there on Ted's cookie?** Ask the children to make a honey drop with a small piece of their Plasticine. Have them place it on their cookie and ask, **How many honey drops are there now? If there were 1 more honey drop, how many would there be?** Model the response, **2, because 1 and 1 more is 2.** The children place another honey drop on the cookie. Continue the 1 more pattern until 6 has been introduced as 1 more than 5.

Have the children clear the honey drops from their cookies one at a time. As they remove each honey drop, ask them to describe the process. **There are 6 honey drops; 1 less than 6 is 5. There are 5 honey drops; 1 less than 5 is 4,** etc.

This time, specify the number of honey drops to place on the cookies and have the children add honey drops one at a time until a set of 6 is created. Repeat this procedure several times using different starting sets. Each time the children should clear their cookies by taking one honey drop off at a time. It is important that the children describe the placing and clearing of honey drops.

You may wish to substitute small objects for Plasticine such as counters, interlocking cubes, or buttons. Ask the children for suggestions on types of cookies to create. Making children's favorite cookies will help maintain a high level of interest.

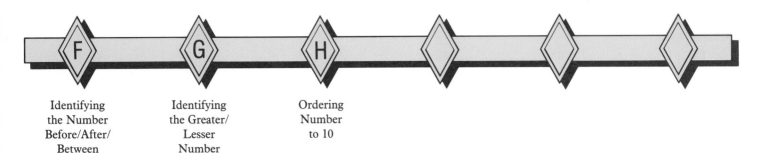

2. One More Penny ◇ C

Provide each child with access to a large collection of pennies and a plastic container with a slit cut in the lid (a bank). Display a penny and ask, **What is this?** Draw the children's attention to the color, the pictures on each side, and the print. Drop the penny in a demonstration bank and say, **1 cent.** Invite the children to copy your actions and encourage them all to say, **1 cent.** Have the children hold up another penny, drop it in the bank as they say, **1 cent and 1 more cent is 2 cents.** Have them open their banks so that they can count to check, **1, 2. 2 cents.** Continue this process adding 1 penny at a time. Change the procedure after the children have added several pennies. Invite each child to place from 1 to 6 pennies in their banks. Have a volunteer tell how much is in her or his bank and add 1 more penny as he or she says, **I have 5 cents in my bank. I put in 1 more penny. How much money do I have?** Invite her or him to empty the contents of the bank to count the collection aloud to confirm the predictions offered.

3. Penny Sale ◇ D

Ahead of time, price a variety of small items. Gather a small group of children around these displayed objects and a collection of pennies. On a posted sheet print Penny Sale and the symbol ¢. Explain the meaning of the symbol. Invite a child to select an item and count out enough pennies to purchase it. Encourage her or him to describe the situation. **I choose the balloon. It costs 3 cents. Here are 3 pennies. 1, 2, 3.** On the posted sheet, record the item and its price. Continue to invite the children to select items and the corresponding number of pennies and record each choice.

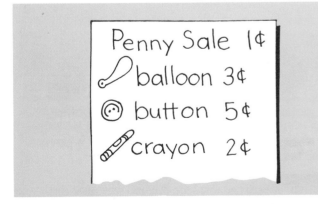

Have the children return all the items selected to the display area. Ask, **What costs 3 cents? If you had 7 cents, what could you buy?** Note that there is more than one answer to this last question. This situation presents an opportunity to compare numbers using the terms more and less.

4. I Wrote Six Letters ◇ D

For this activity you will need a large collection of old envelopes, post cards, greeting cards or papers to represent letters. You will also need numeral cards (0 to 6) cut from Line Masters 8 and 9. There should be enough so that each child receives a card.

Invite the children to sit in a circle. Place a numeral card face down in front of each child with instructions not to peek. Scatter the letters all around the outside of the circle. Demonstrate to the children how they will pass the numeral cards by sliding them along the floor to the next child. Explain that they are to pass the cards for the duration of the song. Begin to pass the cards and chant:

I wrote 6 letters to my friend,
And on the way I dropped them.
A little doggy picked them up,
And put them in its pocket.

Remind the children to stop passing the numeral cards at the end of the song. Tell the children to turn over the numeral cards. The children having the numeral mentioned in the song should now leave the circle to collect the corresponding number of letters and then return to their place. Invite the children to display their letters and state how many they collected. Have these children scatter the letters and continue the activity.

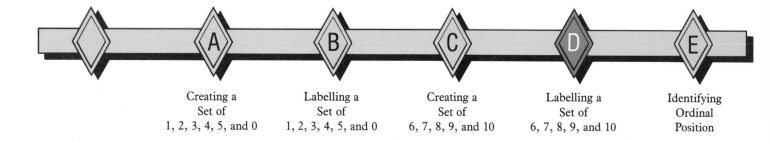

A	B	C	D	E
Creating a Set of 1, 2, 3, 4, 5, and 0	Labelling a Set of 1, 2, 3, 4, 5, and 0	Creating a Set of 6, 7, 8, 9, and 10	Labelling a Set of 6, 7, 8, 9, and 10	Identifying Ordinal Position

5. The Treasure Hunt

D

Direct children to work areas where a collection of pennies or penny cutouts from Line Master 41 have been placed. Have the children make a rubbing of a collection of pennies or cut and paste a collection. Ask them to record the total value of the coins and their names on the back of the sheet. Give the children the opportunity to draw an outline of a treasure chest around the coins before you gather them around a display area.

Collect the treasure chests and display 3 to 5 of them so that they are easy to see. Explain to the children that they are going on a treasure hunt and that you will provide them with some clues that will help them find the treasure. Begin to describe one of the displayed treasures.

- **I'm hunting for a treasure chest containing 9 cents. Does anyone see it?**
- **This is a very valuable treasure. It has more than 6 cents but less than 10 cents. Which treasure is it?**

When a child identifies the correct treasure chest, remove it from the display area and replace it with a different one. When the children are familiar with the process, invite them to take the role of leader.

Try to ensure that you display each child's treasure chest as you play the game over the course of a few days. Eventually these treasure chests may be placed in a center where the children can play the game with a partner.

6. Shopping List

D

Have the children list a random sequence of numerals on a strip of paper. Tell the children that this is their shopping list for a surprise shopping trip. They will have to buy sets of items for each numeral on their list by creating items from the materials available. Direct the children to work areas where magazines, catalogues, crayons, paints, pastels, and large pieces of paper have been placed. Have the children make a picture set to match each numeral on their shopping list. Tell the children to package their sets by drawing a box or a bag around them. Have them label each set with the appropriate numeral. Children should be given the opportunity to share what they bought to go with their shopping list.

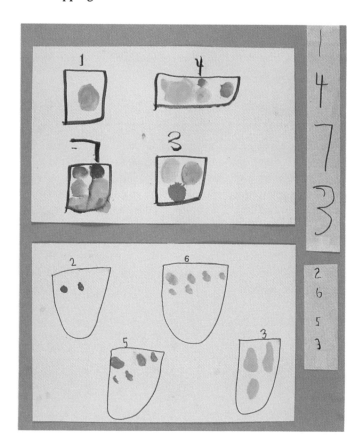

Meeting Individual Needs

This activity is easily adapted for children who need further experiences at the concrete level. Provide a number of boxes or shopping bags and small objects. Have the children make a shopping list and proceed to fill each bag with an appropriate number of objects. Ask the children to tell you the number of purchases in each bag or to place a corresponding numeral card in each one.

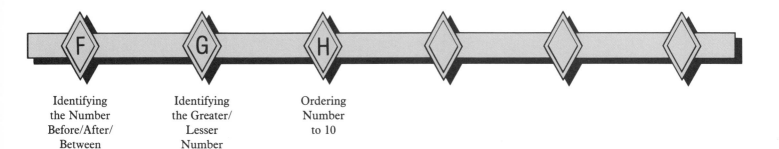

7. Sets of the Sky

Place pictures of the sun, moon, stars, and clouds cut from copies of Line Master 25 at work areas. Distribute a copy of Line Master 42 to each child. Ask the children to identify the number of items in each section. Tell the students that you are going to call out some numbers for them to write in the small boxes in each section. Note that you must dictate a number greater than the number of objects illustrated in each set. Direct the children to work areas to complete each set by gluing the appropriate number of pictures in the sections. As you rotate among the children, ask, **How many were in the box? How many did you add to make (6)?**

The numeral boxes have been left blank to provide flexibility in using this line master. You may wish to focus on one number such as 6. The children then form all sets to equal 6. They may draw the set or cut and paste as suggested here. The same activity may be used several times by having the children insert different numerals in the boxes. Alternatively, you may wish to record the numerals before you distribute the sheets.

This activity provides the children with the opportunity to apply their counting on skills which have been introduced in Five Minute Math and the activity How Many Now?, page 75.

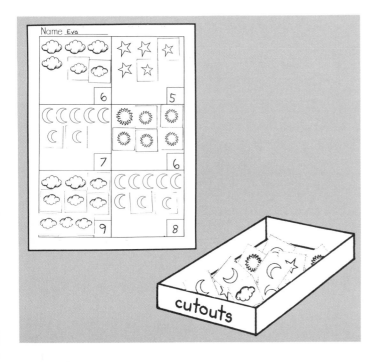

Meeting Individual Needs

Children who continue to need further work at the concrete level may benefit from placing small objects directly on top of the illustrations. They then add objects to that initial set to form a set that corresponds to the numeral.

8. Set Patterns   PS

Invite the children to gather around a large workspace. Place a collection of interlocking cubes (or any other small like objects) within reach of the children. Explain that you are going to make patterns of sets. Ask the children to watch and listen carefully as you begin to create a pattern of sets. Create a pattern similar to the one illustrated.

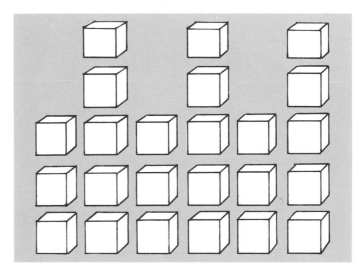

It is important to describe the pattern as you create it. For example, if you create this pattern say, **3 blocks, 5 blocks, 3 blocks, 5 blocks, 3 blocks, 5 blocks,** etc. After you have placed at least 3 repetitions of the pattern, invite a volunteer to place the set that would come next. Continue to ask children to extend the pattern. Encourage the whole group of children to chant the pattern as it is extended further. After the children are familiar with the procedures of the activity, direct them to work areas where they can create their own set patterns. Encourage them to describe their patterns aloud as they work.

After the children have had the opportunity to create a variety of set patterns, suggest that they record one. There are several ways in which they could record these patterns.

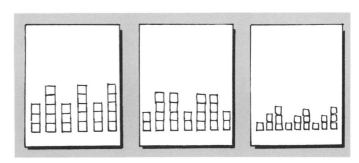

Children can record their patterns using strips cut from Line Master 26, cut and paste squares, or draw them.

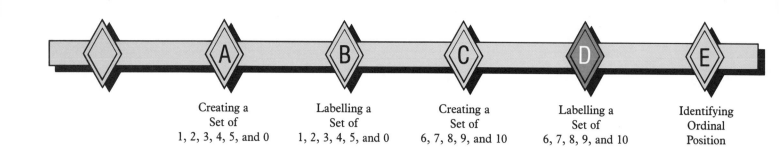

A	B	C	D	E
Creating a Set of 1, 2, 3, 4, 5, and 0	Labelling a Set of 1, 2, 3, 4, 5, and 0	Creating a Set of 6, 7, 8, 9, and 10	Labelling a Set of 6, 7, 8, 9, and 10	Identifying Ordinal Position

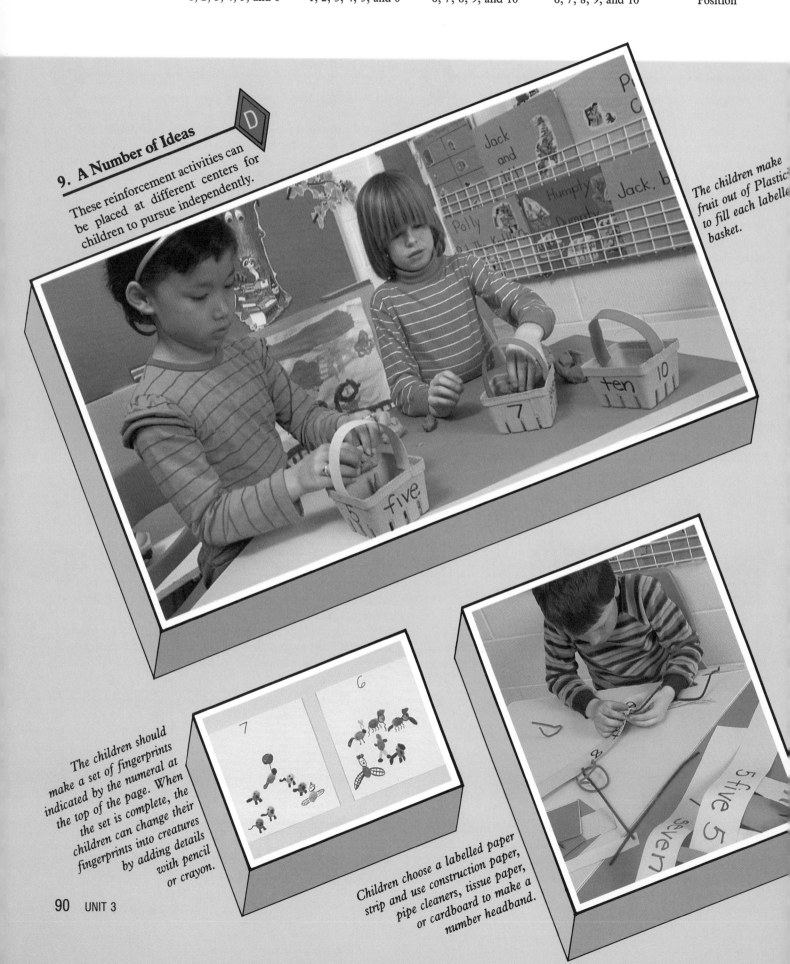

9. A Number of Ideas D

These reinforcement activities can be placed at different centers for children to pursue independently.

The children make fruit out of Plastic... to fill each labelle... basket.

The children should make a set of fingerprints indicated by the numeral at the top of the page. When the set is complete, the children can change their fingerprints into creatures by adding details with pencil or crayon.

Children choose a labelled paper strip and use construction paper, pipe cleaners, tissue paper, or cardboard to make a number headband.

F	G	H			

Identifying
the Number
Before/After/
Between

Identifying
the Greater/
Lesser
Number

Ordering
Number
to 10

The children match each priced item with a wallet of money. These wallets are envelopes containing 1 to 10 pennies. The children can record their matches by drawing the items and making a rubbing of the set of pennies.

The children spin the paper clip and move the number of spaces indicated on the game board (Line Master 43).

Children make a number necklace or bracelet of their choice. Beads can be Cheerios, pieces of straw, commercial beads, or paper squares. This can be labelled with a numeral card.

A	B	C	D	E
Creating a Set of 1, 2, 3, 4, 5, and 0	Labelling a Set of 1, 2, 3, 4, 5, and 0	Creating a Set of 6, 7, 8, 9, and 10	Labelling a Set of 6, 7, 8, 9, and 10	Identifying Ordinal Position

Section 3

Planning the Section

Objective	Level	Activity	Grouping	Program *or* Management Suggestions
E Identifying Ordinal Position	Concrete	1. The Line-up 2. Deliver the Mail 3. Hide and Seek 4. Five Little Imps		Activities 1 to 4 provide a variety of activities with which to explore the idea of ordinal position. You may wish to use 1 or 2 of these activities to reinforce the concept through daily routines. The other activities may be used later to check for mastery or to provide reinforcement for children who need it.
F Identifying the Number Before/After/ Between	Concrete Symbolic	5. The Missing Container 6. Hiding Imps 7. Before and After 8. Who is in the Middle?		In Activity 5 the teacher models the vocabulary before, after, and between. Activity 6 provides the children with an opportunity to practice this vocabulary. In Activities 7 and 8 the children respond to this vocabulary.
G Identifying the Greater/Lesser Number	Concrete Symbolic	9. Compare It 10. More and Less Stories 11. What Do You Think? 12. Number Sort 13. Compare the Cards		As you introduce these activities to small groups, the other children can continue to engage in Activities 1 to 8 independently. Activity 13 can be considered a reinforcement activity.
H Ordering Number to 10	Concrete Pictorial Symbolic	14. Set the Trays 15. Complete My Order 16. Creating Song Books 17. Turn Up the Order 18. Polka Dots 19. What's Missing?		Activity 14 uses the containers prepared earlier for Make It True, page 83. Activity 16 is a reinforcement activity at the pictorial level. While some children are involved in Activity 16, you can introduce Activities 17 or 18 to other small groups or pairs of children.

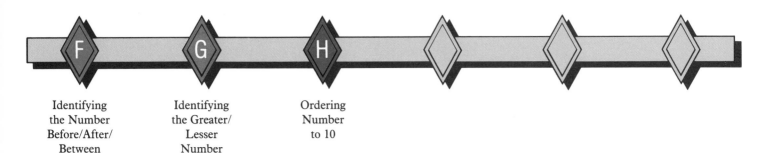
About this Section

In this section, the children focus on the relationship between numbers. These concepts take time and considerable experience to be fully internalized. It is recommended that you engage the children in these activities often and integrate them into following units. As well, there will be more activities to further reinforce these concepts in the Five Minute Math in later units.

Identifying ordinal position may be practiced in the context of daily classroom routines. For example: **Will the 3rd child in line give out the scissors, clean the chalk boards, or feed the gerbil.** The activities in this section give opportunities to explore ordinal position to fifth and to become aware of this vocabulary and the abbreviations 1st to 5th. These activities can be extended to include ordinal position to tenth.

In Unit 1, the children were introduced to the concept of more and less through one-to-one correspondence and concrete graphing activities. They have estimated and identified which of 2 sets is more and which is less. The children have also created sets with more or less members than a presented set. In Sections 1 and 2 of this unit, the children developed an understanding of the relationship between numbers by describing each number in terms of 1 more and 1 less. For example, **2 and 1 more is 3. 2, 3. Or, 2, 1. 1 is 1 less than 2.** In this section, the children explore further the concepts of more and less. They are involved in activities which present the relative nature of number. For example, there are many responses to the direction, **Show me a set less (greater) than 5.** The child discovers that 7 is greater than 4, but also less than 9. Children who demonstrate a solid understanding of the concepts more and less can be encouraged to determine how many more or how many less one set is than another set.

Most children enter grade 1 able to count to at least 10 with confidence. However, often we discover that this is only a rote skill and that children are quite uncertain about ordering sets and/or numerals to 10. The ordering activities involve the children in creating sets in order, completing an order of sets and numerals, and identifying the missing numeral in an order.

The terms "greater" and "less" are used in this book to describe the relationship of numbers. Children, however, naturally use the terms "bigger" and "smaller" when describing numerical relationships. Accept this language, while using the opportunity to model the correct terms.

Observations and Evaluation

You will probably find that most children can identify the ordinal position of first, second, and third. Fourth and fifth positions may need additional reinforcement. Activities 2 and 3 provide assessments of the children's ability to identify ordinal position.

Activities 7 and 8 can be used to assess the children's ability to identify the number before/after/between. To assess the children's ability to identify the greater/lesser number, adapt Activity 7 so that the children respond to the statement, **Show me a number greater (less) than the one I'm showing you.**

To gather more information on the children's ability to identify the greater/lesser number, provide the children with small objects. Display 2 numeral cards and say, **Make the greater (less) number.**

These key questions are suggested to initiate discussion as the children work with the materials.

- **What is the first (second, third, etc.) object in this row?**
- **How many in each set? Which set has more (less)?**
- **How many more (less) in this set?**
- **Show me a number greater than 5.**
- **Show me a number less than 5.**

Suggested Materials

- Cards with the words first — 1st to fifth — 5th [Activities 1 and 4]
- 5 large milk cartons with different colored construction paper chimneys [Activity 2]
- A few old greeting cards, envelopes, and/or post cards [Activity 2]
- 5 containers such as Styrofoam cups, plastic food containers, or cut milk cartons for each pair of children [Activity 3]
- A large quantity of small objects such as interlocking cubes, counters, buttons, beads, bread tags, or pebbles [Activities 5, 9, 14, and 15]
- A container to act as a treasure chest [Activity 6]
- 20 small objects in 2 colors for each pair of children [Activity 11]
- A strip of paper labelled greater-less for each child [Activity 13]
- Shallow boxes labelled 0 to 10 [Activity 14]

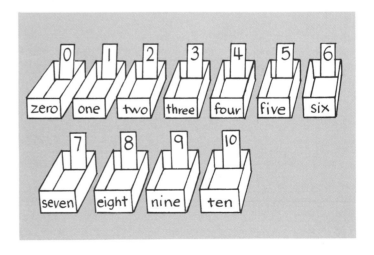

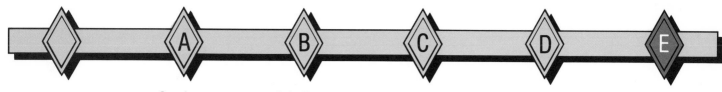

A	B	C	D	E
Creating a Set of 1, 2, 3, 4, 5, and 0	Labelling a Set of 1, 2, 3, 4, 5, and 0	Creating a Set of 6, 7, 8, 9, and 10	Labelling a Set of 6, 7, 8, 9, and 10	Identifying Ordinal Position

Line Masters

Line Master **14**
Activity 3
1 copy

Line Master **44**
Activities 6, 16, and 17
1 per child

Line Masters **8** to **10**
Activities 7, 8, 11, 13, and 19
1 per child

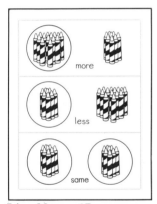

Line Master **17**
Activity 9
1 per child

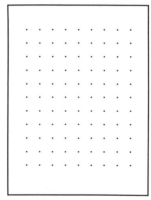

Line Master **27**
Activity 9
1 per child

Any of Line Masters **14** to **16**
Activity 10
1 per child

Any of Line Masters **18** to **23**
Activity 10
1 per child

Line Master **45**
Activity 12
A class set

Line Masters **36** to **40**
Activity 12
1 per child

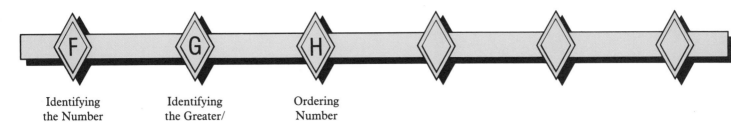

F	G	H			
Identifying the Number Before/After/ Between	Identifying the Greater/ Lesser Number	Ordering Number to 10			

Activities

1. The Line-up

You will need some small slips of paper to represent tickets and a set of cards as illustrated.

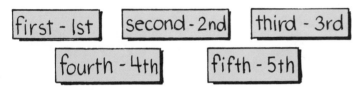

first - 1st   second - 2nd   third - 3rd

fourth - 4th   fifth - 5th

Place the cards in order on the floor at least half a metre apart. Assist the children in reading the word cards a few times before you begin the activity.

Invite 5 children to stand beside the cards so that they form a line. Have them identify their order. **I am first in line.** Tell the children that they have lined up for a reason (to buy tickets for a movie, bus ride, etc.) Give the first 2 people tickets and have them take a seat in the audience. Ask the line to move forward and have 2 more volunteers join the line. Have the children identify their new position in the line. Hand out tickets to the first 2 children in line and continue the procedure.

2. Deliver the Mail

For this activity you will need 5 large milk cartons with the tops slit open and a bag of letters, old greeting cards, envelopes, post cards, or paper strips. Attach a different color chimney to each milk carton "house" with a different colored piece of construction paper. Invite the children to sit in a semicircle. Place the 5 houses in a row. Ask the children to tell you the color of the first, second, third, . . . house. Invite a volunteer to select a letter from the bag. Ask the child to deliver the letter to the house of her or his choice. The child drops the letter through the slit in the top of the milk carton. Ask, **Which house did Lynn deliver the letter to?** Encourage the children to respond together indicating the ordinal position. **She delivered the letter to the third house.** Continue the activity, asking a different volunteer to deliver a letter each time.

Variation

Have a member of the audience group identify to which house the volunteer should deliver the letter.

A	B	C	D	E
Creating a Set of 1, 2, 3, 4, 5, and 0	Labelling a Set of 1, 2, 3, 4, 5, and 0	Creating a Set of 6, 7, 8, 9, and 10	Labelling a Set of 6, 7, 8, 9, and 10	Identifying Ordinal Position

3. Hide and Seek

E

Divide the children into partners. Give each pair 5 containers such as Styrofoam cups, plastic food containers, milk cartons, Dixie cups, etc., and an imp cut from Line Master 14. Have the children sit at a workspace beside each other and ask them to place their containers in a row facing them. Demonstrate the position of the containers for the children. Tell one child in each pair to close her or his eyes while the other child places the imp card in or under one of the containers. When the imp is placed out of view, the child asks her or his partner to guess where the imp is hiding. The child is to respond by describing the ordinal position; **I think the imp is in the third container.** The partner checks the container identified. The child continues to guess hiding spots until the imp is found. The children play again reversing roles.

4. Five Little Imps

E

Distribute the cards first — 1st , second — 2nd , third — 3rd , fourth — 4th , and fifth — 5th to 5 children. Have these children face left or right in a line holding the cards at their side.

Read the cards aloud with the children. Have volunteers identify who is in each position. Engage the children's interest by telling them that you have a poem about 5 little imps.

Recite the poem Five Little Imps. Encourage the children standing to raise their cards when you say the line which corresponds to them. Later, the children will be able to complete the line on their own.

"**Five little imps standing in a row.**
The first little imp said, Let's tickle Ted's toe!
The second imp said, Let's put honey in his shoe!
The third imp said, Let's eat a muffin or two!
The fourth imp said, Drop a feather in his drink!
The fifth imp said, Let's swim in the sink!
Then out came Ted and on went the light,
And away they all ran, off into the night.''

At this point the 5 imps return to their places and pass their cards to other children. These children step forward and repeat the procedure.

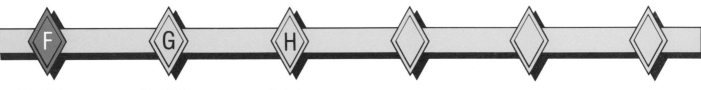

5. The Missing Container

Gather a small group of children around containers of small objects such as interlocking cubes, counters, buttons, beads, bread tags, or pebbles. Have the children makes sets of 0 to 10 in small containers. Enlist the children's help in placing these sets in order from 0 to 10.

Invite the children to close their eyes as a volunteer removes a container from the ordered sets and places it out of sight. The volunteer then tells the children to open their eyes and asks, **How many are in the container I hid?** Encourage the children to explain their answer using the words before, after, or between. For example: **There are 7 things in the hidden container. I know because 7 comes between 6 and 8.** Or, **There are 7 things in the container. 7 comes after 6 and before 8.** The volunteer replaces the set after it has been correctly identified. Repeat this process so that each child has an opportunity to hide a set.

6. Hiding Imps

Invite a small group of children to sit in a semicircle. You will need a container to act as a treasure chest and a deck of shuffled imp cards cut from Line Master 44. On the floor display any card, and ask, **How many imps?** (6) **To put these cards in order, how many imps should be on the card before this card of 6? And after this card of 6?** Continue this line of questioning until the cards are placed in order form 1 to 10. Hold up the container and ask the children to imagine that it is Ted's treasure chest. Ask the children to close their eyes as you place the treasure chest on top of an imp card. Invite the children to open their eyes, and ask, **How many imps are hiding under Ted's treasure chest?** Encourage the children to explain their answer using the order as a reference. For example: **There are 5 imps hiding in Ted's treasure chest. I know because 5 comes between 4 and 6.**

Place numeral cards under each picture card so that the children can quickly recognize the number of each set. Keeping a quick pace will help maintain a high level of interest. Choose volunteers to place the treasure chest on the cards.

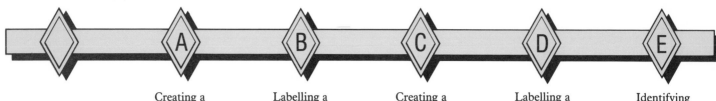

	Creating a Set of 1, 2, 3, 4, 5, and 0	Labelling a Set of 1, 2, 3, 4, 5, and 0	Creating a Set of 6, 7, 8, 9, and 10	Labelling a Set of 6, 7, 8, 9, and 10	Identifying Ordinal Position
	A	B	C	D	E

7. Before and After

Invite the children to sit in a circle. Distribute a set of numeral cards 0 to 10 (Line Masters 8 to 10) to each child. Have the children place the cards face down in order. Ask a volunteer to choose a card and hold it up for the group to see and ask, **What number comes before (after)?** The children select the appropriate card from their deck and hold it up to indicate their response. The child who asked the question waits until everyone has indicated a response and then verbalizes the answer, **4 comes before 5.** Repeat the process many times with different volunteers.

On other days, you might consider having the children record their response as shown.

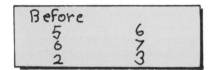

Variation

Have the children play Before and After with a partner. Each child has a set of numeral cards from 0 to 10. Have the children shuffle the cards and place them in a pile face down in front of them. In turn, each child turns up a card from her or his deck and challenges the other child to tell which number comes before or after. The partner looks at the card and says the appropriate number. If a broken sequence is turned up on the 2 piles (for example a 2 and a 4), the child whose turn it is may challenge, **In-between.** The partner responds with the number in-between. When the children have turned over each card in their piles, the children may shuffle and begin again.

Meeting Individual Needs

Provide those children who appear to have difficulty determining before/after with opportunities to work on the mat as illustrated. The children place concrete materials on the board to create sets before and after the one given.

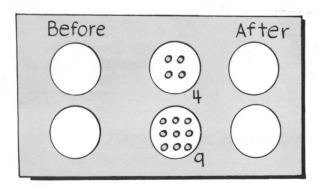

8. Who is in the Middle?

Provide each child with a set of numeral cards 0 to 10 (Line Masters 8 to 10) and invite them to sit in a group with you. Hold up and identify 2 numeral cards, and ask, **Who is in the middle?** The children hold up the numeral that comes between these 2 cards as they say the number. For example: Hold up the 8 and 10 numeral cards and say, **8, 10, who is in the middle?** The children respond **9,** as they hold up their numeral 9 card.

On some days, you might consider having the children record their responses. When children are familiar with the game, have them play in small groups or with a partner.

Variations

• Play the game silently. Do not name the cards as you hold them up. Have the children respond by holding up the appropriate card.

• Play Who is in the Middle? using prepared cards such as the ones illustrated. These cards should be printed on both sides so that the child holding it can read the challenge. Distribute the cards to the children. In turn they ask, **Who is in the middle?** The other children can respond verbally or by holding up a numeral card.

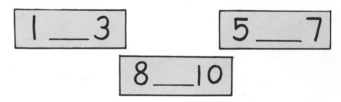

Meeting Individual Needs

Some children may benefit from having a model to refer to. Post a number line or provide number lines for individuals who require a reference.

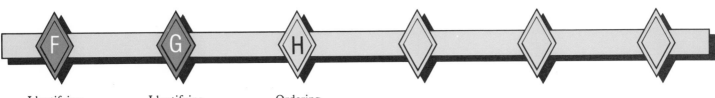

9. Compare It

Invite the children to sit in a circle. Distribute 10 small objects; more , less , and same cards (Line Master 17); and a set of numeral cards 0 to 10 to each child. Have the children make any set of 0 to 10 members with their small objects and label it with their corresponding numeral card. When everyone has made a set, make one of your own with 0 to 10 members on a display board such as a flannel board, overhead projector, or chalk board, and label it with a numeral card. Tell the children to look at their set and compare it with yours. Ask them to label their set with a more, less, or same card this time. Go around the circle and guide each child to describe her or his set in relation to yours. **My set has more than yours. 4 is greater than 2.** Have the children clear the area and repeat the activity. To maintain a high level of interest, invite a volunteer to create the initial set.

Meeting Individual Needs

Ask children who are ready for a further challenge questions such as these.

- **How many more (less) objects are in your set?**
- **How much greater is 4 than 2?**
- **How much less is 3 than 6?**
- **My set has 5 objects. Make a set with 2 more (less). How many are in your set?**

10. More and Less Stories

Provide each child with a story board, (Line Masters 18 to 23) and 10 story characters cut from Line Masters 14 to 16, or small objects to represent the characters. Tell a story which involves creating a set of more or less for the children to act out on their boards. For example, if working with a beach story board, say, **2 fish were swimming close to the shore.** The children place 2 fish on their boards close to the shore. **More than 2 fish were swimming deeper in the ocean.** Have the children describe what they have placed on their story boards. **2 fish are swimming close to the shore. 5 are swimming farther out. 5 is greater than 2.** Discuss why many of the stories are different. Continue to tell stories which involve an initial set and a second set being described as having more or less than the initial set. After the children have acted out a number of these stories, add more action. For example, **4 shells are on the beach.** (The children place 4 shells.) **There are more fish than shells.** (The children place some fish.) **Some fish swam away and now there are less fish than shells.**

If you start out with an initial set of 1 and describe the second set as having less members, everyone will create an empty set. Discuss why everyone in this instance had the same story.

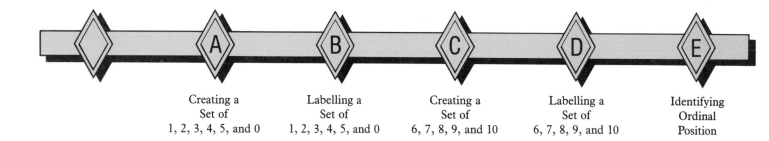

A	B	C	D	E
Creating a Set of 1, 2, 3, 4, 5, and 0	Labelling a Set of 1, 2, 3, 4, 5, and 0	Creating a Set of 6, 7, 8, 9, and 10	Labelling a Set of 6, 7, 8, 9, and 10	Identifying Ordinal Position

11. What Do You Think?

Provide each pair of children with numeral cards 1 to 10, and about 20 small objects such as counters, beans, or interlocking cubes in 2 colors (red and green). Have one child select a secret number of cubes in both colors from the collection and place them in a pile. The child then asks her or his partner, **Do you think there are more red cubes than green cubes?** The partner should state her or his prediction. For example, **No, I think there are less red cubes than green cubes.** Each child then selects a color cube to count and selects the appropriate numeral card to label the set. The child who made the estimate then states her or his discovery. **There are more red cubes than green cubes. There are 6 red cubes and 5 green cubes. 6 is greater than 5; 5 is less than 6.** The children can then reverse roles and repeat the process.

Note if the sets are equal, the children should state this and pick up another handful of objects.

Meeting Individual Needs

Children who are ready for a further challenge will enjoy playing I'm Thinking of a Number. Choose a number between 1 and 10. Have the children try to guess the number you are thinking of by asking questions such as these.

• **Is it greater than 5?**
• **Is it less than 9?**

Keep a tally of the number of questions required to identify the number. Encourage the children to identify the number by asking the fewest possible questions.

12. Number Sort   PS

Provide each child with 2 sorting mats such as pieces of paper, paper plates or cardboard, and copies of picture cards or dot cards for sets 1 to 10 cut from Line Masters 36 to 40. Have the children place their sorting mats in front of them. Ask the children to place the card showing 4 in between the mats. Have them place all the cards showing sets with more than 4 on one mat and all cards showing sets with less than 4 on the other mat. Ask the children to tell which cards they have placed on each mat. Record their responses on a display area. Read this record aloud as a group, **1 is less than 4; 3 is less than 4; 2 is less than 4; 5 is greater than 4.**

Have the children select their own reference card and sort the cards on the 2 mats. Explain that in order to remember the 2 sets they created, they should keep a record such as the one you demonstrated. Distribute Line Master 45 for this recording. Encourage the children to read their recordings aloud to check their work.

Identifying the Number Before/After/ Between	Identifying the Greater/ Lesser Number	Ordering Number to 10

13. Compare the Cards

Provide each pair of children with a strip of paper labelled greater/less at the top and a container holding a large quantity of numeral cards cut from Line Masters 8 to 10. Have each child pick a numeral card from the cup, identify the selected numeral, state whether it is the greater/lesser of the 2 cards, and record it on the appropriate side of the greater/less strip. If 2 cards are the same, the children should then return them to the cup.

less	greater
2	5
7	9
6	8
4	5

You may wish to gather the children together around a display area. Post a few of the completed strips and have the children chant the recordings aloud. For example: **10 is greater than 2; 2 is less than 10. 9 is greater than 8; 8 is less than 9.**

Variation

Have the children divide the numeral cards into 2 stacks. Each child places a stack face down in front of herself or himself. The children turn up the top card in their decks simultaneously. They quickly call out whether they have the greater or lesser number and place the card appropriately on the strip.

14. Set the Trays

Gather the children together so that they are facing 11 randomly placed shallow boxes labelled with the numerals 0 to 10. Place a container of small items such as blocks, beads, toys, or cubes beside the trays. Ask volunteers to place the appropriate number of objects in each tray. Encourage them to describe what they did. **In the 3 tray I put 3 yellow beads. In the 5 tray I put 2 red cubes and 3 blue blocks.** When all trays have been filled and described, invite another volunteer to put them in order. Encourage all children to read the numeral sequence as the volunteer points to the trays in order. Empty the trays and repeat the activity as long as interest is maintained.

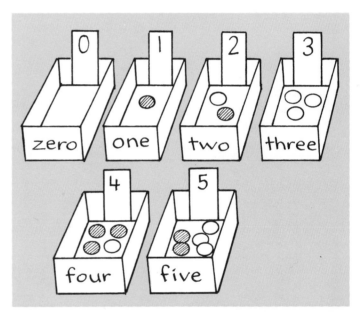

At different centers place sets of containers labelled with the numerals 0 to 10. Place a variety of small materials for forming sets in a bin at each of these centers. Direct small groups of children to each center. Invite the children to fill the containers with the appropriate number of objects and then place them in order from 0 to 10.

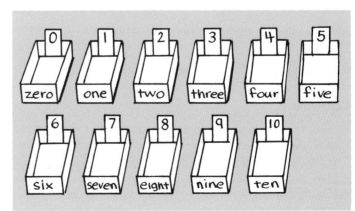

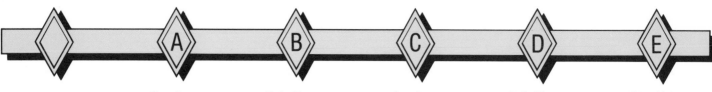

A	B	C	D	E
Creating a Set of 1, 2, 3, 4, 5, and 0	Labelling a Set of 1, 2, 3, 4, 5, and 0	Creating a Set of 6, 7, 8, 9, and 10	Labelling a Set of 6, 7, 8, 9, and 10	Identifying Ordinal Position

15. Complete My Order

Divide the children into pairs, provide them with materials such as counters or beads and direct them to a workspace. The children make a set of materials with anywhere from 1 to 10 members. Explain that they should then say, **Complete my order**, to their partner; exchange places; and continue to make all the sets to 10. For example, if one child made a set of 2, her or his partner would make all the sets from 3 to 10 in order.

Variations

• Have the children play Complete My Order at the pictorial level. Provide cards cut from copies of Line Masters 36 to 40. A child chooses a card and says to her or his partner, **Complete my order.**

• Have the children play Complete My Order at the symbolic level using cards cut from copies of Line Masters 8 to 10.

16. Creating Song Books

Gather the children together. Introduce the song Ten Little Imps to the children.

Ten Little Imps
" 1 little, 2 little, 3 little imps,
4 little, 5 little, 6 little imps,
7 little, 8 little, 9 little imps,
10 little imps a-playing."

You may wish to have the children suggest ways to represent the song through action such as finger plays or mime.

Tell the children that they are going to make a song book for this song. Distribute a copy of Line Master 44 and scissors to each child. Have the children cut out and order the pictures so that they represent the song and the numerical order 1 to 10. The children number the pages and make a book cover before they staple them into booklets.

Note that there are other counting rhymes referenced in Number Across the Curriculum on page 104. You may also wish to invite the children to make up a collective rhyme. The children could draw their own pictures to illustrate an event of their song.

> Imps
> 1   2
> We like you!
>   3   4
> Imps by the door.
>   5   6
> Many new tricks.
>   7   8
> Bang! Goes the gate.
>   9   10
> Gone again.

Meeting Individual Needs

If children appear to be having difficulty ordering pictured sets, provide them with materials such as the one illustrated. These guided exercises further reinforce the order to 10 and help establish other visual displays.

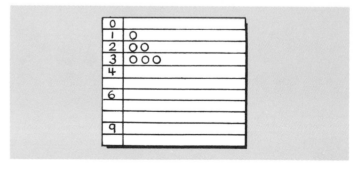

Children place counters on a laminated sheet and add any missing numerals.

F — Identifying the Number Before/After/Between

G — Identifying the Greater/Lesser Number

H — Ordering Number to 10

17. Turn Up the Order

Divide the children into pairs and provide them with a deck of imp cards cut from Line Master 44. Have the children shuffle their cards and place them face down in front of them. Tell the children to begin turning over one card at a time simultaneously. The first child to turn up a card with 1 imp calls out the number 1 and places it face up on the workspace.

The children continue to turn cards simultaneously until a child turns over a card with 2 imps. That child calls out the number 2 and places it face up beside the card of an imp. Play continues in this way until the sequence from 1 to 10 is complete. If the partners exhaust their cards before they complete the sequence, they should turn their stacks over and continue the game.

Variation

Turn Up the Order can also be played using cards cut from copies of Line Masters 36 to 40 or the numeral cards cut from copies of Line Masters 8 to 10.

18. Polka Dots   PS

This activity may be completed as a partner game or individually. If played with a partner, each pair should be provided with a dot sheet (Line Master 27) and 2 different colored crayons. The first player circles 1 dot, the second player 2, and so on, until a set of 10 has been circled. Then the sequence begins again. When a player can no longer circle a set, he or she may get another sheet and take the first turn. To play individually, a child circles the sets 1 to 10 on her or his own. The sequence is repeated until the page is completed.

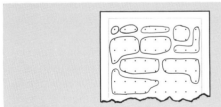

Variation

Have the children try to block her or his partner from being able to circle the next set. For example, in the illustration, the children cannot make a set of 7.

The player who successfully blocked her or his partner begins the next game.

19. What's Missing?

Provide each child with a set of numeral cards 0 to 10 cut from copies of Line Masters 8 to 10. You will also need a set of cards for display purposes. Invite the children to sit in a semicircle facing a display area (chalk ledge, bulletin board, or display stand). Ask the children to lay their numeral cards down in order. Invite a volunteer to order the display numeral cards on the display area. Guide the group to read the sequence aloud. Have the children mix up their numeral cards, and place them in random formation in front of them. Ask them to close their eyes while you remove one card from the sequence of the display board. Invite them to open their eyes and ask, **Which number is missing?** Have the children respond by holding up their numeral card. Ask the children to place this card in front of them and to arrange the other numeral cards in sequence around it. Read the sequence aloud as a group. Invite the children to mix up their cards and repeat the activity as long as interest is maintained.

Rather than having the children respond by holding up a numeral card, you may wish to ask them to print the numeral.

When the children are familiar with the activity, have them play it with a partner or in a small group.

Number Across the Curriculum

Language Arts

- Prepare a set of numeral cards and number name cards for the children to match.

- Write a collective class poem. Explain that in each line there must be a number and a color. You may wish to add other requirements for each line such as something that moves, an animal, or a person's name.

6 blue elephants
walking slowly,

9 pink giraffes
running by,

- In conjunction with this unit, you may wish to read any of these stories (see page 318 for an annotated bibliography):
  - *The Very Hungry Caterpillar* by Eric Carle
  - *Jeanne Marie Counts Her Sheep* by Francoise
  - *Teddybears One to Ten* by Suzanna Gretz
  - *Over in the Meadow* by John Langstaff
  - *Poems for Counting* by Robert M. Quackenbush
  - *1 hunter* by Pat Hutchins

Art

- Provide each child with a certain number of paper strips. Have them count the strips. Invite them to create an interesting sculpture with their strips. After they have completed a sculpture, give them another set of strips. Display these sculptures and have the children describe them.

- Ask the children to think of a number and draw it on a large sheet of paper. Have the children incorporate this numeral into a picture. Post these drawings as Mystery Numbers and challenge the class to identify the mystery number.

- Have the children create a counting mural. Provide each child with a long strip of mural paper. Invite the children to choose 1 thing to draw for a scene of their choice (or a suggested scene). For example, a child could draw a barn for a farm scene, or a house for a town scene. In a following session, have the children draw 2 things for their mural. Repeat this activity until the children have drawn a set of 10 things. Intermittently, have them describe their murals. **In my mural there is 1 barn, 2 horses, 3 goats, 4 chicks,** etc.

Music

- Distribute a variety of instruments to the children. Have the children play a specified number of beats in turn, e.g., 6 beats using the triangle. Have them play 6 beats altogether and then focus on a different number.
- These songs reinforce the concept of number to 10:
  This Old Man
  Ten Green Bottles

Extension Project

Physical Education

Have the children move with one body part touching the floor, 2 body parts touching the floor, 3 body parts touching the floor, etc. Have the children move with 0 feet touching the floor.

Science

• At a center place task cards such as the ones illustrated for the children to complete.

• Melt 6 ice cubes and mark the water level with tape or a grease pencil. Repeat the process for 7 ice cubes. Have the children predict a water level before you melt 8, 9, and 10 ice cubes.

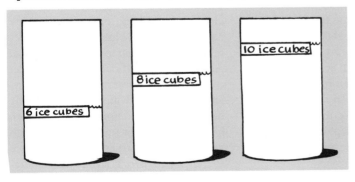

At a center, place different building toys and materials such as Lego, Bristol blocks, interlocking cubes, Cuisenaire Rods, Pattern Blocks, or Parquetry Tiles. Invite the children to build a structure of their choice. After they have completed their structure, have them record the number of different pieces they used. You may want to provide a recording sheet as shown for this purpose. When one structure is recorded, encourage the child to build different structures using the same number (and color) of materials.

These recordings can be posted. Other children can be challenged to build a structure using the same number and type of pieces as the records posted.

Measurement

Unit Objectives

Section 1

A   Sequencing Events
B   Estimating and Measuring Time in Non-standard Units

Section 2

C   Estimating and Comparing Length
D   Ordering by Length or Height

Section 3

E   Estimating and Comparing Capacity
F   Estimating and Comparing Mass

About this Unit

Measurement

Measurement is a skill which children and adults use daily to understand and organize their surroundings. The focus of all of the activities in this unit is on making comparisons. The children consider whether it took them a longer or shorter period of time to complete a task, compare and order objects according to length, weigh 2 objects on a balance to determine which is heavier or lighter, and pour sand, rice, or water from container to container to discover which holds more or less.

Time

Young children usually have a highly distorted sense of time. They refer to yes-

terday, though they mean weeks ago and anxiously wait for their next birthday when they will be all grown up. Most teachers have seen a young child standing ready to go home at recess, or even confused as to whether he or she has had lunch. The activities of Section 1 involve the children in sequencing events that are both personal and familiar in nature. The children also use a variety of timers to determine whether they are performing one task in a longer or shorter period of time than another.

Length

When young children are asked to identify the longer of 2 objects positioned such as the pencils shown here, they frequently choose the yellow one though both, in fact, are the same length.

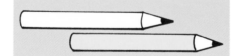

The children are defining length in terms of the position of an end point. Similarly young children might identify the child standing on a chair as the taller child when, in fact, he or she is actually shorter than the other child being considered. The activities provided in Section 2 of this unit involve the children in placing objects on a base line when making comparisons and/or ordering objects according to length. The concept of measuring length is explored and developed further in Unit 10.

Capacity

Even as adults, we are often surprised to find that 2 containers of very different shapes have similar capacities. If you pour an equal quantity of juice into glasses such as these and ask a child to identify the one that contains more juice, invariably he or she will select the tall, narrow glass. The child has relied on the visual clue of the height of the glass rather than the amount of juice. As children pour water, sand, or rice from container to container in the activities of Section 3, they discover that shape is often deceptive and that the capacity of a container is not always what is seems to be.

Mass

The concept of mass is often difficult for children to assimilate, as there may be conflicting visual clues. A small object may be heavier than a much larger one. Also, it may be difficult to make a direct comparison—an object may "feel" heavier depending on which hand it is being held in, or even on how long it has been held. Thus, except for fairly gross comparisons, it is necessary to use a balance to compare masses. It is only through frequent repeated experiences such as those suggested in Section 3 of this unit that the children will understand the function of the balance scale in making comparisons of mass, and will internalize and refine the concepts of heavier and lighter.

Problem Solving

As children participate in the measurement activities of this unit, they develop the problem-solving skills of identifying likenesses and differences and ordering as they compare objects according to length, mass, or capacity. Children must consider cause and effect and reasonable sequences as they order events in Picture Stories, page 114 and Time Clothesline, page 115.

The opportunity for children to further apply and extend their sorting skills exists in the activities: Guess, Sort, Check, page 121; Two the Same and Container Sort, page 130; The Balance of Things, page 132; and Balance Sort, page 133. In addition, activities provided in Five Minute Math, page 109 develop these problem-solving skills:

- sorting
- identifying, extending, and creating patterns
- identifying likenesses and differences
- creating stories

Vocabulary

- Compare
- Heavy, Heavier, Heaviest
- Height
- Length
- Light, Lighter, Lightest
- Long, Longer, Longest
- Mass
- Order
- Short, Shorter, Shortest
- Starting Line
- Tall, Taller, Tallest

Planning Ahead

A solid understanding of number concepts to 10 is a prerequisite for the next unit which introduces addition and subtraction. As you progress through the current unit, it is recommended that you reassess any children whose understanding of number you are unsure of so that you can determine which children need more experience creating, identifying, and labelling sets to 10.

Ongoing Objectives

- Reading the calendar
- Counting on and counting back
- Creating, identifying, and labelling sets to 10
- Identifying the number before/after/between
- Discussing and recording temperature
- Identifying and counting coin collections
- Problem solving
  - Sorting
  - Identifying, extending, and creating patterns
  - Identifying likenesses and differences
  - Creating stories

Five Minute Math

Calendar Activities

- Questions such as these can be included in your calendar time:
  - **How many birthdays do we have this month? When are they?**
  - **Whose birthday is first? Second? Third?**
  - **How many more days to Eli's birthday?**
  - **How many days since our trip to the library?**
  - **How many sunny days were there last week? And this week?**
  - **What was the first sunny day last week? This week?**
  - **Were there more sunny days last week or this week?**

- On separate sheets of paper record the special events noted on the calendar. Present the sheets in random order. Have the children sequence the events using the calendar as a reference.

Counting Activities

- Have the children count silently as you tap the pencil. After approximately 5 taps, make another sound such as ringing a bell or hitting a xylophone or a piano key and invite the children to continue counting aloud.
- Have the children tiptoe on the spot and count in a whisper to a given number; turn to face a different direction; tiptoe on the spot and count in a louder voice back to the original number.
- Have the children count aloud as you point to the numerals on the calendar and/or the cumulative record strip. Cover up the first few numbers and have them begin counting from the first numeral displayed.

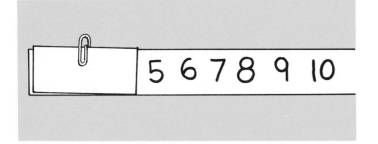

Number Activities

- Any of these games: How Many Now?, page 75; Quick and Quiet, page 82; Silly Sentences, page 83; I Wrote Six Letters, page 87; Before and After and Who is in the Middle?, page 98; and What's Missing?, page 103, can be easily played in 5 minutes to reinforce and review number concepts to 10.
- Ensure that each child has access to interlocking cubes. Make a staircase of towers such as the one illustrated and say, **Make the missing step.** When all the children have completed their step, ask, **How many cubes in your step? Why?**

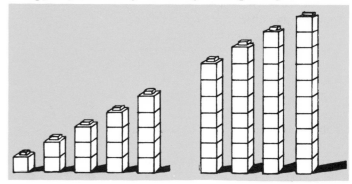

- Play I'm Thinking of a Number. Say, **I'm thinking of a number between 3 and 5. What number am I thinking of? I'm thinking of the number that comes before 2. What number am I thinking of?**

Measurement Activities

- Display an outdoor thermometer and ask, **Does anyone know what this is? What is it used for? Where have you seen one?** Through this discussion, establish that the thermometer is used to measure how hot or how cold it is indoors as well as outdoors.
- Place a thermometer in a glass of cold water and record the mercury level by marking the thermometer with tape or by drawing the level on a picture of a thermometer. Place the thermometer in hot water and mark the mercury level. Ask, **Did the mercury go higher (lower) when it was hot or cold?**

Money Activities

Display a nickel and ask the children to identify the coin and its value. Introduce the word nickel and its value as 5 cents. Ask, **How many pennies would you get if you traded a nickel for pennies?** Print 5¢ and nickel on the board. Have each child take a close look at the nickel and encourage her or him to describe its appearance. Place containers of pennies and nickels within reach of each child. Print 6¢ on the board and ask the children to show you 6 cents. Discuss the 2 different ways children displayed 6 cents. Continue the activity by asking the children to show other amounts of money up to 10 cents.

Problem Solving Activities

Sorting

Present a set of 3 objects such as a pencil, a crayon, and a wooden ruler. Ask, **Which one does not belong? Why?** Encourage the children to explain their answer. For example: **The ruler doesn't belong because you don't write with it. You write with a pencil and a crayon.** Ask, **Does anyone have a different idea?** For example: **The crayon doesn't belong because it isn't made of wood. A pencil and a ruler are made of wood.** Or, **The pencil doesn't belong because it is red. The crayon and the ruler are brown.**

As children become comfortable identifying the object that doesn't belong from a set of 3 objects, increase the number of objects in the set to 4. Invite the children to present the set and have them ask, **What doesn't belong?**

Identifying, Extending, and Creating Patterns

- Be a conductor and conduct a sound pattern. Divide the children into 2 groups. Identify one group as the clapping group and the other group as the patting group (they pat their knees). Conduct the groups to create a sound pattern, then ask children to describe the pattern, **Clap, clap, pat, pat; clap, clap, pat, pat; clap, clap, pat, pat.** Invite a child to take over the role of conductor.
- Display a pattern on the flannel board with felt cutouts. Invite the children to read the pattern. Encourage them to think of many ways to read the pattern. Ask a volunteer to create a pattern and think of various ways to read that pattern.

Identifying Likenesses and Differences

- Display Attribute Blocks or figures cut from Line Master 81. Direct the children to form sets. For example: **Show me a set of 3 blocks of the same color. Show me a set of 4 blocks with the same shape. Show me a set of 3 blocks that are alike (different) in some way.** Have other children consider how they are alike (different).
- Invite a volunteer to select 3 children who are alike in some way, e.g., wearing same color shirt and have her or him ask, **How are these children alike? Is there anyone else who could join this set of children?** Have those identified children join the 3 children. Ask, **Why is Sita not in the group? Why is Jeanne in the group?**

Creating Stories

- Tell a short story with a number in it. For example: **There were 5 monkeys swinging in the tree.** Invite the children to retell the story with a different number in it. You may wish to have the children illustrate their choices. After the children have had the opportunity to retell a number story by substituting a different number, have them substitute the subject or context. For example:
  - **There were 3 boys playing in the sandbox.**
  - **There were 3 boys playing in the haystack.**
  - **There were 3 dogs playing in the sandbox.**

Encourage the children to suggest the initial story. You might consider telling and posting the initial story. Over the course of the week the children could draw their retelling of the story. Gather the children together to hear all their different versions of the story.

- Tell stories such as these for the children to discuss and solve. As you tell the story, act it out with small objects. (The objects can be displayed effectively on an overhead projector.)
  - **There are 4 children at the party. There are 3 ice cream cones. Is there an ice cream cone for each child?**
  - **There are 5 dogs in the backyard. There are 7 bones buried in the backyard. Is there at least 1 bone for each dog?**

Using the Poem

The poem Am I Short? provides the children with a link between measurement and real life. **What is bigger? Who is the tallest? Which is the longest?** These are familiar questions to children. The poem indicates that measurement will give them the answers. The poem also introduces the vocabulary of comparatives and superlatives which the children will need for measurement.

Each verse might be used separately to introduce or to reinforce a specific kind of measurement and could become a basis for discussion about various kinds of things Ted might compare or measure in a specific way.

As an alternative, the complete poem might be used as an introduction to the whole idea of measurement. It would again serve as the basis for an initial discussion and lead into the measurement activities.

You may choose to use it as an action verse by leading the children in a demonstration of the various sizes, heights, or masses.

Am I Short?

Am I short? Am I tall? Am I in the mid-dle of us all?

Line us up, You will see. Short, Tal-ler, Tal-lest, Which is me?

Supplementary Material

Ted is my Friend: Mathematics Activity Book, pages 27-31; and ordering mat, pages 43 and 50.

Am I Short?

Am I short? Am I tall?
Or in the middle of us all?
Line us up, you will see;
Short, taller, tallest? Which is me?

Is it big? Is it little?
Do I put it in the middle?
Line them up, you will see;
Little, bigger, biggest? Which will it be?

Is it heavy? Is it light?
Does it feel to be just right?
Put it on the balance, you will see;
Light, heavier, heaviest? Which will it be?

Is it short? Is it long?
If it's neither, then we're wrong!
Measure it and you will see;
Short, longer, longest? Which will it be?

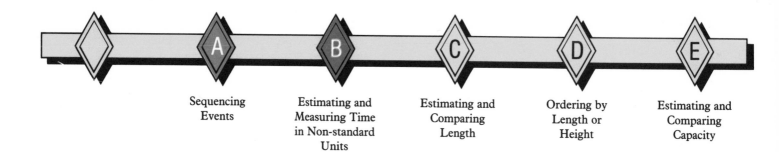

A	B	C	D	E
Sequencing Events	Estimating and Measuring Time in Non-standard Units	Estimating and Comparing Length	Ordering by Length or Height	Estimating and Comparing Capacity

Section 1

Planning the Section

Objective	Level	Activity	Grouping	Program *or* Management Suggestions
A Sequencing Events	Pictorial	1. Before and After School 2. Picture Stories 3. Time Clothesline 4. A Glass of Lemonade	♦♦♦♦♦♦♦ ♦♦♦♦ ♦♦♦♦♦♦♦ ♦♦♦♦	These activities stress language development (before, after, next, last, first). Further suggestions for sequencing activities are described on page 134 under Language Arts. Activity 3 forms the basis for many possible Five Minute Math Activities. You may wish to set up a cooking center where single portion recipes are posted weekly.
B Estimating and Measuring Time in Non-standard Units	Concrete	5. Time It 6. Beat the Timer 7. Watch It Sink!	♦♦♦♦♦♦♦ ♦♦♦♦ ♦♦♦♦	In Activity 5 the whole class is involved in a cooperative effort. This activity introduces a non-standard timer. Activities 6 and 7 require a timer for each pair of children. Materials should be collected ahead of time. Some of the timers can be made with the children, others are best prepared ahead of time.

About this Section

In Unit 3 the children were introduced to the concept of ordering sets and numbers and the associated vocabulary: before, after, between, first, second, third, etc. While sequencing events in Activities 1 to 4, the children apply and extend these ideas.

Activities 5 to 7 reinforce and review ordinal numbers. The children also extend their understanding of more and less to include a comparison of time. For example, **It took more time to clean up today than it took yesterday.**

The objectives of this unit are best met through frequent and almost incidental exposure. Many opportunities arise in daily classroom routines and activities to discuss the sequence of events and the passage of time. Many experiences measuring time and constant references to the passage of time are essential for a child to internalize these concepts.

Activity 4 is a cooking activity. Cooking provides children with further opportunity to focus on a sequence of specific steps and also informally introduces different meaningful measures.

Observations and Evaluation

The goal of the activities in this section is to help children develop an awareness of the duration of time rather than to meet a specific behavioral objective. These key questions should form the basis of many discussions:

- **What happened first? Second?**
- **What did you do before/after recess?**
- **What do you think happened next?**
- **What do you think took longer? Why?**
- **Did it take more or less time?**

Suggested Materials

- Many interesting pictures cut from magazines, calendars, brochures, or old storybooks [Activity 2]
- Pieces of cardboard about 20 cm by 25 cm [Activity 3]
- Clothespins [Activity 3]
- A long piece of yarn or rope to act as a clothesline [Activity 3]
- Ingredients and utensils for lemonade: lemons, sugar, teaspoon, hand juicer, and cups [Activity 4]
- A large clear container [Activity 5]
- Sand or salt [Activity 5]
- A timer for each pair of children [Activity 6]
- A lid with a hole in it for each pair of children [Activity 7]
- A container for water for each pair of children [Activity 7]

Line Masters

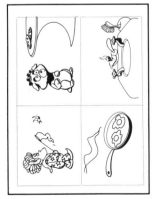

Line Master **46**
Activity 2
A large quantity

Line Master **47**
Activity 4
1 per center

Activities

1. Before and After School

Gather the children together. Engage them in a discussion of what they did before they came to school. Provide each child with 2 or more small sheets of paper (a standard sheet cut in half). Invite the children to draw pictures of the different things they do before coming to school. Direct them to work areas where drawing materials are available.

Gather the children together to discuss their pictures with their classmates. Printed descriptions may be recorded for each page. On another day repeat the procedure for relating events occurring after school.

You may wish to have the children sequence their 2 pictures and assemble them into a book.

Variation

Have the children discuss and illustrate events before and after a non-school activity such as lunch, swimming lessons, or bedtime.

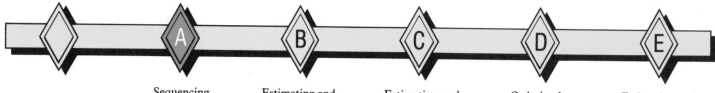

2. Picture Stories   PS A

At different work areas provide large sheets of newsprint and interesting pictures cut from magazines, old storybooks, and/or pictures cut from Line Master 46. Direct small groups of children to different areas.

Invite the children to choose a picture about which they would like to create a story. Have them glue it in the center of a sheet of newsprint. Encourage the children to take time to think of a story for their picture. Explain that once they are sure of their story, they should draw pictures on each side of the picture they chose. To the left of the picture, have them draw something that happened before the middle scene; and to the right, something that happened after it.

Give the children an opportunity to tell about their story. You may wish to have the children share their story with a partner, a small group, or a parent. They may record the story in print, on a tape recorder, on a computer, or on a typewriter. Ensure that the children have an opportunity to explain their stories. Their interpretation of the pictures and the events they depict will determine an acceptable sequence.

Variation

Cut out simple cartoons (3 to 5 frames). Put all the frames from one cartoon in an envelope. Place the envelopes at a center. Invite the children to select an envelope and put the frames in order to tell a story. Encourage the children to tell the stories they create with the frames. Note that some children will not necessarily sequence pictures in the original order. It is important to hear their story before deciding the validity of their particular sequencing.

Meeting Individual Needs

Some children may have difficulty creating a story about a given picture. To point out the various possibilities, engage these children in a discussion about the scene they have chosen. Questions such as these may be asked in this discussion:

- **Who is in this picture?**
- **What are they doing?**
- **Do they look happy? Sad?**
- **What may have just happened to make them feel that way?**
- **Where do you think the people are?**
- **How did they get there?**
- **What do you think they'll do next?**

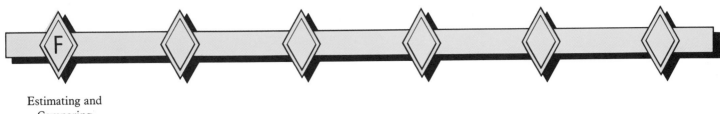

3. Time Clothesline   PS   A

For this activity you will need pieces of cardboard (about 20 cm by 25 cm), clothespins, and a long piece of string or yarn to make a clothesline. Post the pieces of cardboard in a row on a flat surface such as a chalk board. Gather the children together for a discussion of what they do each day in the classroom. Begin this discussion by asking, **What do we do first when we enter the classroom?** Reach a consensus and record the event on a piece of cardboard. This record should take the form of a simple phrase and quick sketch. Continue the discussion and recording of daily events until the last activity of the day is recorded. Promote time sequencing vocabulary through your questions. **What do we do next? And after that? What do we do before recess? After recess?**

Hang the clothesline in a spot easily accessible to the children (from the chalk board ledge). Invite the children to clip the events in order on the clothesline. You may wish to mix up the pieces of cardboard and have the children select the first event, second event and so on until the order is complete. Alternatively, a child could select any event and clip it on the clothesline. The next volunteer could search for and add the event that takes place before or after the one hanging. This process would continue until all events were hanging in order.

You may wish to have the children participate in illustrating these events. Invite volunteers to illustrate the phrases you have recorded. There may be activities which take place only on certain days of the week. For example, gym, library, or music activities may occur on only a few days each week. Discuss the situation with the children to determine a way of handling these events. For example, additional cards could be made to be inserted in the order when appropriate.

Meeting Individual Needs

Children who are ready for a further challenge may be interested in creating a personal time clothesline for a specific day in their week, a time block (from after school to bedtime), important life events, etc.

4. A Glass of Lemonade   A

Gather a small group of children together and tell them that they are going to make lemonade. Hold up a sample set of sequence cards cut from Line Master 47. Discuss the recipe and the order of the steps to be followed. Emphasize why a recipe follows a specific sequence.

Direct the children to the cooking table where the ingredients and utensils have been arranged under each sequence card. Direct their attention to the chef's schedule. Decide who will go first, second . . . and have them sign up. The first child begins the procedure and works her or his way through each step before the next child begins.

Variations

- Discuss the steps that were involved in making lemonade. Have the children draw a series of pictures to illustrate the recipe. This pictorial recipe can be used by the child at home.
- You may wish to provide other simple cooking activities to reinforce the sequencing of steps. For example, by adding sequence cards the children could make lemonade popsicles.

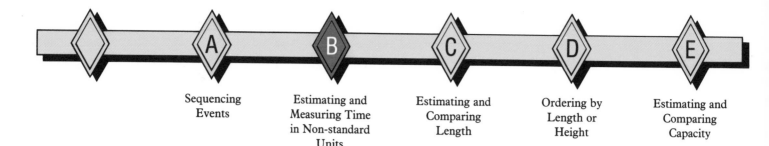

5. Time It B

For this activity you will need a large clear container, a funnel, and sand to make a sand clock. Place the funnel in the container. Use the sand clock to determine how long it takes to complete a set task such as class cleanup after math activities, getting ready for recess, or lining up for library. Clearly identify for the children what will signal the beginning and end of the cleanup.

When the task is complete, mark the sand level on the container. Clear tape with a magic marker line, colored tape, or a pencil mark work well. Label the mark as their first timed cleanup.

Repeat the procedure several times over the course of a few days. Always compare the length of time it took to complete the task with their previous records. These questions may be useful for initiating discussion.

- **What did we find out today?**
- **Did it take more or less time to clean up today? How do you know?**
- **Do you think it will take us more or less time tomorrow?**
- **How often have we timed ourselves?**

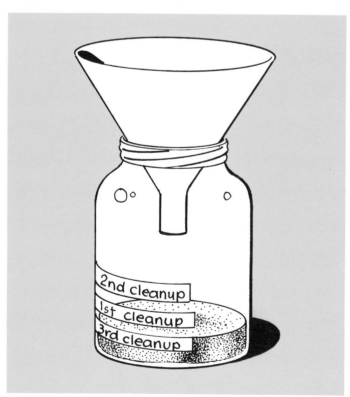

You may wish to use an egg timer for this activity. This may become a Five Minute Math activity which you complete each day. A new activity such as getting a snowsuit on or tying shoes may be picked each week.

6. Beat the Timer B

Each pair of children will need a timer made from classroom materials such as those illustrated on page 113 as well as a pencil and paper for recording the results of their game.

The children prepare their recording sheet by folding it in half to make 2 sections. At the top of one section, the child prints his or her name. On the top of the other section ask the child to draw the timer he or she selected.

Decide on a set task for the children to perform such as putting a specific number of pegs in a board, snapping a specific number of blocks together, buttoning a painting shirt, dressing for recess, etc. Have the children work with partners. One child is the time watcher; the other child is the performer. The time watcher starts the timer and says, **Go**. The performer tries to complete the task before the time runs out. If the child beats the timer, he or she records it in the section with his or her name. If the timer wins, it is recorded on the corresponding section of the recording sheet. You may have the child draw a picture of the activity, or use some symbol for representation. The children reverse roles and repeat the process.

You may wish to set up several activities at centers with different timing materials at each one. Alternatively, the children can perform one activity so that they can see the similarities or differences in their performance during a set period of time. When determining the activity, ensure that it is possible to complete it during the set time period.

7. Watch It Sink!

Divide the children into pairs. Each pair will need a lid with a hole in it, and a container of water. One child is the time watcher; the other is the performer. The performer selects a task to complete such as stringing beads or pieces of straw, snapping interlocking cubes together, or making a paper chain. The time watcher places the lid in the container of water and says, **Go**. The performer begins the task.

When the lid sinks, the time watcher says, **Stop**. The performer stops the activity and places the result of her or his effort to one side. The children reverse roles and the procedure is repeated several times. Each time have the children compare their performance to the length of the first attempt. Encourage them to discuss whether they accomplished more or less the first, second, or third time they performed the task.

You might want to have the children create a concrete graph of the result of each timed interval. For example, they could place each train of interlocking cubes, string of beads, or paper chain they created in each timed interval on a graphing mat or along a table top edge to compare their different performances. You may wish to link this comparison of measurement to a comparison of numbers by counting the number of cubes snapped, beads strung, etc.

A few drops of detergent in the water will ease the surface tension and allow the lids to sink faster.

Variation

Have the children select a task such as printing numbers or drawing circles to perform while the lid sinks. They can record these performances on a strip cut from Line Master 26. You might have the children glue these strips on a large piece of paper to create a graph of their work.

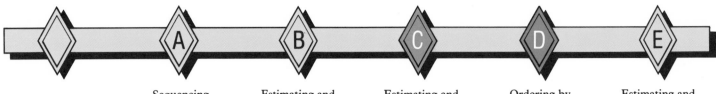

A	B	C	D	E
Sequencing Events	Estimating and Measuring Time in Non-standard Units	Estimating and Comparing Length	Ordering by Length or Height	Estimating and Comparing Capacity

Section 2

Planning the Section

Objective	Level	Activity	Grouping	Program *or* Management Suggestions
C Estimating and Comparing Length	Concrete	1. Detective 2. The Starting Line 3. Guess, Sort, Check 4. What Did You Choose?		Activity 1 focusses on items of the same length whereas Activities 2 to 4 develop the concepts of longer and shorter. Activity 2 is considered a key activity — as a starting line is introduced. The children are introduced to estimating before measuring in Activity 3. If you are introducing any unfamiliar material for these activities, remember to allow for free exploration.
D Ordering by Length or Height	Concrete Pictorial Concrete and Pictorial	5. Plasticine Snakes 6. Place It 7. Place Your Order 8. Making Tracks 9. Tall, Taller, Tallest 10. Height Tapes 11. Family Pictures 12. The Order of Things		In Activities 5 to 8 the children order objects by length. In Activities 9 to 12 objects are ordered by height. Activities 7, 8, 11, and 12 are reinforcement activities. Activity 12 suggests a number of ideas for a center. Place materials at a center and check to know when to replenish it. Children can continue to rotate to this center as you begin the activities of the next section.

About this Section

Children develop and extend their skill of comparing and ordering objects to include the consideration of length and height. They begin by comparing 2 objects. Increase the number of objects only after the children are using appropriate vocabulary to compare the length of 2 objects. It is recommended that you direct the children to read their ordering sequences from left to right. As the children work at centers, in small groups, or with a partner, encourage them to describe aloud the sequences they create.

Estimation is a skill used frequently in daily life. In most activities, the children are asked to estimate which object is longer, shorter, or the same length. The actual measuring of objects follows these estimations. It is important that you accept all estimates. The children should be made aware that estimates are not precise and therefore there are no correct or incorrect responses. Through a variety of estimating and measuring activities, the children's estimates will gradually become more and more accurate. You may wish to use the familiar word "guess" initially with the children. As they grasp the concept of estimation, gradually interchange guess with estimate.

The introduction of a starting line helps children to understand that direct comparisons of length are only valid when made from a common base line. The terminology "starting line" is used because it is familiar to children in the context of games and races.

Observations and Evaluation

It is important that children use the base line appropriately when comparing and ordering objects by length. Circulate among the children while they are involved in the activities to make sure that they are placing objects properly on the base line.

These key questions can form the basis of discussions as you observe children at work:

- **Which is longer/shorter? Show me.**
- **Show me something longer/shorter than this.**
- **Where does this belong in the order?**
- **Read this order aloud.**

If you want to gather more information about how some children compare and order objects by length, engage them (individually or as a small group) in this simple task. Provide each child with an ordering mat (Line Master 48) and 2 items to compare according to length. Say, **Show me the thing you think is shorter/longer.** Ask, **How could you check your guesses (or estimates)? Show me. What thing is shorter? Longer?** Distribute another object and ask the children to place it on their mat. Have them read the order aloud. Say, **Show me the longest/the shortest.** If necessary, repeat the task with different materials.

Suggested Materials

- An envelope for each pair of children [Activity 1]
- A collection of materials for comparing length such as straws, ribbons, popsicle sticks, toothpicks, pencils, crayons, paper strips, or pieces of string or wool [Activities 2, 3, 4, 6, and 7]
- A base line such as paper, string, or wool [Activities 2 and 3]
- Label cards shorter , longer , and same for each child [Activity 3]
- Plasticine for each child [Activity 5]
- Adding machine tape or balls of string or yarn [Activity 10]
- Materials that lend themselves to stacking such as cans, blocks, and cubes [Activity 12]
- Materials to make flowers such as pipe cleaners, toothpicks and tissue paper [Activity 12]

Line Masters

Line Master **48**
Activities 4, 5, 6, and 7
1 per child

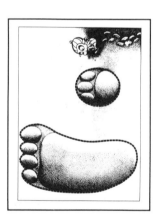

Line Master **49**
Activity 8
1 per child

Line Master **1**
Activity 12
A large quantity

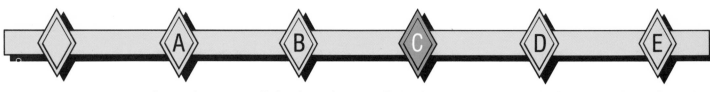

A	B	C	D	E
Sequencing Events	Estimating and Measuring Time in Non-standard Units	Estimating and Comparing Length	Ordering by Length or Height	Estimating and Comparing Capacity

Activities

1. Detective

C

Cut paper into strips of 6 different lengths. You will need at least 40 paper strips of each length. Place 6 paper strips, 2 of which are the same length, in an envelope. Prepare an envelope for each pair of children participating in the activity. Take the remaining paper strips and divide them into bins. Each bin should have at least 12 paper strips.

Invite the children to sit in a circle and empty the contents of an envelope into the center of the circle. Engage the children's interest by telling them that they are going to be detectives. Their job is to find out which 2 paper strips are the same length. Lead a discussion on how to approach this task. Accept all reasonable responses and try them out. Once the 2 matching paper strips have been identified, display one of the bins containing more paper strips and check them against the original 2 until another one is found.

Divide the children into pairs and give each pair an envelope. Place the bins of paper strips at different work areas. Explain that now they each have a chance to be a detective. Guide the children to these areas and explain that first they must find the 2 paper strips the same length in the envelope and then another paper strip the same length from the bin. Once the items have been identified, have partners switch envelopes and repeat the process.

Ribbons, string, wool, or straws can be substituted for paper strips. You may wish to have the children participate in cutting the strips and assembling the envelopes and bins.

Repeat this activity on another day increasing the number of paper strips in each envelope. If, however, this activity has been difficult for some children, you should decrease the number of strips and ensure that the differences in length are quite substantial.

These envelopes can be stored in a shoe box and be available to the children so that they can engage in more detective work if they are so motivated.

2. The Starting Line

C

Invite the children to sit in a circle around several bins of materials. Ask each child to take a handful of objects from a bin. Distribute a piece of paper to each child. Have the children run their finger lightly along the straight line made by the bottom of the paper. Tell them that this will be the starting line for comparing the lengths of different objects. Explain that the starting line provides each object with a fair chance just like the starting line for runners in races.

Have the children pick an object from their collection and place it very carefully on the starting line. This object will be used for comparison. Give verbal instructions such as these:

- **Pick an object you think is shorter/longer. Place it on the starting line beside your other object to check if it is shorter/longer.**
- **Put your thumb on the longer object.**
- **Touch the shorter object.**

Take the children through several examples of longer and shorter picking a new reference object.

There are a number of different items the children could use as starting lines such as the edge of a table, a floor tile, a baseboard, or a taut piece of string.

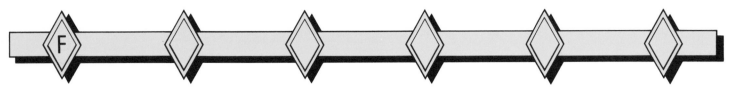

Estimating and
Comparing
Mass

3. Guess, Sort, Check PS

Provide each child with a starting line such as a piece of paper or string and label cards: shorter , same and longer . Have the children take a handful of materials from the bin.

Engage the children's interest by telling them that they are going to play a guess and check game. Ask the children to choose an object and place it on their starting line. Based on this reference object, have them guess and sort their collection of objects into 3 possible groups: shorter, same, or longer. Have the children label the groups with their cards. Then, ask the children to check their guesses by placing each object in turn on the starting line beside the reference object. After they check each object, they should place it in the appropriate group: shorter, same, or longer. Repeat, using a new object on the starting line for comparison. Continue the checking process until all objects are sorted appropriately.

You can elaborate on the sets created to include a discussion of number by asking these questions:

- **How many things did you find that are longer than (shorter or the same length as) your object?**

- **Are there more things that are longer or more things that are shorter? How many more?**

Variations

- Guess, Sort, Check may be played with partners. One child sets the object on the starting line and sorts the rest of the objects into 3 possible groups. The other child verifies by comparing the lengths. The children then switch roles.
- Guess, Sort, Check may be used as a recording activity. Have the children select one item for comparing (their shoe). Give each child at least 4 small sheets of paper (a standard size sheet cut in 4). Ask the children to draw a picture on each page of something in the classroom that they think is longer than their shoe. The children compare the length of their shoe with the length of each object on a starting line. All pictures of objects that were actually longer than the shoe can be assembled into a small book. The other pictures of objects which were found to be shorter could be stapled to form another book entitled Shorter Than My Shoe. Provide more paper so that the children can continue to record their guesses and checks.

A	B	C	D	E
Sequencing Events	Estimating and Measuring Time in Non-standard Units	Estimating and Comparing Length	Ordering by Length or Height	Estimating and Comparing Capacity

4. What Did You Choose?

Invite a small group of children to sit in a semicircle around an ordering mat (Line Master 48). Engage the children in a discussion about the ordering mat. Ask, **Where is the starting line? Who are the characters? Who is shorter? Who is taller?**

Display 2 similar items such as string or popsicle sticks cut to different lengths. Demonstrate how you will conceal the length of the objects by placing them in your closed hand so that only a portion is revealed.

Invite 2 volunteers to step forward, pick an item from your closed hand, and state whether they think they have the longer or shorter object. Have the children place the shorter item on the ordering mat near Kalaloo and the longer item near Slider to confirm their guesses. Repeat the activity as long as interest is maintained.

Variation

Have the children play What Did You Choose? in small groups at work areas. When children are on their own, it may be easier if the objects are placed in a bag rather than having a child hold them.

5. Plasticine Snakes

Provide each child with a piece of Plasticine and an ordering mat (Line Master 48). Invite each child to use some of the Plasticine to make a snake, which is then placed on the ordering mat. Have the children break off 2 more pieces of their Plasticine. They then roll out a piece to make a snake longer than the one on the ordering mat. Encourage them to check during the rolling process to see whether the snake is longer, shorter, or the same length. Have the children place this second snake on the starting line beside the first snake to check whether it is longer. Have the children point to the snakes and describe them in terms of length. **This snake is longer than that one. This snake is shorter than that one.** Ask the children to use the other piece of Plasticine to make a snake shorter than the first one. Encourage them to compare and describe the length of their third and first snakes.

After 3 snakes have been ordered on the mat, lead a discussion based on these questions:

- **Which is the longest snake? Show me.**
- **Which is the shortest snake? Show me.**
- **How could you describe this order? Read the order aloud.**
- **Can you think of another way to read the order?**
- **Make another snake. Where would you put it in the order? Show me.**

You may wish to have the children repeat the activity with a snake of a different length for their initial reference object.

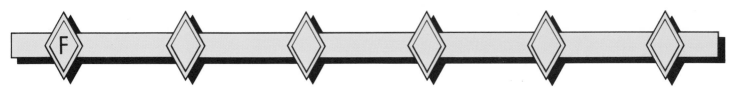

6. Place It

This is a partner game. Have each pair of children take a handful of objects from the bin of materials and an ordering mat (Line Master 48). Guide the pairs to a work area. One child chooses 3 objects from the collection and orders them on the mat using the edge as a starting line. Encourage each child to read aloud the order created. Have the child choose one more object and challenge her or his partner to place it in the order. If the object is not in the appropriate position, the child should try again before switching roles with her or his partner.

Variation

One child places an object on the ordering mat. The child then challenges the partner to place 2 objects on the mat, namely, one that is shorter and one that is longer. After the partner successfully orders the objects, he or she may then offer a new challenge.

7. Place Your Order

Place the bins of materials and glue at different work areas. Guide small groups of children to different work areas. Invite the children to select at least 3 items and then place them in order on their ordering mats (Line Master 48). Have the children repeat this process a number of times. Encourage them to describe the order they create to the other children. After the children have ordered different groups of items, ask them to select at least 3 items to glue in order on their mats. Encourage the children to describe these final ordering sequences.

You may wish to have the children record their descriptions of the order on their mats.

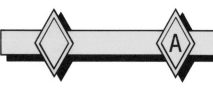

A	B	C	D	E
Sequencing Events	Estimating and Measuring Time in Non-standard Units	Estimating and Comparing Length	Ordering by Length or Height	Estimating and Comparing Capacity

8. Making Tracks
D

Provide each child with a piece of paper. Invite the children to take off a shoe and place it carefully on their paper. Show the children how to trace the outline of their shoe on the paper. Ask the children to cut out this picture of their shoe. Provide the children with a large sheet of paper, glue, and a copy of Ted and Troll-teddy's footprints (Line Master 49). Engage the children's interest by saying, **These are the footprints made by Ted and Troll-teddy.** Ask the children to cut out these footprints. Have the children order the footprints (including their own) according to length on the mat and glue them down.

Note that some children may wish to trace a friend's foot to insert in the order. You may wish to leave additional paper and copies of Line Master 49 at a center. The children may wish to make and/or cut out several footprints and lay them out end to end on the floor, or glue them to large pieces of paper to make foot tapes.

9. Tall, Taller, Tallest
D

Gather the children together. Tell the children that they will be comparing their height with others. Discuss how the floor will be used as a starting line. Invite 2 children to stand in front of the rest of the group. Ask the children, **Who is the taller of the 2?** Invite another child to come forward. Ask a volunteer to compare this child's height with the other 2 children's and position her or him so that the 3 either increase or decrease in height. Invite a volunteer to describe the order. Have the children return to the other group and choose new volunteers to repeat the procedure.

When the children are familiar with ordering 3 people by height, increase the number of children in the sequence.

*Children have previously engaged in activities which illustrate the relative nature of number. Take this opportunity to draw their attention to the relative nature of height. For example, **Jenny is shorter than Dianne but taller than Kim.***

Variation

If you have individual pictures of the children, photocopy them and place 3 or 4 in an envelope. Have a child take an envelope, find the children pictured, compare their heights, and paste the pictures on an ordering mat (Line Master 48). Name cards could be substituted for pictures.

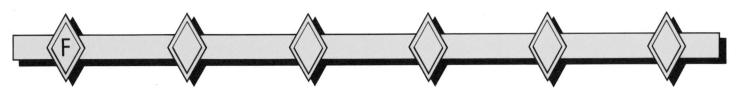
10. Height Tapes

Provide a few rolls of adding machine tape or balls of string or yarn, pencils, and scissors at a center. Invite a small group of children to this center at a time. Divide the group so that each child has a partner. Have one child lie down on the floor with her or his heels at the edge of a floor board or floor tile while the other child unrolls the adding machine tape the length of her or his partner. Tell the child to mark the partner's height on the tape with a pencil. The strip is then cut and the process is repeated for the second child. Ask the children to go to their own work area to print their names on their tapes. (If string is used, have the children print their names on a piece of masking tape and affix it to the string.) Call all members of the small group to the center again to order the height tapes. Have the children line up from shortest to tallest against a wall and tape their adding machine tapes to the wall in order. Ensure that each tape touches the floor (which should be discussed as the starting line).

You may wish to display these tapes along a hallway wall. The children could order themselves by height and then post their tapes in that order. This would be an effective method to organize a display of the tapes of the whole class.

Record the date on the tapes with a date stamp. Repeat the activity in a few months' time and compare the child's growth.

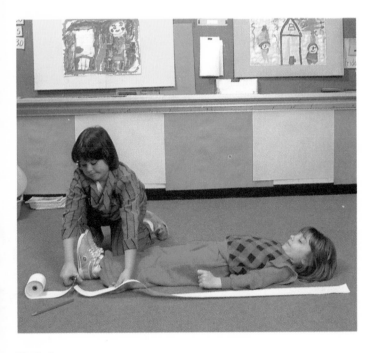

Variation

Have the children lie on large sheets of mural paper while their partners trace their bodies. Invite the children to cut out their silhouettes. Order these paper models according to height.

11. Family Pictures

Gather the children together for a discussion. These questions are suggested as a basis for this discussion:

- **Who is the tallest/shortest in your family?**
- **Who is taller/shorter than you in your family?**
- **Who is taller/shorter than your mother/father/brother/sister?**

Distribute picture-making materials at the different work areas and invite the children to draw their family. Encourage the children to describe their pictures. **My dad is the tallest. My sister is shorter than I am. I am taller than my brother but shorter than my mommy.**

Variation

Have the children bring in family photos from home. Encourage the children to present their photos and describe the height of the family members.

12. The Order of Things D

At centers set up a variety of materials for the children to order. Circulate among the small groups and encourage the children to describe the orders they create.

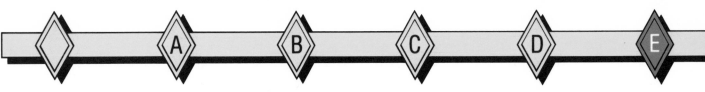

A	B	C	D	E
Sequencing Events	Estimating and Measuring Time in Non-standard Units	Estimating and Comparing Length	Ordering by Length or Height	Estimating and Comparing Capacity

Section 3

Planning the Section

Objective	Level	Activity	Grouping	Program *or* Management Suggestions
E Estimating and Comparing Capacity	Concrete	1. Exploring Capacity 2. More or Less? 3. Two the Same 4. Container Sort	♦♦♦♦ ♦♦♦♦ ♦♦♦♦ ♦♦♦♦	You may wish to introduce Activities 2 to 4 informally through questioning as the children explore capacity. If there is an available water table, it would be worthwhile borrowing it for the duration of this section.
F Estimating and Comparing Mass	Concrete	5. Heavy or Light? 6. Exploring the Balances 7. On the Balance 8. The Balance of Things 9. Balance Sort 10. Which is Heavier?	♦♦♦♦♦♦♦ ♦♦♦♦ ♦♦♦♦ ♦♦♦♦ ♦♦♦♦ ♦♦♦♦	Activity 5 introduces the vocabulary heavy and light. A variety of homemade balances are illustrated in the Suggested Materials. It is recommended that you borrow as many commercial balances as possible from other classrooms. You may wish to introduce Activities 6 to 9 informally through questioning while the children are exploring mass in Activity 5.

About this Section

In this section children compare the mass and capacity of objects. The activities which develop these concepts require a number of materials. You may wish to set up both the mass and capacity centers at the same time so that small groups of children can be involved in a variety of activities. Rotation charts and record keeping suggestions are offered on pages xviii-xxi.

Note that there are 2 different activities described in which children explore materials, namely, Exploring Capacity, page 129 and Exploring the Balances, page 131. This focus once again reflects the importance of free exploration of materials. Children will discover many properties of objects during this exploratory stage. It is recommended that after each exploratory session you gather the children together and invite them to share their discoveries. These group discussions can help you decide on activities to follow, as well as provide the children with an opportunity to verbalize and often to consolidate much of their learning.

Observations and Evaluation

These key questions can form the basis of discussion as you circulate among the groups:

- **Which do you think holds more/less?**
- **How can you find out? Show me.**
- **Which do you think is heavier/lighter?**
- **How can you find out? Show me.**

If you want to gather more information about how some children estimate and compare capacity, engage them (individually or as a small group) in this simple task. Have the children select 2 containers from a collection of containers. Say, **Show me the container you think holds more (less). How could you find out?** Have the children demonstrate their response.

To gather more information about how some children estimate and compare mass, display familiar objects, choose one item, and ask the children to identify an object that they think is

heavier (lighter). Have them hold both objects and refine their estimate if they wish. Ask, **How could you find out?** Have the children demonstrate their responses. Have the children repeat this process to estimate and compare the mass of several objects.

Suggested Materials

- A collection of containers such as Dixie/Styrofoam/plastic cups, cans, plastic jars, margarine tubs, pudding or yogurt cups [Activities 1, 2, 3, and 4]
- Material to measure capacity such as sand, salt, rice, kernels, or water [Activities 1, 2, 3, and 4]
- Containers of different shape but equal capacity [Activity 3]
- A container marked Ted's Tub for each work area [Activity 4]
- 3 label cards: more , less , and same for each work area [Activity 4]
- A collection of balances; commercial and/or made from materials as illustrated [Activities 6, 7, 8, 9, and 10]

- A collection of materials of varying masses [Activities 5, 6, 7, 8, and 9]
- 3 label cards: heavier , lighter , and same for each work area [Activity 9]
- A box or container marked Ted's Box for each work area [Activity 9]
- 2 containers of the same size such as yogurt, Styrofoam or Dixie cups for each work area [Activity 10]
- A large number of small objects of varying masses such as pennies, nuts, bolts, rice, corn, buttons, puffed rice, or cotton balls [Activity 10]

Activities

1. Exploring Capacity

At different work areas provide a collection of containers in various sizes and shapes as well as material with which the children can compare capacity such as dried corn, rice, sand, or water. Guide small groups of children to each area to freely explore these materials. Invite the children to pour, empty, and fill the containers. Circulate among the groups to observe the children and encourage discussion. At the end of each period of exploration, gather the children together and ask them to describe their discoveries. You may wish to record these findings on a chart.

It is important that the children have frequent opportunities to explore these materials before they are directed to investigate them for a specific purpose.

Comparing capacity requires special preparation. It is suggested that a large container, covered surface, or box be placed at each work area to collect the overflow as children pour material from one container to another. Establish with the children that they are expected to clean up all materials before leaving the work area.

A	B	C	D	E
Sequencing Events	Estimating and Measuring Time in Non-standard Units	Estimating and Comparing Length	Ordering by Length or Height	Estimating and Comparing Capacity

2. More or Less?

Collect a variety of containers of different sizes and shapes. Label these containers with different colored symbols. Gummed stickers cut into different shapes (circles, stars, squares, or semicircles) or symbols drawn with markers can be used to label the containers. Place these containers and dried corn, rice, sand, or water at different work areas. Gather a small group of children at one of these areas. Select 2 containers, and ask, **Which do you think holds more/less; the container with the red circle or the container with the blue circle?** Have the children respond to this question before any testing is carried out. Lead a discussion on how they could find out which container holds more. Accept all reasonable responses and try them. After a conclusion is reached, demonstrate how it can be recorded on a piece of newsprint.

Invite the children to go to a work area in groups of 2 or 3 to investigate further the capacity of various containers. Encourage the children to follow the steps of estimating, checking, and stating their conclusions each time they compare the capacity of 2 containers.

As you circulate among the centers, observe and question the children as they investigate capacity. Encourage the children to describe the process and their conclusions. These questions are suggested to promote discussion:

- **What were you trying to find out?**
- **Which container did you guess held more/less?**
- **What did you do first? Next? What did it show you?**

Note that often the children's concept of full needs to be clarified. It must be pointed out to them that they must fill the container to the top and then level if off with their hands before comparing the capacity of the containers.

Meeting Individual Needs

Invite the child who is ready for a further challenge to order 3 (or more) containers by capacity.

3. Two the Same   PS

For this activity you will need to add 2 containers of different shapes but equal capacity to each collection of containers. Explain to the children that at each work area there are 2 containers which hold the same amount. Invite the children to go to the work areas to carry out investigations to find these containers. You may wish to have the children switch work areas after they discover the containers of equal capacity.

If the children have difficulty accepting the fact that containers of widely differing shapes may have the same capacity, encourage the children to pour the rice from the second container back into the first one to ensure that the same amount is still there. Not all children will understand the concept of conservation of volume. Give them opportunities to explore the materials further, but do not expect internalization of the concept.

You may wish to challenge the children to bring containers from home with the same capacity as the 2 they identified at the work area. Have them display the container and check to see if it is in fact a container of the same capacity.

4. Container Sort   PS

For this activity you will need to add to each work area 3 hoops (or pieces of yarn to form circles); 3 cards to label each hoop: more , less , and same ; and a container to be used as a standard marked Ted's Tub. Show the children the hoops at a work area. Help them to read the labels, if necessary, and place one in each hoop. Tell the children they are going to check all the containers against Ted's Tub and sort them in the appropriate hoop. Have a pair of children come and choose a container. They estimate how its capacity compares with Ted's Tub, before testing with a material such as rice to confirm their prediction. They place the container in the appropriate circle. Repeat the process with another pair of children to ensure that the children understand the procedure. Send as many children as materials will allow, in pairs, to work areas to sort the containers.

Ensure that all the children have several opportunities to work with the materials over a period of a few days. You can extend this activity to involve a discussion of number by asking these questions:

- **How many containers did you find that hold more (less) than Ted's Tub?**
- **Which set has the most (least) containers?**
- **How many more (less) in this set than in that one?**

5. Heavy or Light?

Gather the children around a collection of items of varying mass. Select 2 objects which obviously have different masses such as a pencil and a book. Ask, **Which is heavier?** Invite the children to state their opinion; then hold an object in each hand.

Encourage the children to use the words "heavier" and "lighter" in their descriptions of the objects. **The book is heavier than the pencil. The pencil is lighter than the book.**

Continue to select items and ask the children to compare them using the words "heavier" and "lighter". Ensure that the children have a solid grasp of the concepts of heavy and light before you ask them to compare objects with masses which are not as obviously different.

Variation

Have the children contribute items to lists of Very Light Things and Very Heavy Things. Read the lists aloud with the children.

6. Exploring the Balances

Collect and make (see illustrations on page 129) as many different balances as possible. At different work areas place a balance and a number of objects of varying mass. Direct small groups of children to different areas to explore these materials. Circulate among the groups and encourage the children to describe their discoveries and pose questions to generate further exploration.

- **Why do you think one arm of the balance is hanging lower?**
- **Can you find something that you think is heavier/lighter than this object?**
- **Are you finding that bigger things always make the balance go lower?**

At the end of the exploration sessions, gather the children together and ask them to describe their discoveries. Encourage them to state what they expected to happen when they placed objects on the balance as well as what they actually observed. Have the children demonstrate these discoveries to the group. Through these exploration sessions and discussions, the children should learn the mechanics of a balance and what conclusions they can draw from the position of the arms on the balance.

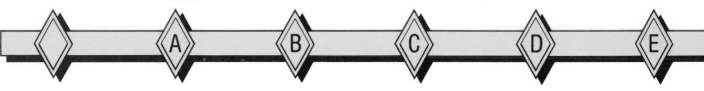

7. On the Balance F

At different work areas place balances and a number of objects of varying mass. Invite the children to gather at one of these areas. Choose and display 2 objects. Ask, **Which do you think is heavier/lighter?** Review what it means when one arm of the balance is lower/higher than the other. Invite volunteers to hold the items and ask again which they think is heavier/lighter. Discuss how you could find out using the balance. Invite a volunteer to place the objects on the balance and repeat your initial question. Model a comparison of the masses of the 2 objects for the children. **The crayon is lighter than the eraser. The eraser is heavier than the crayon.** Repeat the process of estimating, checking, and stating a conclusion until the children appear comfortable with the process. Invite small groups of children to go to the different work areas to compare the masses of a variety of objects. Encourage them to hold an object in each hand before they place them on the balance.

You may wish to have the children record the discoveries they make comparing masses. Have the children fold a piece of paper in half. At the top of one half, have them draw a light object and at the top of the other half a heavy object (a feather and a brick). Each time they weigh and compare objects, they can record their discoveries in the appropriate sections, i.e., the crayon under the feather and the eraser under the brick.

Meeting Individual Needs

Invite the child who appears ready for a further challenge to order 3 (or more) containers by mass.

8. The Balance of Things PS F

Ahead of time select an object. Fill a plastic container so that it has the same mass as the selected object. Gather the children around a balance and a collection of objects of varying mass. Draw the children's attention to the position of the arms on an empty balance. Review what it means when one arm is lower, higher, or the arms are balanced. Place the container on the balance. Invite the children to conduct a search for the object with the same mass as the container. Encourage the children to select an object they estimate has the same mass, then test it, and state their conclusions.

You may wish to set up a display area where children can place objects with the same mass. Children could search for items at home or on the playground to add to the sets created.

Estimating and
Comparing
Mass

9. Balance Sort PS

At different work areas provide a large number of objects of varying shapes and mass, balances, one object designated as a standard marked Ted's Box, 3 hoops or yarn circles, and 3 label cards for each set of circles: heavier , lighter , and same .

Tell the children that there is a box marked Ted's Box at each set of balances. Show them the yarn circles at each balance. Help the children read the labels and place one in each circle. Invite the children to compare all the objects at the balances against Ted's Box to see which is heavier/lighter/same. Ask a volunteer to come and choose an article, guess which set it belongs in, check it on the balances, and state a conclusion. **The paste brush is lighter than Ted's Box.**

Have the child place the object in the appropriate circle. Repeat the process until the children appear comfortable with the routine. Invite as many children as materials will allow to work at the balances estimating, testing to confirm, stating conclusions, and sorting the objects appropriately. Ensure that each child has several opportunities to work with the materials over several days. You may designate any article as a standard with which to compare.

You can extend this activity to involve a discussion of number by asking these questions:

- **How many things did you find that are heavier (lighter) than Ted's Box?**
- **Were there more things that were heavier or lighter?**
- **How many more things did you find that were heavier?**

10. Which is Heavier?

You will need 2 containers of the same size for each set of balances and a number of objects of widely varying mass such as pennies, nuts and bolts, or rice.

Gather the children around you facing a set of balances. Ask the children to look at the 2 containers and tell if they hold the same amount. You may wish to have a child fill one container with rice and pour it into the other to ensure that they are of equal capacity. Fill the 2 containers with objects of widely differing mass such as pennies and rice. Ask, **Is one heavier or do they weigh the same?** Invite a child to place the 2 containers on the balance. Encourage the children to try to verbalize what they see. **The containers are the same. They hold the same amount. But this container is heavier than that one.**

Give the children an opportunity to explore and discuss this concept in small groups at the balances. Not all children will be able to understand the concept. Give them the experience, but do not expect internalization at this stage.

Measurement Across the Curriculum

Language Arts

- Invite the children to make a filmstrip of their favorite story. Provide paper, a cardboard box, and 2 paper towel rolls. Have them draw their story in sequence and tape the paper together in order. Demonstrate how the paper rolls and box can be assembled into a filmstrip projector.

- Have the children contribute to a list of long and short words. Keep the list posted so that children can add to it periodically.

- Invite the children to think of what it would be like if they were as big as an elephant, as small as an ant, as tall as a skyscraper, or as short as a blade of grass. Have them write a story and/or draw a picture to illustrate their thoughts.
- In conjunction with this unit, you may wish to read any of these stories and poems: (see page 318 for an annotated bibliography).

  - *Pancakes, Pancakes* by Eric Carle
  - *The Three Billy Goats Gruff* by Paul Galdone
  - *The Little Red Hen* by Paul Galdone
  - *The Carrot Seed* by Ruth Krauss
  - *The Story of Ferdinand* by Munro Leaf
  - *Do You Want to See Something?* Eve Merriam
  - *The Apple Bird* by Brian Wildsmith

Music

- Attach separate loops of string to a number of metal objects, e.g., a nail, a fork, or a spoon. Suspend each object from a coat hook, chalk board ledge, etc. Have the children strike each object in turn and order the objects according to pitch.

Begin with 3 objects and increase the number of objects as the children appear ready.

It may help children to decide whether the note is a high or a low one if you have them hum the sound produced.

- Partially fill a number of jars with varying amounts of water. Have the children strike the rim of the jar lightly with a xylophone mallet or pencil and listen for the sound. Have them order the jars according to pitch. Begin with 3 jars and increase the number of jars as the children appear ready.

Science

- Have the children discover whether it takes an ice cube a longer or shorter time to melt than it takes a sugar cube to dissolve.
- Have the children grow a plant from a seed. Pick one day a week to mark the height of the plant on a popsicle stick placed in the pot.

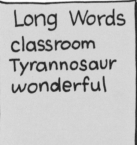

- Have the children collect blades of grass, leaves, flowers, dried twigs, etc., and order them according to length.

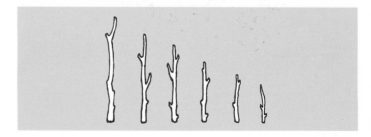

Extension Project

- Place a clear container full of water in a spot where it will be undisturbed. Use masking tape to mark and date the level of water. Record the level of water each week. Discuss how quickly the water evaporates.

- Place a container outside to collect rainfall. Mark the water level and date on the container. Repeat this on other rainy days and discuss on which day the most rain fell.
- Compare and order fruits and/or vegetables by size (large pumpkin, medium pumpkin, or small pumpkin). Have the children weigh them to compare the mass of the objects.
- Have the children compare the mass of a dry and wet sponge. Provide a variety of materials for children to weigh dry and then wet, e.g., pieces of cloth, wool, cotton balls, or cork.
- Display a variety of containers. Have the children place them on shelves so that the largest box is in the back and the smallest box is up front. Discuss the ways items are displayed in supermarkets.

Physical Education

- Have the children line up on a starting line with 3 bean bags. Ask them to throw each bean bag a different distance: close, far, and farther. Describe the order in which the children are to collect the bean bags, **The one closest to you. In the middle. Farthest from you.**
- Compare and order the balls in the equipment room by size.
- Have the children move to music. Ask them to make their bodies as small or big as they possibly can as they walk, skip, run, slide, or crawl. After they respond to your instruction of making their body big or small, ask them to become even bigger or smaller.
- Have the children stretch their bodies to be as tall as possible, even taller; as short as possible, even shorter.

Read Goldilocks and the Three Bears. Have the children create a model of the house for the bears. Explain that each set of objects they make for the house should relate to the size of the bears. For example, if the child were to make beds, he or she would make a small one for baby bear, a larger one for mama bear, and an even larger one for papa bear. You may wish to post a list to suggest different items that the children could consider making for the diarama. At a center, place boxes (shoe boxes are a good size) and materials such as cardboard, construction paper, wallpaper pieces, or felt scraps for the children to use to create these dioramas.

As children create wallpaper, carpets, and furniture, a great deal of measuring will be required.

Addition and Subtraction to 5

Unit Objectives

Section 1

A Combining Sets to 3, 4, and 5
B Creating and Solving Addition Story Problems
C Recording Addition Sentences
D Solving Addition Sentences

Section 2

E Separating Sets to 3, 4, and 5
F Creating and Solving Subtraction Story Problems
G Recording Subtraction Sentences
H Solving Subtraction Sentences

Section 3

I Creating and Solving Story Problems
J Solving Number Sentences to 5

About this Unit

Addition and Subtraction

If one were to ask adults what they remember about their mathematics classes, no doubt most would recall spending day after day learning and practicing basic facts. When one listens to the concerns of teachers regarding children's mathematical performance, it is typical to hear them observe that no matter how much drill, reinforcement, and review of the basic facts they provide, many children do not master these facts. These observations reflect the need to question the approach traditionally taken to teaching basic facts. Typically, children have been presented symbols and number sentences early in grade 1. Many children successfully complete their number work and can respond verbally without hesitation to questions such as, **What is 3 plus 2?** Often, however, they are only demonstrating good recall. Frequently, teachers incorrectly interpret these rote responses as a solid understanding of addition and subtraction concepts.

This unit presents the concepts of addition and subtraction through concrete experiences. The children manipulate concrete materials, participate in, observe and discuss addition and subtraction situations. Only after they have experienced additive and subtractive action, verbalized their actions, and internalized the concepts, do they begin to connect symbols to the actions they perform and observe. It is important that children read what they record to reinforce the connection between their actions and the symbols represented.

Considerable research has been generated to investigate how children best learn and acquire the basic whole number addition and subtraction concepts. Educators continue to debate whether children should learn the operations of addition and subtraction together or separately. This unit reflects the latter approach. Section 1 is devoted to developing the concept of addition and the addition facts to 5. Section 2 presents activities to develop the concept of subtraction and the subtraction facts to 5. Only after the language patterns, the processes, and symbols particular to each concept are firmly established and internalized, do children participate in activities which involve both concepts. A child must understand that the language patterns; "added to", "joined", "altogether", "another", "as well", and "too" all express the addition process. After participating in and describing concrete experiences to develop this awareness, the connection between the action and symbols is modelled. It is recommended that the child demonstrate an understanding of the concept of addition, i.e., what type of situations are additive, and know how to express the action verbally and in print, e.g., 1 + 2 = 3 before being introduced to the concept of subtraction.

The concept of subtraction is developed in the same way as was addition. Various language patterns and types of action reflecting a subtraction situation are emphasized. Children should be comfortable expressing their observations and experiences before symbols are connected to these actions.

When children have a solid grasp of the language patterns, processes, and symbolic representation of addition and subtraction, they are directed to the activities in Section 3. In Section 3, addition and subtraction are brought together in the context of familiar activities. The children are asked to apply their understanding of the concepts when they interpret situations as either additive or subtractive in nature. Because children have grasped the concepts of addition and subtraction, combinations are developed together throughout the rest of the program.

Children should be able to generate and solve number sentences to 5 after participating extensively in the activities of this unit. Many different reinforcement activities are suggested. It is recommended that you place these reinforcement games at a center so that the children pursue them as they engage in the next unit. Children should master the number sentences to 5 before they embark on Unit 7 which presents combinations for 6 through 10.

Problem Solving

Throughout this unit, children have opportunities to create and solve story problems. As they participate in the activity Let's Tell Stories, pages 149 and 162, they generate other stories to describe an action. In Pick a Card, pages 153 and 164 children select a number sentence card and tell a story to correspond to it. Children tell story problems and record number sentences as they observe and interpret addition and subtraction situations. This activity is somewhat reversed when children select a + or − card and tell a story or act out a situation to reflect the chosen symbol in What's My Card?, page 169. Children generate number sentences for a given number as they participate in the open-ended activity The Name Game, page 170. In addition, activities provided in Five Minute Math, page 139 develop these problem-solving skills:

- sorting
- identifying likenesses and differences
- creating stories

Vocabulary

- Addition
- Equals
- Minus
- Number Sentence
- Plus
- Subtraction

Planning Ahead

The success of the next unit, which deals with 3-dimensional geometry, depends on the availability of a large collection of geometric solids for the children to manipulate. It is suggested that you refer to page 179 to see what types of materials will be required and enlist the help of the children to begin collecting them now.

Ongoing Objectives

- Reading the calendar
- Ordering days of the week
- Counting
- Estimating and comparing objects by length, mass, and/or capacity
- Reading a thermometer
- Recognizing time names
- Counting coin collections
- Problem solving:
    - Sorting
    - Identifying likenesses and differences
    - Creating stories

Five Minute Math

Calendar Activities

- Draw the children's attention to the days of the week printed at the top of the calendar and have them chant the days in order. Ask the children to chant the days of the week in order but instead of saying (**Wednesday**), they are to clap their hands.
- Cover one of the days on the calendar and ask, **Which day is under cover? How do you know?**

Sunday	Monday		Wednesday	Thursday	Friday	Saturday
			1	2	3	4

- Provide 7 children with days of the week cards and have them pop up in turn as you all chant the days of the week in order. Ask, **What is the day before Tuesday? After Friday? Between Monday and Wednesday?**
- Mix up the ordered days of the week cards posted on the calendar display and have the children re-order them.

Counting Activities

- Enlist the children's help in taking attendance by having them help to count how many children are present. Involve them in determining how many children are absent.
- Divide the children into 5 groups. Have one group begin to count aloud. Encourage the other groups to count along silently. When you point to a group, the members should continue to count without breaking the sequence. Change the groups after every 10 numbers initially. Once the children begin to expect changes at 10, 20, 30, etc., begin to make random changes.
- Have the children count to 100 using motions. Have them change the motion at each decade. For example, as the children count from 1 to 10, they clap their hands; from 11 to 20 they bend from side to side; from 21 to 30 they swing their arms; etc. As you approach each decade, point to a child who will choose the motion for the next decade count.

Measurement Activities

- Any of these games: What Did You Choose? and Plasticine Snakes, page 122, or Tall, Taller, Tallest, page 124 can easily be played in 5 minutes to reinforce and review the skill of comparing and ordering objects by length.
- Have the children predict which of 2 items is heavier or lighter. Ask, **Which do you think is heavier; the eraser or the crayon?** Have a volunteer place the objects on a balance and ask, **Which is heavier?** Compare the mass of a variety of objects.
- Ask the children to find something which is heavier than a pencil, lighter than an eraser, or with about the same mass as a paper clip. Have the children test their predictions on a balance. You may wish to keep a continuous record of their discoveries.

- Ask the children to find a container in the room that they think holds more (less) than the one you display. Have the children check their estimates.
- Begin to take a daily reading of the temperature outside. Have a volunteer take a thermometer outside and then return to class and give it to you. Print the temperature on the board and manipulate a large display thermometer to the corresponding temperature. Compare the day's temperature with the previous day's temperature. Ask, **Is it warmer today than it was yesterday or is it cooler? How do you know?**

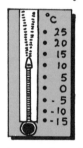

A large demonstration thermometer can be made from a long zipper.

- Ask the children questions such as these:
    - **That was the bell to start school; what time do you think it is?**
    - **Time to eat lunch! What time do you think it is?**
    - **In 5 minutes it will be time to go home; what time will it be?**

Money Activities

Place collections of nickels and pennies within reach of the children. Pass a paper plate or sheet of paper with an amount shown on it to each child. Have the children place a corresponding number of coins on the plates. In turn, ask the children to read the amount printed on their plates, display the placed coins, and count them aloud. Encourage all children to join in the counting. Have the children exchange plates and repeat the activity.

Problem Solving Activities

Sorting

List and sketch a mystery set such as the ones illustrated. Read the list aloud with the children and invite them to identify the mystery set. Encourage the children to think of other objects which belong in the mystery set and add their suggestions to the list.

Identifying Likenesses and Differences

Ahead of time, prepare 2 pictures of 2 similar objects such as an airplaine and a boat; a glass of milk and a cup of juice; or a flower and a tree. These pictures can be drawn or cut them from magazines, old story books, catalogues, or old calendars. Post the pictures and ask, **How are these 2 things alike?** You may wish to list the children's responses as they are offered.

Focus on a few of the descriptions and continue with questions such as, **What else can you think of that is used for transportation? That is metal? How are these 2 things different?** Record the responses. Leave the lists posted so that the children can add to them as they think of additional likenesses and differences. On other days, continue to post pictures for the children to compare. Initially, display pictures which are similar. Once the children readily suggest likenesses and differences, increase the challenge by posting pictures which are less similar such as a banana and a glass of juice; a horse and a monkey; a chair and a mug; or a coat and a belt. Encourage children to search for pictures of 2 objects for their classmates to compare.

Creating Stories

* Tell a story with numbers. As you tell it, act out the story with small objects. (The objects can be displayed effectively on an overhead projector.) Your story may be similar to this one.
   - **One day, 2 flowers were blooming in the garden. The next day, there were 4 flowers blooming. What could have happened?**
   The children may respond.
   - **More flowers bloomed. The gardener planted more flowers.**
   Some children may include a number in their explanation. For example, **2 more flowers bloomed.** The focus, however, should not be on the numbers; but on the concepts more and less.

   - **There were 4 apples on the table. Now there are 2 apples on the table. What could have happened?**
   The children may respond.
   - **Someone ate some apples. Some apples rolled off the table. Someone put some apples in the fridge. Someone used the apples to make a pie.**

* Print a numeral on the chalk board, e.g., 4 and tell a story about that numeral. **There were 4 kittens in the basket.** Show the story with small objects (4 cubes in a container). Have the children make up a story about 4. Ask them to demonstrate their stories with objects as well. Change the numeral and continue the activity. You may wish to title the bulletin board Stories of 7 and invite children to contribute stories and/or illustrations during the course of a week.

Using the Story

The story Raisin Bread deals with a situation with which most children can readily identify; the search for the perfect bedtime snack. Ted's clever manipulation of raisins to make his own raisin bread when there is none available provides the basis for the activity Raisin Bread, page 146. This activity allows the children to experience and verbalize the joining of sets. It is important that children see number in the context of familiar activities and not as something divorced from real life. Discussion of the story may lead into further experiences with number.

You may wish to have the children make up another verse for Ted and Troll-teddy's Sleepy Song.

Ted and Troll-teddy's Sleepy Song

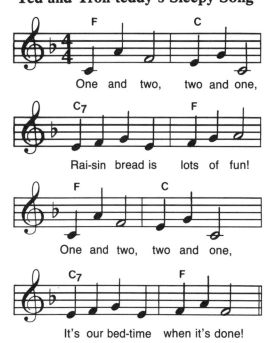

Supplementary Material

Ted is my Friend: Mathematics Activity Book, pages 3-10, 32-36 and 57-62; story boards, pages 39-42 and 51-54; and game boards, pages 45-48.

Raisin Bread

One evening, when the sky was dark blue, Ted hummed a little hum and danced a little dance. His tummy was telling him it was time for a bedtime snack, so of course he felt very, very good. But this evening, Ted didn't feel like having honey drop cookies.

"Raisin bread," he said thoughtfully to Troll-teddy. "Raisin bread will be the perfect bedtime snack for tonight."

Troll-teddy rolled over and wagged her tail to show that she thought having raisin bread was a good idea too.

Ted looked on the high shelf. He took down some bread. But it wasn't raisin bread; it was brown bread. Ted looked on the low shelf. He picked up some bread. But it wasn't raisin bread; it was oatmeal bread. Ted looked on the in-between shelves. There were Ted's cookie jar and some brambleberry muffins, but not one slice of raisin bread.

"Oh no, Troll-teddy," said Ted sadly. "I really did want a piece of raisin bread for our bedtime snack. Now what can we do?"

Ted wiggled his toes to help him think and he looked at all the good things on the shelves, but his tummy kept hoping for raisin bread.

Troll-teddy trotted to a little cupboard. She looked at Ted, and then at the cupboard and back at Ted once more.

"Do you want something in there, Troll-teddy?" asked Ted. He opened the cupboard door. He peered inside, and suddenly his face was lit by a sunny smile. There on the shelf sat a full jar of raisins!

"You are the cleverest Troll-teddy in the whole wide world! We'll make our own raisin bread!" said Ted happily. He took the jar of raisins and the loaf of brown bread over to the counter. Troll-teddy wiggled her tail expectantly. Her tummy wanted raisin bread too! She watched Ted put two slices of bread on the table.

Now, Ted never cut bread into two ordinary pieces, oh no, that was too dull. Ted liked to tear his bread into two lovely zigzaggy pieces. It looked so much more interesting that way! So Ted carefully tore each slice of bread into two zigzaggy pieces — just right!

"Now comes the best part, Troll-teddy," said Ted, lifting Troll-teddy onto his round tree-trunk stool so that she could see the fun too.

Ted picked up one raisin and poked it into one end of a piece of bread. He picked up another raisin and poked it into the other end of that piece of bread. He picked up two more raisins. He poked one into the end of the other piece of bread and popped the other one into his mouth. Ted closed his eyes. "Mmmmmmm!" he said.

Then, something made him open his eyes. Troll-teddy sat on the stool staring at Ted. Her mouth was opened in a round, hopeful O. Ted laughed out loud and popped a raisin into Troll-teddy's mouth. Then he poked three raisins into the other slice of bread, only stopping to pop a very occasional one into his own mouth or into Troll-teddy's.

At last he took out two blue plates. They were perfect bedtime snack plates because they were the color of the evening sky.

Ted put a slice of raisin bread for Troll-teddy on one blue plate and a slice of raisin bread for himself on the other plate and carried them over to the fireplace.

"One and two," Ted started singing as he looked at the raisins in the two zigzaggy pieces of Troll-teddy's slice. "Two and one," Ted sang as he looked at the raisins in the two zigzaggy pieces of his own slice. Then Ted made up a song:

"One and two, two and one,
raisin bread is lots of fun!
One and two, two and one,
it's our bedtime when it's done!"

Ted and Troll-teddy munched their raisin bread by the fireplace, and in no time at all both slices of bread had disappeared. Then Ted and Troll-teddy yawned and tumbled into bed, singing sleepily, "One and two, two and one; one and two, two and o-o-o-o-nnnne."

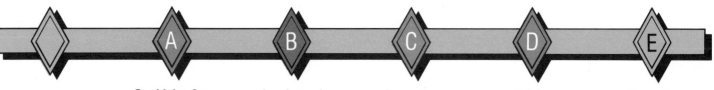

Combining Sets to 3, 4, and 5	Creating and Solving Addition Story Problems	Recording Addition Sentences	Solving Addition Sentences	Separating Sets to 3, 4, and 5

Section 1

Planning the Section

Objective	Level	Activity	Grouping	Program *or* Management Suggestions
A Combining Sets to 3, 4, and 5	Concrete	1. Raisin Bread	👥👥	Activities 1, 2, and 3 are games in which children manipulate objects to form combinations of 3 (4, 5). These games should be introduced in small groups so that each child has the opportunity to participate actively. While you are teaching a game, the other children can be directed to further exploration at the number centers.
		2. Open the Flower	👥👥	
		3. The Water Slide	👥👥	
B Creating and Solving Addition Story Problems	Concrete	4. Lights! Camera! Action!	👥👥👥👥	Activities 4 to 6 present the children with different addition situations to describe. Activity 4 should be introduced at the outset of this section and should be continued throughout the entire unit.
	Semi-concrete	5. Let's Show a Story	👥👥	
	Concrete	6. Let's Tell Stories	👥👥	
C Recording Addition Sentences	Concrete and Symbolic	7. The Script	👥👥👥👥	Activity 7 is a key activity as the teacher demonstrates the appropriate way to record number sentences and models the corresponding vocabulary. This activity should be repeated frequently. Children should proceed to any of Activities 8 to 10 after they show they can record appropriate number sentences for actions as described in Activity 7.
	Concrete, Pictorial and Symbolic	8. Our Own Number Stories	👤	
		9. Combinations and Arrangements	👤	
		10. Recording the Games	👥👥	
D Solving Addition Sentences	Concrete and Symbolic	11. Pick a Card	👥👥👥👥	Activity 12 suggests a number of different games to reinforce the combinations to 5. You will need to prepare these games ahead of time. While some children are engaged in these games, continue to direct pairs of children to play the manipulating games (Activities 1 to 3). Initiate the activities by asking them to find all the ways they can to make raisin bread using 5 (4 or 3) raisins (place seeds on petals, or have children go down the water slide).
		12. Find the Solution	👥👥	

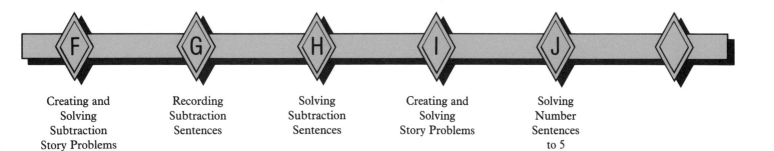

About this Section

Four types of activities are presented in this section to develop the concept of addition to 5. They are:

- manipulating games to generate the combinations to 5;
- addition situations to develop an understanding of the addition process in the real world and to relate it to classroom activities;
- recording activities to connect pictures and symbols to the addition situations;
- review and reinforcement games which present the number sentence for children to interpret and solve.

In order to internalize and consolidate the combinations of a number, children need to manipulate objects. In addition, it is important that they express and hear a description of the action they perform and/or observe. The first 3 activities in this section are games which meet these requirements.

It is recommended that all children learn these games while developing combinations for 3. Although these combinations may seem quite elementary for many of your children, the goal is to teach the games in an easy, non-threatening situation. This gives each child the opportunity to experience immediate success. Teach these manipulating games in 3 different sessions so that the children are comfortable learning the procedures unique to each one. Once the children are familiar with the games, feel free to have them play any or all 3 in one session. It is not the activity that is important, but the opportunity for children to experience combinations for a number over and over again. By varying the games, the children's interest and motivation remain high. It is also important to vary the set that children manipulate. If children manipulate different sets, they have the opportunity to see relationships between numbers and they do not fall into the habit of simply giving rote descriptions of their actions. It is suggested that you introduce the children to combining sets of 4 and then 5 after they have successfully combined sets of 3 and recorded their actions.

Activities 4, 5, and 6 involve the children in experiencing different types of addition situations. The focus of these activities is to present a variety of situations in which addition occurs and to expose the children to the different language patterns which express the addition process. It is suggested that you present these 3 activities in the order in which they appear. However, it is highly recommended that you introduce Activity 4 as the children are learning the first 3 games. Activity 4 can introduce your daily math sessions or act as a break in the day. The activity is most effective if you focus on addition processes as they arise spontaneously in the classroom.

The third objective of this section is to introduce the children to the recording of number sentences. In the first recording activity, The Script, page 150, the teacher models the number sentence. Once again, this is an activity which should take place frequently for children to internalize that the symbols express the actions they observe.

Activities 11 and 12 present number sentences to be interpreted and solved. Activity 12 (a reservoir of games) reinforces the combinations introduced in this unit. Children should participate in Activities 11 and 12 only after they have worked extensively generating combinations to 5 and demonstrated an understanding of the addition process and related language patterns. Keep these materials at a center and encourage children to visit the center throughout the next unit so that the concept of addition to 5 is reviewed before introducing addition to 10.

Some children may intuitively discover the commutative property (2 + 1 is equal to 1 + 2) as they manipulate the materials to form the combinations to 5. Discuss their insights and observe whether they apply this understanding in Unit 7 when they explore sums to 10. You may wish to draw an individual's attention to this property if the child appears ready to accept it.

Observations and Evaluation

As children participate in the activities of this section, you will have ample opportunity to make observations. These informal observations and the discussions you have with the children can provide you with insights into the level of children's thinking and their understanding of the concept. These observations can also help you to determine the activities and experiences individual children should engage in to further their understanding. These key questions can form the basis of discussion as you circulate among individuals and small groups.

- **How many are in each set? How many are there altogether?**
- **Show me 3 with 2 different sets. Can you show 3 again another way? And another way?**
- **Are these all the different ways you can make 3?**
- **What game have you played? What have you discovered? Show me the combinations.**
- **Show me 2 and 1. How many are there altogether?**
- **What have you recorded? Read it to me, please. Now show it to me.**
- **Show me 2 + 1** (sentence printed on card or chalk board).

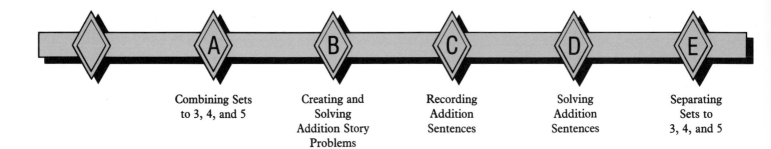

This chart describes typical observations you may make and suggest some directions you may wish to provide.

Observations	Teacher Direction
A child has played the manipulating games (Activities 1 to 3) often and is describing the materials and actions with confidence.	Have the child observe as you play Open the Flower or The Water Slide, page 147. Include a step which involves the child making a prediction. For example; if you play Open the Flower with 4 seeds, open one hand (petal) and ask, **How many seeds are in this petal? How many seeds do you think are in the other petal?** Use an uncut paper roll as you play The Water Slide. Place 2 of the 4 objects (children) in the pool. Ask, **How many children are in the pool? How many will go down the slide? How many are in the pool now?** Lift the tube to check.
The child demonstrates a solid understanding of 4 by making accurate predictions.	Have the child begin to develop combinations for 5 and introduce her or him to the stage of recording (see The Script, page 150).
The child hesitates or makes inaccurate predictions.	Involve the child further in exploring number at the number centers and in playing the manipulating games.
A child has difficulty recording an addition play or story as a number sentence. For example, you may observe: $2 + 3\ 5$ $\quad$ $\begin{array}{r} 2 \\ +\ 2 \\ \hline =\ 4 \end{array}$ $\quad$ $1 = 3 + 4$ $4\ 1\ 5$	Continue to model number sentences as described in The Script. Have the children read the number sentences aloud with you as you point to each part of the sentence. Delay the recording until the child has observed and participated often in Activities 1 to 6. Have the child begin by choosing number sentence strips cut from Line Masters 54 and 55.
A child solves number sentences successfully but cannot show it to you using concrete materials.	The child has learned how to manipulate symbols but does not understand the meaning behind the symbols. Give the child many opportunities to participate in Activities 4, 5, 6, and 11.
A child is expressing Activities 1 to 6 as number sentences correctly and consistently.	Have the child interpret and solve number sentences as suggested in Activities 11 and 12. In addition, you can assess whether all combinations of 3 (4 and 5) have been internalized by giving the child Line Master 50 (in parts) to interpret and solve. Also, have the child show you what the number sentence means using concrete materials. This will show whether the symbols have meaning or if they have been memorized.

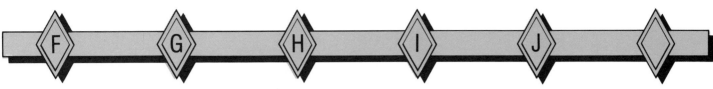

F — Creating and Solving Subtraction Story Problems

G — Recording Subtraction Sentences

H — Solving Subtraction Sentences

I — Creating and Solving Story Problems

J — Solving Number Sentences to 5

Suggested Materials

- 3 to 5 small objects such as counters, beads, beans, interlocking cubes, bread tags, or buttons per child [Activities 1, 2, 3, 6, and 10]
- A paper towel or toilet paper roll cut in half lengthwise for each child [Activities 3 and 10]
- Records made at number centers (Unit 3) [Activity 9]
- Many cards with addition problems such as $\boxed{2+2}$ $\boxed{4+1}$ [Activities 11 and 12]
- Puzzle addition number sentences such as $\boxed{2+3}\boxed{=5}$ [Activity 12]
- A game board [Activity 12]
- Containers to act as flower pots [Activity 12]
- A number sentence wheel [Activity 12]

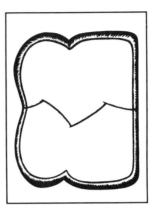

Line Master 51
Activity 1
1 per child

Any of Line Masters 14 to 18
Activities 5 and 8
A large quantity

Line Masters

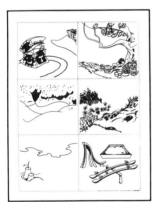

Line Master 52
Activities 8 and 12
1 per child

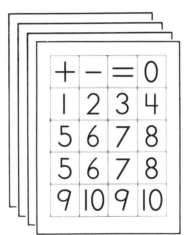

Line Masters 53 to 56
Activities 8, 9, 10, and 12
A large quantity

Any of Line Masters 18 to 23
Activities 5 and 8
A large quantity

Line Masters 56 to 58
Activity 10
1 per child

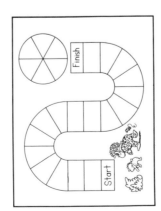

Line Master 43
Activity 12
1 copy

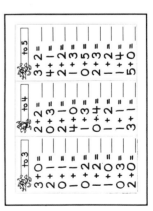

Line Master 50
Page 144 and Activity 12
A large quantity

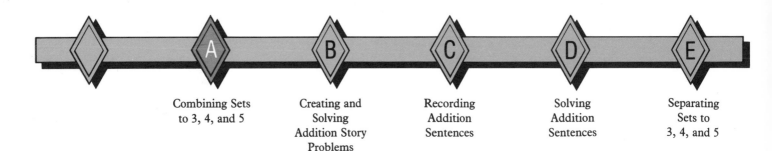

Combining Sets
to 3, 4, and 5

Creating and
Solving
Addition Story
Problems

Recording
Addition
Sentences

Solving
Addition
Sentences

Separating
Sets to
3, 4, and 5

Activities

1. Raisin Bread

Invite a small group of children to sit in a circle. Provide each child with a piece of raisin bread (Line Master 51) and 3 small objects to represent raisins. Engage the children's interest by recalling with them how Ted makes raisin bread for a bedtime snack by poking raisins into a slice of bread. Tell the children that in this game they can make raisin bread like Ted does.

Have the children cut the raisin bread into 2 pieces along the zigzag line. Tell them to place their 2 pieces of bread in front of them so that they are slightly apart. Demonstrate with your 2 pieces. Ask, **How many raisins do you have?** Tell the children to watch while you put some of your raisins on one piece of bread and some on the other.

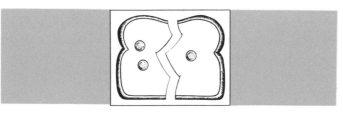

As you point to each piece of bread, ask, **How many raisins are here? And here?** The children respond, **2 raisins . . . 1 raisin.** Ask, **How many raisins will you have altogether when you slide the 2 pieces of bread together?** Slide the pieces together as you say, **2 raisins and 1 raisin is 3 raisins. There are 3 raisins**

altogether. Repeat the process a number of times. Ensure that the children follow the routine of reading the sets as someone points to them, and then reading the sum when the 2 pieces of bread are pushed together. Have the children decide individually how many raisins they will put on each piece of bread. Encourage all of the children to read the sets and sums as the child who made them points to each set and performs the actions. After all the children have had a turn making raisin bread, have them remove their raisins, separate their pieces of bread, make new sets on each piece of bread, and repeat the process.

Once the children are comfortable with the game and are describing their actions without cues, remove yourself from the group. It is important that the children play the manipulating games often in small groups or in pairs to internalize the concept of combining sets. As children play in pairs, one child should perform the operation while the other child watches and verbalizes the actions.

Note that the child who is pointing to her or his set and the combination should concentrate on the actions and the other children's description rather than on saying the combinations. Having the other children responsible for verbalizing the combinations, focusses their attention on the process. These children cannot rely on the child demonstrating to give them verbal cues.

Watch for the child who places all the raisins on one portion of the raisin bread and creates an empty set on the other portion. If necessary model the appropriate verbal description.

It is recommended that you laminate the pieces of raisin bread since they will be handled frequently.

F	G	H	I	J
Creating and Solving Subtraction Story Problems	Recording Subtraction Sentences	Solving Subtraction Sentences	Creating and Solving Story Problems	Solving Number Sentences to 5

2. Open the Flower

Invite a small group of children to sit in a circle. Provide them with 3 seeds or 3 small objects to represent seeds and have the children count their seeds. Ask the children to put 1 seed in one hand and 2 seeds in the other hand. Have them pretend that their hands are the petals of a flower and that when their hands close, they form the bud. Tell them to close the petals to protect the seeds.

Open one hand, and ask, **How many seeds are here?** Open your other hand, and ask, **How many seeds are here?** Cup your hands together, and ask, **How many seeds are there altogether? 1 seed and 2 seeds is 3 seeds.** Have several children demonstrate this process individually while the other children read the sets in each hand and the sum, **1 seed and 2 seeds is 3 seeds. There are 3 seeds altogether.** Ask the children to decide how many seeds they will put in each hand the next time. In turn, have each child display the sets on each petal and the total in the bud. Have the children read the sets and sums as each child opens her or his hands. Repeat this process until the children are able to play without cues in small groups or with a partner.

After the children have had much experience playing this game and are playing it comfortably, consider extending it to include the step of predicting. Before the child opens her or his second hand, invite other children to predict how many seeds they will see. Continue the rest of the game as described.

3. The Water Slide

Invite a small group of children to sit around a work area. Provide each child with half a paper roll (toilet or paper towel roll cut in half lengthwise), a piece a blue paper (or a blue Styrofoam food tray), and 3 small objects. Explain that the paper roll represents a water slide, the blue paper is the swimming pool, and the 3 small objects are children. Hold the paper roll at an angle to the paper so that it looks like a water slide adjacent to a pool. Place 2 small objects on the paper, and ask, **How many children are in the pool?** Place 1 counter at the top of the slide, and ask, **How many children are going down the slide?**

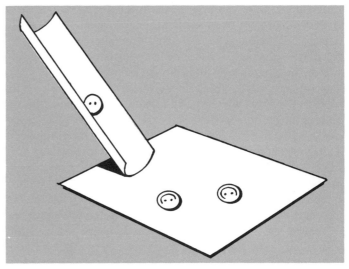

Let the counter go so that it slides into the pool below, and ask, **How many children are in the pool altogether? 2 children and 1 child is 3 children. There are 3 children altogether.** Repeat the process several times to ensure that the children understand the process of this manipulating game. Invite the children to decide how many children to place in their pools. In turn, have each child point to the children in her or his pool and then let the counters go down the slide. The other children read the sets and sum aloud. Repeat this process until the children are able to proceed without cues. Have them continue the game in small groups or with a partner.

*After the children have had much experience playing this game and are comfortable with it, consider extending the game to include the step of predicting. To do so, have the children use a whole paper roll (a tube). Invite them to place up to 2 counters in the pool and hold their tube adjacent to the pool. Have them show how many counter(s) (all of the remaining ones) are going down the slide before they let them go down the tube. Ask, **How many children do you think are in the pool altogether? Why?** A child might respond, **3. I know because 1 counter was in the pool and 2 counters went down the slide. 1 and 2 is 3.** Have the child raise the tube so that everyone can check. Encourage them to describe the action again correctly if necessary.*

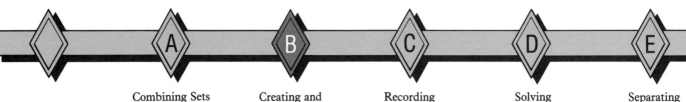

A	B	C	D	E
Combining Sets to 3, 4, and 5	Creating and Solving Addition Story Problems	Recording Addition Sentences	Solving Addition Sentences	Separating Sets to 3, 4, and 5

4. Lights! Camera! Action!   PS ◆ B

Tell the children that today they are going to have a chance to be actors. Explain that they must listen carefully for their own names so that they will know what to do and can help answer questions. Have the children act out the number of addition situations according to your descriptions. Vary your language so that the children are exposed to a variety of language patterns which describe addition in different situations. **She lined up too. They also went to paint. He chose a red paper as well. He added 2 more. · . . . And another imp joined them.** The words "too, also, as well, added, more, and another" represent different language patterns which are interpreted as meaning addition. Through this incidental, but frequent exposure the children will hear and begin to identify and understand the different ways that addition situations can occur.

Keep the action moving quickly. Try to ensure that every child gets a chance to act. The scripts given here are examples of an unlimited number which you can create. Initially model the retelling using numbers. After the children have heard a few examples, encourage them to describe the play using numbers. The first example describes the process in detail. You may wish to have the children give group answers. Later you might consider inviting individual responses.

- **Tony and Sarah lined up to go to the library.** (The children named should actually line up.) **Lise wanted to change her book so she lined up too.** (Lise joins Tony and Sarah.) **Now, let's tell about this play using numbers. We could say 2 children and 1 more child lined up.** Ask, **How many children are lined up to go to the library?** (Children respond, **3 children are lined up.**) Say, **Let's tell about the whole play using numbers,** (Children respond, **2 children and 1 more child is 3 children.**) To end the play, say, **The children sat down when they came back from the library.** (Children return to their places.)

- **Kathy went to the art center to paint a picture. Manuel and Fred also went there to paint pictures. Let's tell about this play using numbers.** (Children respond, **1 child and 2 more children went to the art center to paint pictures.**) Ask, **How many children are painting at the art center?** (Children respond, **3 children are at the art center.**) Say, **Let's tell about the whole play using numbers.** (Children respond, **1 child and 2 children is 3 children altogether.**) Continue, **When the children finished their paintings, they went back to their places.**

- **Maria, Ian, and Alex went to the playhouse to pretend they were imps playing tricks on Ted. No one else went to be imps. Let's tell about this play using numbers.** (Children respond, **3 children went and 0 children joined them.**) Ask, **How many children are pretending to be imps at the playhouse?** (Children respond, **3 children are pretending to be imps altogether.**) Say, **Let's tell about the whole play using numbers.** (Children respond, **3 children and 0 children is 3 children.**) End the play saying, **When they finished their game, the children pretended to disappear into a crack in the floor and tiptoed back to their place.**

Encourage the children to think of short stories for their classmates to act out. This activity may be used to introduce your math period over several days or to act as a break between activities. It is useful to vary the familiar and factual stories with ones that are more imaginative and whimsical to keep the interest level high. You may wish to include stories which relate to themes in which the children are currently involved. Use as many natural classroom situations as you can to draw the children's attention to addition situations. For example, **Orisha and Jan chose red paper. Neil chose red paper as well. How many children chose red paper?** *Or,* **Stephan drew 1 red flower. He added 2 more blue flowers. How many flowers did he draw?**

Variation

Have the children make up puppet plays using imp finger puppets. These finger puppets can be made by rolling the imp characters (cut from Line Master 14) and taping the sides as they meet. You may wish to have the children color these before they roll and tape them. Each child will need at least 3 puppets. Have the children designate a particular spot to be the crack in the floor where all the imps disappear at the end of each story. It is helpful to model a couple of stories before encouraging the children to think of their own. For example, **2 imps came out of their hiding place to slide down Ted's sofa. It looked like so much fun that another imp joined them. How many imps were sliding? When the imps heard a footstep, they ran and hid in a crack in the floor.**

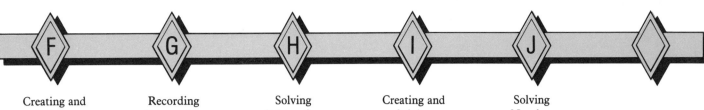
5. Let's Show a Story

Invite a small group of children to sit in a circle. Provide each one with a story board selected from Line Masters 18 to 23 and a quantity of story characters cut from Line Masters 14 to 16. The stories told here for the forest story board are representative of an unlimited number you can present to the children. Remember to vary the language you use so that different addition situations are modelled. Have the children clear their story boards after each story.

- **Once upon a time, 2 black rabbits were hopping in the forest.** (Children place 2 black rabbits on the story board.) **They were playing in the leaves when a white rabbit came along to join them.** (Children place a white rabbit on the story board.) **Let's tell the story again using numbers.** (Children respond, **2 black rabbits and 1 white rabbit joined them.**) Ask, **How many rabbits were hopping in the forest altogether?** (Children respond, **There were 3 rabbits hopping in the forest altogether.**) Say, **Let's tell the whole story using numbers.** (Children respond, **2 black rabbits and 1 white rabbit is 3 rabbits altogether.**)
- **A squirrel ran into the forest to look for a tall tree to climb.** (Children place 1 squirrel on the story board.) **2 other squirrels were also looking for a tall tree.** (Children place 2 more squirrels on the story board and retell the story using numbers, **1 squirrel and 2 more squirrels.**) Ask, **How many squirrels are looking for a tall tree altogether?** (Children respond, **There are 3 squirrels looking for a tall tree altogether.** They tell the whole story, **1 squirrel and 2 squirrels is 3 squirrels looking for a tall tree.**)

6. Let's Tell Stories   PS

Invite a small group of children to sit in a circle. Display 3 small objects such as counters and a piece of paper. Identify the counters as cars and the piece of paper as a parking lot. Tell the children that you are going to show a story about the cars and the parking lot and that they are going to tell the story. Slide 2 cars onto the parking lot. Slide another car onto the parking lot. Say, **Who would like to tell me about what you just saw?** A child might respond, **2 cars went into the parking lot at the restaurant to park. Then, 1 more car drove in.** Ask, **How many cars are in the parking lot altogether?** The child responds, **There are 3 cars altogether. 2 cars and 1 car is 3 cars.** Ask, **Who has another story they'd like to tell about what I just showed you?** A child might respond, **2 cars drove into the parking lot at the shopping center. 1 other car pulled in and found a space.** Ask again, **How many cars are in the parking lot altogether?**

Continue to encourage children to tell stories about the situation you demonstrated. After each volunteer has had a chance to tell a story, redefine the setting and the objects. The paper could become the moon and the counters space stations or the paper could be an ocean and the counters motor boats. The possibilities are unlimited. Once again, encourage children to tell stories about the situation you demonstrate.

On another day, provide children with the objects and a piece of paper. Have each child in turn, identify her or his objects and paper and show a story. Have the other children tell stories for those actions.

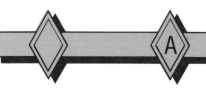

A	B	C	D	E
Combining Sets to 3, 4, and 5	Creating and Solving Addition Story Problems	Recording Addition Sentences	Solving Addition Sentences	Separating Sets to 3, 4, and 5

7. The Script

After children have had opportunities to perform plays as described in Lights! Camera! Action!, page 148 and act out and tell stories with story boards or counters as in Let's Show a Story and Let's Tell Stories, page 149, start to model the number sentences which represent the actions as they unfold. It is important that children have many opportunities to see the number sentence evolve as the action takes place. Children can internalize the true meaning of the + sign only after they have seen it represent the different language patterns for addition situations. As you tell and record a variety of stories, children will have the opportunity to experience the + sign as representing many different language patterns for addition. Explain that from now on you are going to write a script for each play or story acted out. Tell a story similar to the type you told in Lights! Camera! Action!

Mary and Lily were listening to a tape at the listening center. (These children go to the listening center.) **Andy also wanted to listen so he joined them.** (Andy goes to the listening center.) **Let's tell about this play using numbers.** On a display area (chalk board or on an overhead projector), record the number sentence as a child responds. For example: the child responds, **2 children** (you print 2) **and 1 more child joined them** (you print, + 1; 2 + 1 is now on the chalk board). Say, **I made a record of the number story that (Julie) told us.** As you point to the symbols, say, **2 children and 1 more child. The script is 2 and 1** (again, point to the corresponding symbols).

Say, **Let's end our script. How many children are at the listening center altogether?** Print = 3 to complete the number sentence as a child responds, **There are 3 children at the listening center.** Point to each corresponding symbol as you say, **Our script is 2 and 1 is 3.** Repeat this process as children act out many stories. On other days, repeat the same process of modelling a number sentence when the children tell about their stories as they engage in Let's Show a Story and/or as they tell stories to describe the situations in Let's Tell Stories.

When children are comfortable reading the number sentences, start to model the terms "plus" and "equals" as you point to the corresponding symbols. **Another way to read the script is 2 plus 1 equals 3.** Expect many children to continue to read the number sentences using the words "and" and "is" rather than "plus" and "equals." Accept this language as it reflects understanding. However, continue to model the mathematical terms.

When children are thoroughly comfortable reading the horizontal form, explain that there is another way to record number sentences. Model the vertical form and read it aloud with the children. Begin to use both forms interchangeably.

Give the children opportunities to be script writers after they have observed you model number sentences on several occasions. Initially, have the children actually copy the number sentences you record and ask them to read the sentences. Then, have the children record a number sentence for a play before you print the appropriate one on the board. Reinforce that there are 2 ways to record number sentences (horizontally and vertically). Record a vertical number sentence on the chalk board. Have the children record the corresponding horizontal number sentence on paper or individual chalk boards.

8. Our Own Number Stories

After the children have observed you model number sentences on many different occasions as described in The Script, they can begin to keep records of Activities 4, 5, and 6 as they play these activities individually or with a partner. These records can be verbal, pictorial, and/or symbolic as shown here.

Children tape the stories and plays they have created.

Children can draw stories on copies of the story boards (Line Masters 18 to 23) or on mini-story boards (Line Master 52). The plays performed and the stories acted out with counters can be illustrated on paper and these illustrations can be compiled into a class storybook. The storybooks can be labelled with cards or strips cut from Line Masters 53 to 55 or number sentences printed by the child.

9. Combinations and Arrangements

In Unit 3, children combined and arranged a variety of materials to form sets of 3, 4, and then 5 (see pages 76 to 78). These combinations and arrangements were recorded and filed for later reference. Gather a small group of children together and provide them with the records of their sets of 3 created at the number centers. Ask the children to display and describe these recordings.

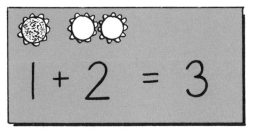

There are 3 bottle caps. 1 is red and 2 are yellow. 1 and 2 is 3.

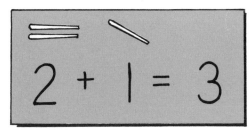

In my picture of 3 toothpicks, 2 go across and 1 goes down. 2 and 1 is 3.

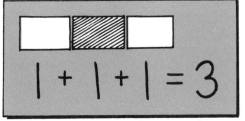

My train has 1 blue cube, 1 red cube, and 1 blue cube. 1 and 1 and 1 is 3.

After the children have had the opportunity to become reacquainted with their recordings, ask, **What is the number sentence for your record?** Invite volunteers to display their records and tell a corresponding number sentence, **2 plus 1 equals 3.** After each child has had a chance to tell a number sentence for at least one of her or his recordings, guide the children to work areas to record the number sentences below their sets. They can glue the appropriate number sentence strips (Line Masters 53 to 55) or print their own. These records can be compiled into class or individual books and read aloud with the children when completed.

A	B	C	D	E
Combining Sets to 3, 4, and 5	Creating and Solving Addition Story Problems	Recording Addition Sentences	Solving Addition Sentences	Separating Sets to 3, 4, and 5

10. Recording the Games

Children can begin to keep a record of the 3 manipulating games (Raisin Bread, page 146, Open the Flower and The Water Slide, page 147) as they play them. This should be done only after they have had many opportunities to observe you model number sentences as described in The Script, page 150. Line Masters 56 to 58 are provided for recording purposes. The large frame at the top of each of these line masters is designed to accommodate the actual objects used to play the games.

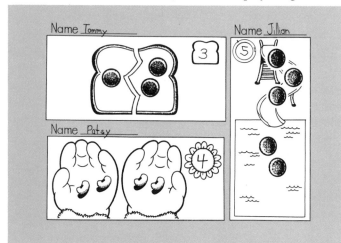

Children should have several opportunities to transfer the materials to this large mat. For example, they should first manipulate the objects, e.g., seeds from Open the Flower, in their hands and then transfer the seeds to the large frame. Placing the materials in the large frame is the first step of transferring the action to paper. When children are successfully reproducing their actions concretely on the top large frame, have them begin the second step of recording their actions. This can be done by having them draw a picture of the materials on the top frame in a smaller frame. They should then choose an appropriate number sentence strip or cards (Line Masters 53 to 55) or print a number sentence to label the action.

Children must be comfortable printing numerals before being asked to use them to express their new number learning. These same children, however, may be ready to record the number combinations they discover. Provide them with access to numerals, symbols, and/or number sentence scripts cut from Line Masters 53 to 55 to use for recording their actions. The third and final step in recording these games requires a blank sheet of paper and the concrete materials.

Do not rush children to this final step. Children who do not require the picture of the action will likely stop drawing it spontaneously. The drawing of the action (as described in the second step) is useful as it provides you with a more complete record of the action. You can tell if children are recording a number sentence which accurately describes the action by seeing how the sentence corresponds to their picture.

If children are playing a game with a partner, one child can perform the actions with the materials while the other child records the actions by drawing the material, choosing a number sentence strip, or printing the corresponding sentence.

It is important that the children say aloud what they are recording when working alone or with a partner. These verbal statements help the children see the connection between their actions with the objects and the printed record. You might consider gathering small groups of children together at intervals to read their records aloud. You may also wish to have children use the game materials to act out each other's records.

You may wish to provide a motivation for these recordings. When playing Raisin Bread, the children could be waiters or waitresses keeping a record of their customer's (partner's) orders. They could be keeping a diary of blossoming flowers as if they were scientists as they play Open the Flower. The children could be pool lifeguards keeping track of all the swimmers as they play The Water Slide.

Line Masters 56 to 58 can be used for recording number sentences for 3, 4, or 5. Ask the children to record the number of materials they are working with in the top corner. If children are working on combinations of more than one number, have them record all the numbers in the top corner. To keep an up-to-date record of the children's progress, intermittently collect completed recording sheets for your files.

Some children may need a set goal to ensure that their time is used purposefully. Mark a certain number of frames you expect to be recorded in a set time. This can be accomplished by designating a finishing point with a symbol such as a star, happy face, or stop sign.

11. Pick a Card

PS

Place cards with addition problems to 5 as shown in a bag.

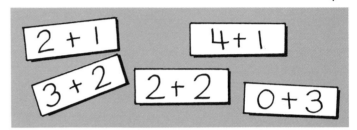

Provide the children with at least 5 objects and a piece of paper. Invite a volunteer to select a card from the bag and display it so that everyone can see it easily. Encourage the children to think of a story to match the card. Have them show their story using the objects and piece of paper. For example, if 2 + 2 was picked, a child might identify her or his objects as racing cars and the paper as a track and, say, **2 cars were testing the track for a big race. 2 more racing cars started to practice.** (He or she would place the objects on the paper at the appropriate time in the story.) Encourage many children to tell their stories before you invite another volunteer to pick a card.

On other days, children can play this game with partners or in small groups.

Variation

Have the children select a card as shown in the activity. Tell them that it is their script and encourage them to make up puppet plays using the imp or animal finger puppets (made from Line Masters 14 to 16). They could also treat the card as a caption and create a story for it on a story board of their choice. This story could be drawn on the story board or story character cutouts could be glued in place.

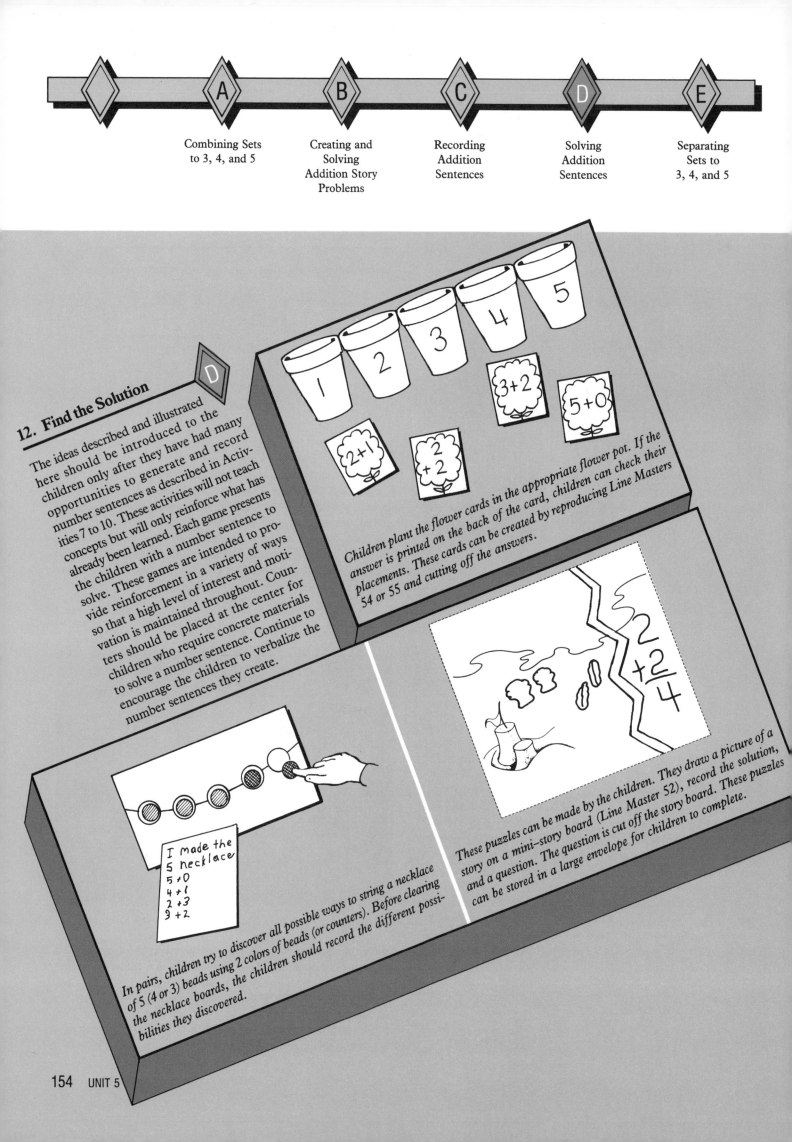

12. Find the Solution

The ideas described and illustrated here should be introduced to the children only after they have had many opportunities to generate and record number sentences as described in Activities 7 to 10. These activities will not teach concepts but will only reinforce what has already been learned. Each game presents the children with a number sentence to solve. These games are intended to provide reinforcement in a variety of ways so that a high level of interest and motivation is maintained throughout. Counters should be placed at the center for children who require concrete materials to solve a number sentence. Continue to encourage the children to verbalize the number sentences they create.

Children plant the flower cards in the appropriate flower pot. If the answer is printed on the back of the card, children can check their placements. These cards can be created by reproducing Line Masters 54 or 55 and cutting off the answers.

In pairs, children try to discover all possible ways to string a necklace of 5 (4 or 3) beads using 2 colors of beads (or counters). Before clearing the necklace boards, the children should record the different possibilities they discovered.

I made the 5 necklace
5 + 0
4 + 1
2 + 3
9 + 2

These puzzles can be made by the children. They draw a picture of a story on a mini-story board (Line Master 52), record the solution, and a question. The question is cut off the story board. These puzzles can be stored in a large envelope for children to complete.

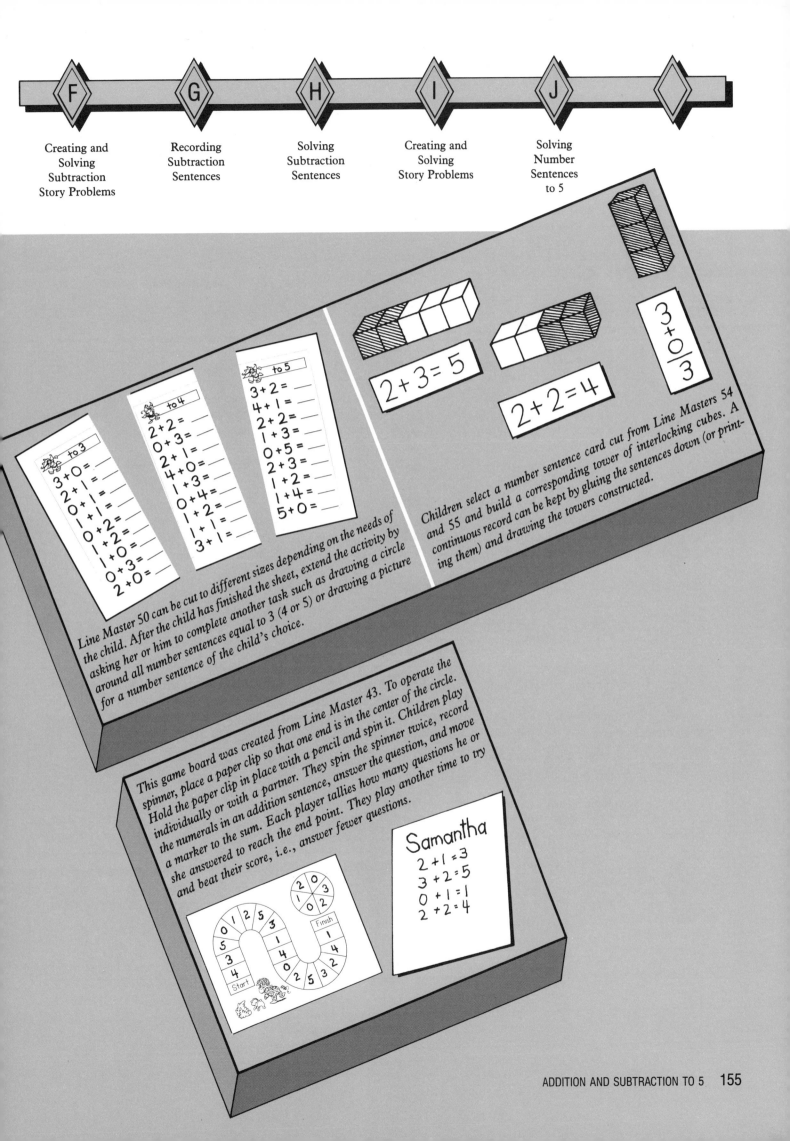

to 3

3 + 0 =
2 + 1 =
0 + 1 =
1 + 1 =
0 + 2 =
1 + 2 =
1 + 0 =
0 + 3 =
2 + 0 =

to 4

2 + 2 =
0 + 3 =
2 + 1 =
4 + 0 =
1 + 3 =
0 + 4 =
1 + 2 =
1 + 1 =
3 + 1 =

to 5

3 + 2 =
4 + 1 =
2 + 2 =
1 + 3 =
0 + 5 =
2 + 3 =
1 + 2 =
1 + 4 =
5 + 0 =

2 + 3 = 5

2 + 2 = 4

3 + 0
  3

Line Master 50 can be cut to different sizes depending on the needs of the child. After the child has finished the sheet, extend the activity by asking her or him to complete another task such as drawing a circle around all number sentences equal to 3 (4 or 5) or drawing a picture for a number sentence of the child's choice.

Children select a number sentence card cut from Line Masters 54 and 55 and build a corresponding tower of interlocking cubes. A continuous record can be kept by gluing the sentences down (or printing them) and drawing the towers constructed.

This game board was created from Line Master 43. To operate the spinner, place a paper clip so that one end is in the center of the circle. Hold the paper clip in place with a pencil and spin it. Children play individually or with a partner. They spin the spinner twice, record the numerals in an addition sentence, answer the question, and move a marker to the sum. Each player tallies how many questions he or she answered to reach the end point. They play another time to try and beat their score, i.e., answer fewer questions.

Samantha
2 + 1 = 3
3 + 2 = 5
0 + 1 = 1
2 + 2 = 4

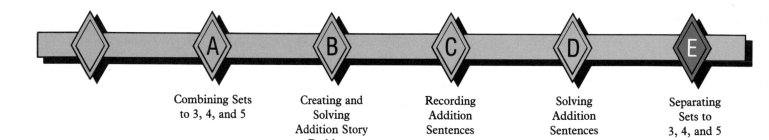

A — Combining Sets to 3, 4, and 5

B — Creating and Solving Addition Story Problems

C — Recording Addition Sentences

D — Solving Addition Sentences

E — Separating Sets to 3, 4, and 5

Section 2

Planning the Section

Objective	Level	Activity	Grouping	Program *or* Management Suggestions
E Separating Sets to 3, 4, and 5	Concrete	1. Breakfast Orders 2. Washed Away 3. Pitch the Tent 4. Abracadabra!	🙍🙍🙍🙍 🙍🙍🙍🙍 🙍🙍🙍🙍 🙍🙍🙍🙍	Activities 1 to 4 are games in which children manipulate objects to separate sets of 3 to 5. Activities 1 and 2 have materials which clearly define the initial set and are recommended to introduce children to the concept of subtraction. Children should have numerous opportunities to play these manipulating games.
F Creating and Solving Subtraction Story Problems	Concrete Semi-concrete Concrete	5. Lights! Camera! Action! 6. Let's Show a Story 7. Let's Tell Stories	🙍🙍🙍🙍🙍🙍🙍 🙍🙍🙍🙍 🙍🙍🙍🙍	Activities 5, 6, and 7 develop along the same lines as activities by the same name in the last section. Begin Activity 5 at the outset of the section and continue it throughout the unit.
G Recording Subtraction Sentences	Concrete and Symbolic Concrete, Pictorial, and Symbolic	8. The Script 9. Our Own Number Stories 10. Recording the Games	🙍🙍🙍🙍🙍🙍🙍 🙍 🙍	In Activity 8, the teacher models subtraction number sentences. It is important that children have numerous opportunities to observe these number sentences unfold as action occurs before they engage in Activities 9 and 10.
H Solving Subtraction Sentences	Concrete and Symbolic	11. Pick a Card 12. Find the Solution	🙍🙍🙍🙍🙍🙍🙍 🙍🙍🙍🙍	Prepare subtraction number sentence cards referenced in Activity 12 ahead of time. While some children are engaged in these games, continue to direct pairs of children to play the manipulating games (Activities 1 to 4).

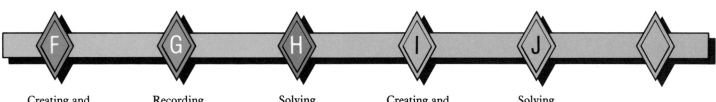

About this Section

This section deals with separating sets to 5 and follows the same progression as the last section on combining sets to 5. Children generate the different ways sets can be separated as they play 4 different manipulating games (Activities 1 to 4), experience and describe a variety of subtraction situations (Activities 5 to 7), record subtraction number sentences to express these actions (Activities 8 to 10), and solve subtraction sentences (Activities 11 and 12).

It is recommended that Activities 4, 5, and 6 of the previous section become your Five Minute Math activities as you proceed through this section. These activities will further reinforce and review the addition process.

Observations and Evaluation

As in the previous section on addition, each child should be working at her or his own level. As you circulate among the children, these key questions can form the basis of your discussion.

- **What number are you working with? How can you separate it into 2 sets? Show me. Show me another way. And another way. Have you shown me all the ways you can think of to separate 4?**
- **Show me 3 take away 1. How many are left?**
- **What have you recorded? Read it to me please. Could you show it to me with counters?**
- **Show me 3–1** (printed on a card or on the chalk board).

Observations	Teacher Direction
A child creates stories which are impossible to act out. For example, **3 turtles were in the brook. 5 turtles left the brook. How many turtles are still in the brook?**	The child needs more work separating concrete materials. Direct the child to Activities 1 to 4 where he or she manipulates a given set. Also, encourage the child to demonstrate her or his story. A child who does not see why the situation is impossible may benefit from participating in activities to further develop number concept. (See Unit 3.)
A child has difficulty recording a subtraction play or story as a number sentence. For example, you may observe: 5 4 1 5-4 1 5=4-1 5 5 -4 = 1 4 1	Continue to model number sentences as described in The Script. Have the child read number sentences aloud as you point to each part of the sentence. Delay the recording until he or she has observed and participated often in Activities 1 to 7. Have the child begin by choosing the appropriate number sentence strip cut from Line Masters 60 and 61.
A child solves number sentences successfully but cannot show them to you using concrete materials.	The child has learned how to manipulate symbols but does not understand the meaning behind the symbols. Give the child many opportunities to participate in Activities 5, 6, 7, and 11. Ensure that the child verbalizes her or his actions.
A child is expressing Activities 1 to 7 as number sentences correctly and consistently.	Have the child interpret and solve number sentences as suggested in Activities 11 and 12. In addition, give the child Line Master 59 (in parts) to interpret and solve. Also, have the child show you what the number sentence means using concrete materials. This will determine whether the symbols have meaning to the child or if they have simply been memorized.

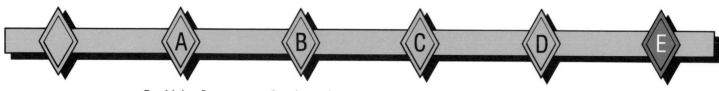

A	B	C	D	E
Combining Sets to 3, 4, and 5	Creating and Solving Addition Story Problems	Recording Addition Sentences	Solving Addition Sentences	Separating Sets to 3, 4, and 5

Suggested Materials

- Egg cartons cut into sections of 3, 4, and 5 [Activities 1 and 10]
- 3 to 5 small objects such as counters, beads, interlocking cubes, bread tags, buttons, or shells for each child [Activities 1, 2, 3, 4, 7, and 10]
- A piece of Plasticine for each child [Activities 2 and 10]
- An index card or stiff piece of paper for each child [Activities 3 and 10]
- A tissue for each child [Activities 4 and 10]
- Several cards with a subtraction problem such as

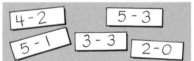 [Activities 11 and 12]

- Flip cards [Activity 12]

Line Masters

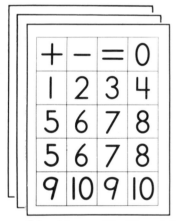

Line Masters **53, 60,** and **61**
Activities 9, 10, and 12
A large quantity

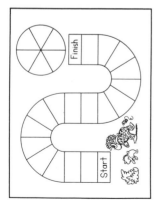

Line Master **43**
Activity 12
1 copy

Any of Line Masters **18 to 23**
1 per child
Activities 6, 9, and 12

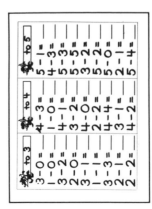

Line Master **59**
Page 157 and Activity 12
1 per child

Any of Line Masters **14 to 16**
1 per child
Activities 6, 9, and 12

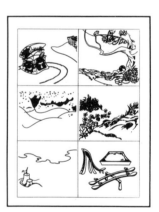

Line Master **52**
Activities 9 and 12
1 per child

Line Masters **62 to 65**
Activity 10
1 per child

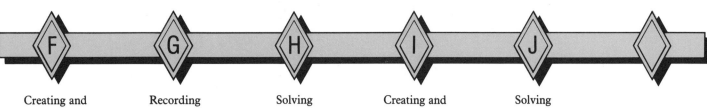

F	G	H	I	J	
Creating and Solving Subtraction Story Problems	Recording Subtraction Sentences	Solving Subtraction Sentences	Creating and Solving Story Problems	Solving Number Sentences to 5	

Activities

1. Breakfast Orders

Invite a small group of children to sit in a circle. Provide each child with an egg carton that has been cut into 3 sections and 3 small objects to represent eggs. Engage the children's interest by telling them that they are short-order cooks filling breakfast orders. Have the children count their eggs and place one in each section of their egg carton. Demonstrate the process of filling a breakfast order. Point to the eggs in the carton and say, **3.** Say, **I need 1 egg sunnyside up.** Remove an egg as you say, **3 take away 1. How many are left? 3 take away 1 is 2.** As you say, **2,** point to the eggs remaining in the carton.

Invite the children, in turn, to complete this order. Encourage the children to describe the process as each child fills the order. After all the children have completed the order, have them fill the egg carton so that once again there is an egg in each section. Place another order for them to fill such as 2 scrambled eggs or a 3-egg omelet. Have each child fill the order as the other children describe the initial set of eggs, the number of eggs taken away, and the number left in the egg carton once the order is filled. Remove yourself from the group once the children are able to perform and verbalize their actions without cues.

On another day, you may wish to have the children take turns placing orders or provide numeral cards 0 to 3 which children interpret as orders.

2. Washed Away

Gather a small group of children around a work area. Provide each child with 3 shells (or any small objects) and a piece of Plasticine. Explain that the Plasticine will represent a beach in this game. Have them flatten the Plasticine and lightly press the shells into it to make an imprint. Explain that large waves often roll onto the beach and carry away things lying on the beach into the water. Point to the shells on a demonstration beach and have the children count them. **There are 3 shells.** As you move your hands towards the beach and remove 1 shell say, **A wave rolled in and washed away 1 shell. How many are left? 3 take away 1 is 2.** As you say, **2,** point to the shells left on the beach. Invite the children, in turn, to move their hand as if a wave washed away the shell. Encourage each child to describe the action as, **3 take away 1 is 2.** After all the children have had a turn, have them replace the shell so that once again there are 3 shells on the beach. Invite the children to repeat this process washing away a different number of shells.

When the children are able to perform and describe the actions without cues, remove yourself from the group. You may wish to have the children place the Plasticine on a piece of sandpaper to add to the appearance of the beach. Small pails can be used as storage containers for the shells.

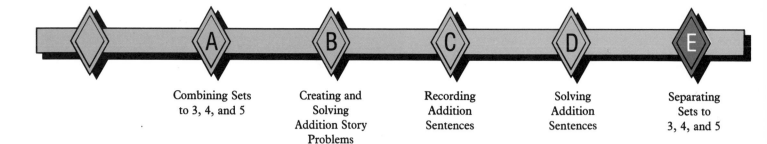

A	B	C	D	E
Combining Sets to 3, 4, and 5	Creating and Solving Addition Story Problems	Recording Addition Sentences	Solving Addition Sentences	Separating Sets to 3, 4, and 5

3. Pitch the Tent

Invite a small group of children to sit in a circle. Provide each child with 3 small objects and a folded index card or a piece of stiff paper. Explain that the objects represent people and the folded index card represents a tent. Have the children count their objects and place them in a line in front of themselves.

Point to your demonstration counters, and ask, **How many people are there?** Hold up the folded index card and demonstrate how to pitch the tent by covering 1 counter as you say, **1 person is in the tent. How many are outside? 3 take away 1 is 2.** Have the children watch as you repeat the process.

Once again, model the description, **3 take away 1 is 2.** In turn, have the children pitch their tents in the same manner. As each child does so, encourage those watching to describe the action.

Invite the children, in turn, to pitch their tents over as many of their objects as they choose. Each time a child pitches a tent, have the children describe the action. Repeat the process until the children are able to continue without cues in small groups or with a partner.

4. Abracadabra!

Invite a small group of children to sit in a circle and provide each child with 3 small objects and a tissue. Engage the children's interest by telling them that they are going to pretend to be magicians and perform some disappearing acts.

Ask the children to count their objects. Place your 3 objects so that everyone can see them. Ask, **How many objects do I have?** Hold up your tissue, wave it over the objects, then cover and slide 1 object away. As you perform this action say, **Abracadabra! 1 had 3 and made 1 disappear. How many are left? 3 take away 1 is 2.** Have all the children perform this disappearing act. As each child makes an object disappear, encourage those watching to describe the actions.

Have the children restore their original set and invite them to decide on another disappearing act. Repeat the process of having a child perform while the audience describes the act. When children are familiar with the activity, encourage them to continue to play with a partner or in a small group.

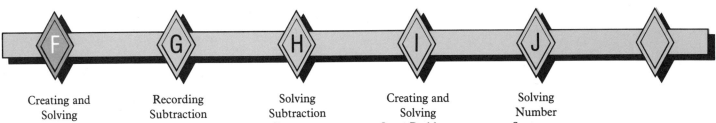

F	G	H	I	J
Creating and Solving Subtraction Story Problems	Recording Subtraction Sentences	Solving Subtraction Sentences	Creating and Solving Story Problems	Solving Number Sentences to 5

5. Lights! Camera! Action!

Tell the children that they are going to be actors again and that they should listen carefully for their cues. Keep the action moving quickly and try to ensure that each child has an opportunity to act. All stories should involve a subtraction situation. As with addition, it is important to vary the language patterns you use so that children are exposed to a wide range of subtraction situations. **He went away. She gave the blue crayon to Ann. The frog hopped away.** The words ''went away, gave, and hopped away'' represent the type of language you can use to describe a subtraction situation.

- **Jennifer, Leo, and Kim were playing a game of catch.** (These children start to act.) **Leo heard his brother call him and he went home.** (Leo leaves the group.) **Let's tell about this play using numbers.** (A child may respond, **3 children then 1 boy went away.**) Ask, **How many children are still playing catch?** (Children respond, **2 children are still playing catch.**) Say, **Let's tell about the whole play using numbers.** (Children respond, **3 children then 1 boy went away is 2 children.**) To end the play, say, **When it got dark, Jennifer and Kim went home.**

- **Hilary had 3 crayons. She gave away the blue crayon to Ann. Let's tell about the play using numbers.** (Children respond, **3 crayons then she gave away 1 crayon.**) **How many crayons does Hilary have left?** (Children respond, **She has 2 crayons left.**) Say, **Let's tell about the whole play using numbers.** (Children respond, **3 crayons then she gave away 1 crayon is 2 crayons.**)

- **Tony, Lynn, and Jon were pretending to be frogs at the playhouse. They hopped and hopped. They got tired so all the frogs hopped away. Let's tell about the play using numbers.** (Children respond, **3 frogs then 3 frogs hopped away.**) **How many frogs are hopping at the playhouse now?** (Children respond, **0 frogs are hopping now. The whole play is, 3 frogs then 3 frogs hopped away is 0 frogs.**)

Encourage the children to tell stories for their classmates to act out. As with addition, it is most effective to use as many classroom situations as you can to illustrate subtractive action.

Variation

Have the children make up puppet plays involving subtraction situations. Have them use finger puppets made from Line Master 16 (these puppets are described on page 148). It is helpful to model a couple of stories before inviting the children to think of their own.

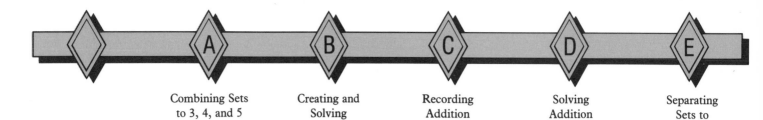

A	B	C	D	E
Combining Sets to 3, 4, and 5	Creating and Solving Addition Story Problems	Recording Addition Sentences	Solving Addition Sentences	Separating Sets to 3, 4, and 5

6. Let's Show a Story F

This story board activity follows the procedure outlined on page 149. Each story you tell should involve a subtractive action. Remember to vary the language you use so that different subtraction situations are modelled. These stories (on the story board of Ted's room, Line Master 18 with the imp story characters cut from Line Master 14) are representative of an unlimited number you can tell the children. Have the children clear the story board after each story.

- **One evening 3 imps were playing on Ted's shelves.** (Children place 3 imps on their story board.) **They decided that they would rather play outside, so they went away to play outside.** (Children remove all imps from the story board.) **Let's tell the story using numbers.** (Children respond, **3 imps then the 3 imps went away to play outside.**) Ask, **How many imps are playing on Ted's shelves now.** (Children respond, **Zero imps are playing on Ted's shelves.**) Say, **Let's tell about the whole story using numbers.** (Children respond, **3 imps then 3 imps went away is 0 imps.**)
- **3 imps were playing in Ted's treasure chest.** (Children place the imps on the story board.) **2 of the imps thought they heard Ted and slipped away through the crack in the floor.** (Children remove those 2 imps from the story board.) **Let's tell the story using numbers.** (Children respond, **3 imps then 2 imps slipped away.**) Ask, **How many imps remain in Ted's room?** (Children respond, **1 imp is playing in Ted's treasure chest. 3 imps then 2 imps slip away is 1 imp.**)

Invite volunteers to tell stories for their classmates to show on the story board. Encourage each child to participate as the leader.

Variation

On other days, have the children work in pairs. Each child tells a story for her or his partner to act out on a story board. You might have to guide children in selecting their initial sets.

7. Let's Tell Stories PS F

Invite a small group of children to sit in a circle. Display 3 small objects and a piece of paper. Use the procedure outlined on page 149 to have the children tell stories which describe your actions. You could identify the counters as airplanes and the piece of paper as a runway. Place the 3 airplanes on the runway. Slide 1 counter off into the air as if it were taking off. Say, **Who would like to tell me about what you just saw?** Encourage several children to describe the same action in their own words. Demonstrate another action, e.g., 2 airplanes taking off. Redefine the counters and paper to maintain a high level of interest. Invite the children to make suggestions.

On another day, provide children with the objects and a piece of paper. Have each child, in turn, identify her or his objects and paper and show a story. Have the other children tell stories for those actions.

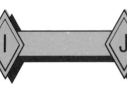 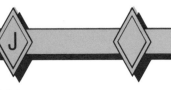

F	G	H	I	J	
Creating and Solving Subtraction Story Problems	Recording Subtraction Sentences	Solving Subtraction Sentences	Creating and Solving Story Problems	Solving Number Sentences to 5	

8. The Script G

Begin to model scripts (number sentences) for the plays described in Lights! Camera! Action!, page 161 and stories from Let's Show a Story and Let's Tell Stories, page 162 only after the children have had several opportunities to participate in those activities. As with addition, it is important that the children see the number sentence evolve as the action takes place. Vary the type of subtraction situations so that children see the − sign as representing any subtraction action.

Nancy, Ryan, and Evan were painting at the art center. (These children go to the art center.) **The boys finished painting and went to the library.** (Ryan and Evan leave the art center.) **Let's tell about this play using numbers.** On a display area, record the number sentence as the child responds. For example, the child responds, **3 children were at the art center** (you print, 3) **2 children went away** (print −2; 3 − 2 is now on the chalk board.) Say, **I made a record of the number story that (Carlo) told us.** As you point to the symbols, say, **3 children take away 2 children. The script is 3 take away 2** (again point to the corresponding symbols). Continue to record the story as a child responds to the question, **How many children are left at the art center?** Print = 1 to complete the number sentence as a child responds, **There is 1 child left at the art center.** Point to each corresponding symbol as you say, **Our script is 3 take away 2 is 1.** Repeat this process as children act out many stories. On other days, repeat the same process of modelling a number sentence as children tell the stories in Let's Show a Story and Let's Tell Stories.

When children are comfortable reading the number sentences, start to model the terms "minus" and "equals" as you point to the corresponding symbols. **Another way to read the script is 3 minus 2 equals 1.** As with addition, continue to accept the familiar language "take away" and "is" as you model these terms.

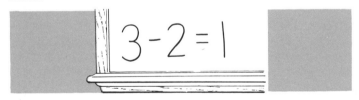

$$3 - 2 = 1$$

Remind the children that there are 2 ways of recording a number sentence. Use the horizontal and vertical forms interchangeably so that children become familiar with both forms.

After children have observed you model number sentences on several different occasions, invite them to be script writers as the number story is told. These scripts (number sentences) can be recorded on sheets of paper or individual chalk boards. Initially, have children copy the number sentences you record. If you record a horizontal number sentence, have them record it in the vertical form.

9. Our Own Number Stories G

After the children have observed you model number sentences on many different occasions as described in The Script, they can begin to keep records of Activities 5, 6, and 7 as they play them individually or with a partner. Children record verbally, pictorially, and/or symbolically as they did for addition, page 151.

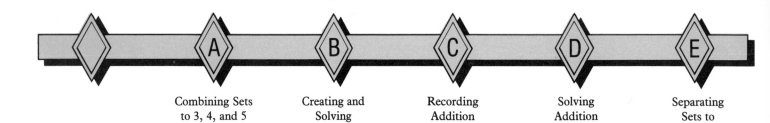

A	B	C	D	E
Combining Sets to 3, 4, and 5	Creating and Solving Addition Story Problems	Recording Addition Sentences	Solving Addition Sentences	Separating Sets to 3, 4, and 5

10. Recording the Games

Children can begin to keep a record of the 4 manipulating games (Breakfast Orders and Washed Away, page 159; Pitch the Tent and Abracadabra!, page 160) as they play them. This is done only after they have had several opportunities to observe you model number sentences as described in The Script, page 163.

Line Masters 62 to 65 are provided for recording purposes. Once again, the first step of transferring the action to the paper is placing the concrete objects in the large top frame as shown.

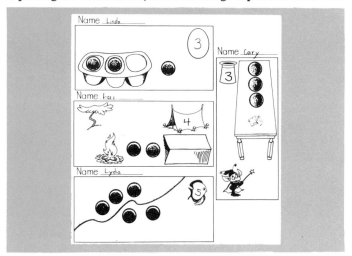

Children proceed to the next recording step after they have had several opportunities to describe the materials as they appear in the top frame. Children draw a picture of the objects in the top frame in a smaller frame. They also record the number sentence by making a label using cutouts from Line Masters 53, 60, and 61 or by printing their own. Discuss reasonable ways to draw the tent and tissue. Model their suggestions so that every child approaches the task with an idea of how to represent those concrete objects.

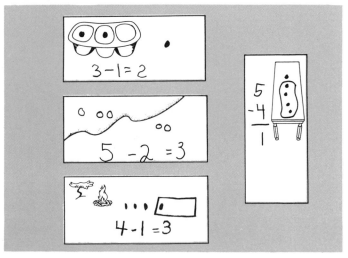

The third and final step in recording these games is shown here. Remember not to rush this step. Most children will spontaneously start to eliminate the second step of drawing the objects.

It is important that children say aloud what they are recording when working alone or with a partner. The verbal statements reinforce the number sentence through another mode.

Once again, you may wish to provide motivation for these recordings. The children could be recording the orders they fill as short-order cooks when they play Breakfast Orders; be scientists recording the movement of the waves when they play Washed Away; be counselors keeping track of all campers on a camping trip when they play Pitch the Tent; or be reporters writing up a magic act as they play Abracadabra!

Note that Line Master 62 is appropriate for recording actions when working with 3 eggs. You must add a section for 4 eggs and 2 for 5 eggs before you reproduce the line master.

11. Pick a Card   PS

Follow the procedure outlined on page 153 and change the cards to subtraction questions.

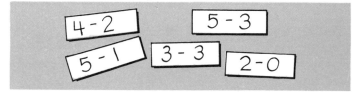

12. Find the Solution ◆ H

The reinforcement activities illustrated and described on pages 154 and 155 can easily be adapted for differences to 5. The activities are intended to reinforce the concepts of this section; not to teach them. In addition, it is recommended that you add a collection of flip cards to the center.

Children play with the flip cards in pairs or small groups. A leader selects a card and the other child places the same number of concrete objects down. The leader flips the card up and the child removes the same number of objects. The child chooses a number sentence strip (Line Masters 60 and 61), prints it, or tells an appropriate number sentence to describe the action.

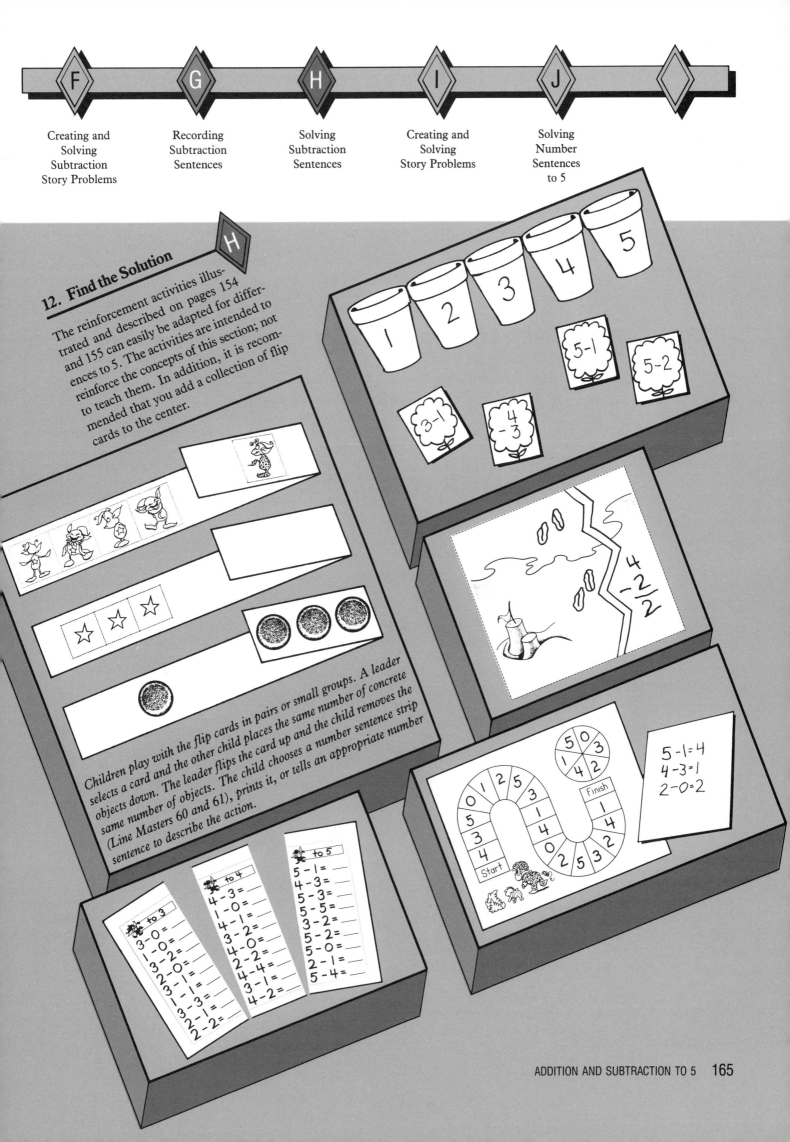

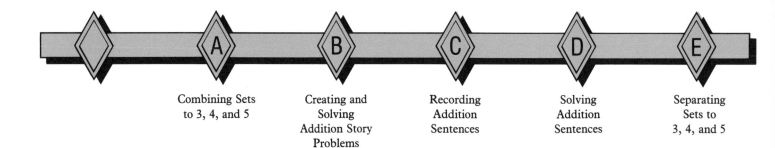

Section 3

Planning the Section

Objective	Level	Activity	Grouping	Program *or* Management Suggestions
I Creating and Solving Story Problems	Concrete	1. Lights! Camera! Action!	♦♦♦♦♦♦♦	These activities have been listed for large groups. However, you might consider gathering small groups together to ensure greater participation. While small groups are involved with you, other children can work independently with the games suggested in the activity Find the Solution on pages 154-55 and 165 or proceed to Activity 6.
		2. Choose a Card	♦♦♦♦♦♦♦	
	Semi-concrete	3. What's the Story?	♦♦♦♦♦♦♦	
	Pictorial	4. Number Sentence Captions	♦♦♦♦♦♦♦	
	Symbolic	5. What's My Card?	♦♦♦♦♦♦♦	
J Solving Number Sentences to 5	Symbolic	6. Solve, Sort, and Staple	♦	Activity 7 suggests a variety of ways for children to display the number sentences they generate. This activity can be repeated frequently throughout the year. It provides an excellent opportunity for children to recall the facts they have generated.
		7. The Name Game	♦	

About this Section

This section provides the children with many opportunities to interpret both addition and subtraction situations as they are acted out, simulated with objects, shown on story boards, and told verbally. Children should be given many opportunities to explain why they chose a particular symbol (+ or −) or wrote a specific number sentence. It is important to hear the reasoning that went into their choice. Though a child may select a sign or number sentence that appears inappropriate, her or his interpretation may, in fact, lead to the response offered. Remind the children that they must watch and/or listen very carefully as each situation unfolds.

It is suggested that the children participate often in activities at the concrete and semiconcrete levels (Activities 1 to 3) before moving to Activities 4 and 5 at the pictorial and symbolic levels. You may wish to continue to integrate these activities slowly as you begin the next unit. Activity 7 can easily be set up as a center for children to review and reinforce the combinations to 5 as you engage in the next unit.

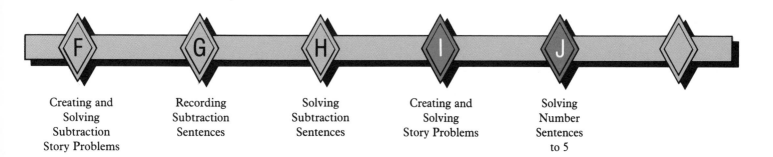

Observations and Evaluation

It is important to assess those children who choose an inappropriate symbol and/or number sentence. Try to establish through questioning whether the children are observing and listening as attentively as they should to interpret the situation. Ask, **What did you see? Tell me in your own words what you heard.** If the child's response indicates that he or she was observing and listening attentively, consider whether the concept of the addition and subtraction process has been internalized and if the symbols have been connected to the actions. These key questions may help you ascertain how well these concepts have been internalized.

- **What did you see? Did children join or leave the group? What sign could we use to show joining (leaving)? How do we read this sign?**
- **Show me a story that this sign could describe. Tell it to me.**
- **What does this number story say? Show it to me with counters.**
- **What story could go with those actions?**
- **Show me a number story with your counters. How could you print it?**

Children who are unable to answer these questions successfully need more opportunities to participate in the activities of Sections 1 and 2.

Suggested Materials

- A **+** and **−** card for each child [Activities 1, 2, and 5]

Line Masters

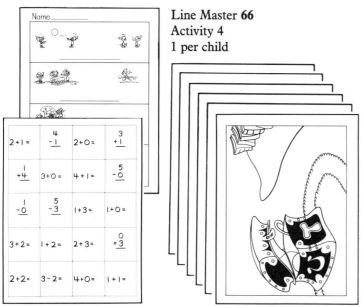

Line Master **66**
Activity 4
1 per child

Line Master **67**
Activity 6
1 per child

Any of Line Masters **18** to **23**
Activity 3
1 per child

Activities

1. Lights! Camera! Action!

Tell the children that today they are going to be actors and script writers again. Explain that, as on other days, you are going to tell stories for the children to act out. They are to listen for their names (cues) and join the play while it is in progress. Point out that on previous days the stories had only addition action or subtraction action. Today, however, some stories will have addition action and others will have subtraction action. The audience will be script writers and their role is to watch the play and determine whether the action was additive or subtractive. After each story has been acted out, discuss the type of action that took place. These questions can form the basis for the discussion.

- **What happened in this play? Tell me in your own words.**
- **Did groups of children come together?**
- **Did a child(ren) leave the group during the play?**
- **Which sign (+ or −) describes the action in this play?**
- **What is the number sentence for this play?**

Invite a volunteer script writer to record the number sentence on the chalk board or display chart. After a few stories have been performed and the children are discussing the action of the play with confidence, provide each child with + or − cards, a piece of paper, and a pencil. After the next performance, ask the children to hold up the card that describes the action. If some children select an inappropriate card, discuss the action. If not, invite them to print the number sentence that describes the play. Have the script writers read these scripts aloud before going on to the next play.

Try to ensure that every child has an opportunity to participate in a play. The stories should be short to keep a quick pace and maintain a high level of interest. Remember to make number sentence strips (Line Masters 54, 55, 60, and 61) and cards cut from Line Master 53 available.

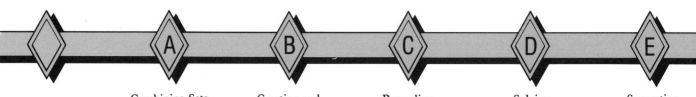

A	B	C	D	E
Combining Sets to 3, 4, and 5	Creating and Solving Addition Story Problems	Recording Addition Sentences	Solving Addition Sentences	Separating Sets to 3, 4, and 5

2. Choose a Card

Provide each child with + and − cards. Explain that you are going to act out a story problem with counters (any objects which are easy to see can be used) on the overhead projector. After you have completed the action, ask the children to hold up the sign that appropriately identifies the action. For example, if you placed 5 counters on the overhead projector and then removed 2 counters; the children would hold up a − card. Alternatively, if you placed 2 objects on the overhead projector and then placed 3 more objects; the children would hold up a + card.

Invite the children to tell a story in their own words for the actions they observed. You may have to prompt them by identifying what item the counters were representing. If you offer the counters as rockets a child might respond, **There were 5 rockets on the launching pad. 2 rockets took off and there were 3 rockets left.**

If an overhead projector is not available, have the children sit in a circle. Perform the action so that everyone can see the counters clearly.

Variation

- Have the children play Choose a Card with a partner. The children can display the action on any flat surface. Encourage them to identify the action by selecting a card as well as telling a story in their own words.
- Display a story using story characters cut from Line Masters 14 to 16 on a story board (Line Masters 18 to 23). Have the children identify the action and then tell the story in their own words.

3. What's the Story?

Provide each child with a story board (Line Masters 18 to 23) and several story characters (Line Masters 14 to 16). Tell a story that involves a number of additive and subtractive actions. After each action, invite the children to tell a number sentence which describes that particular moment in the story. This sample story takes place on the playground story board (Line Master 23) with story characters cut from Line Master 16.

- **One sunny afternoon 3 children were playing in the sandbox. 1 child left to go to the teeter-totter. Tell the number sentence.** (Children respond, **3 minus 1 equals 2**.) **The child on the teeter-totter was having no fun alone so he went back to the sandbox. Tell the number sentence.** (Children respond, **2 plus 1 equals 3**.) **After a while, he persuaded a friend to go to the teeter-totter with him. The 2 children went to play on the teeter-totter. Tell the number sentence.** (Children respond, **3 minus 2 equals 1**.) **2 more children came to play at the playground. They went to play at the slide. Tell the number sentence that describes how many children are on the slide.** (Children resond, **0 plus 2 equals 2**.)

Continue as long as interest is maintained. Invite children to participate in the story telling.

When you are telling a story involving both addition and subtraction, it is a good idea to use related facts often so that children can gradually acquire the concept of fact families.

Variation

- Provide the children with number sentence strips cut from Line Masters 54, 55, 60, and 61. They can choose and display the appropriate strip to tell the number story.

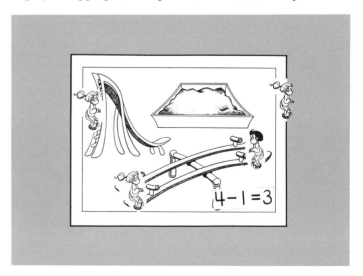

- Have the children print a number sentence in response to the statement, **Tell a number sentence.**

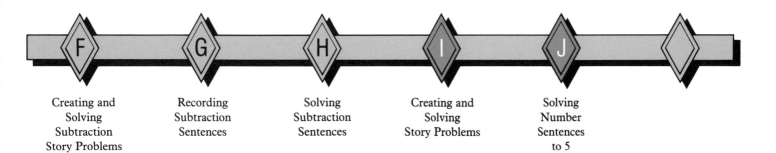

F	G	H	I	J	
Creating and Solving Subtraction Story Problems	Recording Subtraction Sentences	Solving Subtraction Sentences	Creating and Solving Story Problems	Solving Number Sentences to 5	

4. Number Sentence Captions

Distribute a copy of Line Master 66 to each child and draw their attention to the top section. Invite the children to tell stories about this illustration. After all children have had the opportunity to voice their stories, ask, **What number sentence do you think best tells about this picture?** Accept all reasonable responses. Unusual responses might be better understood if the child also explains her or his interpretation of the story. Point out the space below the illustration and explain that this is where the corresponding number sentence should be printed. Direct small groups of children to work areas where they can tell stories about the other illustrations on the page. After they have shared stories about all the illustrations, have them print number sentences under each one.

You may wish to have the children print or tape stories to go along with the illustrations. Have number sentence strips (Line Masters 54 55, 60, and 61) available for children who need them.

Meeting Individual Needs

Encourage the children who are ready for a further challenge to search through magazines, brochures, or calendars to find pictures that illustrate additive or subtractive action. Have them mount a picture and print the appropriate number sentence as a caption. These can be posted as a bulletin board display or stapled into a class book and placed in the library.

5. What's My Card? PS

Invite the children to sit in a circle and provide each child with + and − cards. Display a + card and a − card. Have the children give examples of the type of action each card represents. Hold the display cards so that the children cannot see the signs. Invite a volunteer to come forward, view the cards, and select a card of her or his choice. Ask the child to tell a short story that goes with the card selected. This story should end with the question, What's my card? **I had 5 cookies. I was very hungry so I ate 2 cookies. What's my card?**

Have the children answer by holding up one of their cards to indicate their response. If children have difficulty identifying the action, have them act out the story. Call on volunteers and repeat the process as long as interest is maintained.

Variation

Have the volunteer select a + or − card and ask her or him to act out an appropriate story using counters. Invite the children to guess which card prompted the story.

6. Solve, Sort, and Staple J

Provide each child with a copy of Line Master 67 and explain that after they complete the page of questions, they are to cut along the dotted lines. This will produce pages for a booklet. Tell the children that they are to sort their number sentences to form booklets of sentences that all equal the same numeral. Have additional strips cut so that children can add pages to their books if they choose. When the sorting is complete, have the children make a cover using a small blank sheet and staple it in their booklets.

Invite the children to illustrate the number sentences in their book. Each number sentence can be illustrated on the back of the previous page.

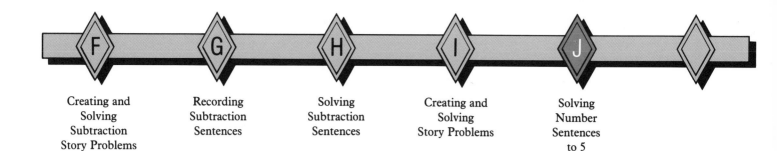

F	G	H	I	J	
Creating and Solving Subtraction Story Problems	Recording Subtraction Sentences	Solving Subtraction Sentences	Creating and Solving Story Problems	Solving Number Sentences to 5	

7. The Name Game PS J

Lead a discussion with the children on personal names. Ask, **Does anyone here have a nickname?** List the child's name and nickname. If no one responds, ask the children to think of variations for names such as Robert or Elizabeth.

Print a numeral from 1 to 5 on a display area and ask the children to name the numeral. Print the number name (five) beside the numeral. Ask, **What are other names for 5?** If necessary, prompt the children by questioning, **Is 3 + 2 another name for 5? Is 5 − 0 another name for 5?** List each appropriate name as it is mentioned. Carry on this discussion until children have started to see the numerous possible names for 5. Have the children continue to generate names for 5 (or any other number). Ensure that the children have access to counters. There are many different ways to have children present these names; they can be generated individually, with a partner, or as a group effort.

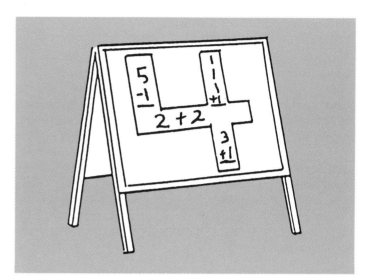

Numerals can be drawn on large sheets of paper and posted on easels. Children can help to print appropriate names in the numeral.

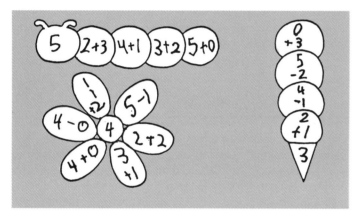

Children can present the different names as illustrated using precut figures (or ones they cut themselves from construction paper or newsprint).

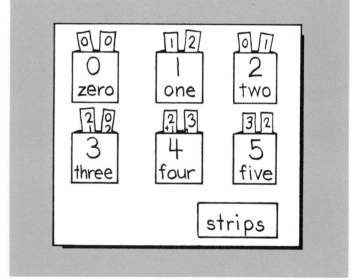

Children print number sentences on strips and then place each strip in the corresponding pocket. Other children can then remove the strips, shuffle them, and sort them into the appropriate pockets.

These activities provide a good opportunity for review and reinforcement. You may wish to introduce the activities over a number of days, and then leave them at a center where children can participate as they choose. Some children will discover patterns that will lead to creating many number sentences for the first time.

Meeting Individual Needs

If a child is ready for a further challenge, encourage her or him to choose a number. Have the child generate many ways to express the selected number. Provide a variety of art materials and magazines for this endeavor.

Addition and Subtraction Across the Curriculum

Language Arts

In conjunction with this unit you may wish to read any of these books (see page 318 for an annotated bibliography):
- *Pancakes for Breakfast* by Tomie de Paola
- *There Was an Old Lady Who Swallowed a Fly* by Pam Adams

Art

Draw children's attention to their art work by asking questions such as these:

- **How many red flowers are in your picture? How many blue flowers are in your picture? How many flowers are there altogether in your picture?**
- **Anna painted 4 cats in her picture. If she painted 1 more cat, how many would there be altogether?**

Physical Education

When you are involved in activities in the gym, ask questions such as these:

- **There are 2 children on the red mat and 2 children on the green mat. How many children are on the mats?**
- **Elizabeth threw 5 beanbags at the basket. How many landed inside the basket? How many landed outside the basket?**

Social Studies

Have the children identify when they must add or subtract in their daily lives. Ask them to interview their parents, brothers, sisters, or babysitters to find other occasions when people must add or subtract. You may wish to compile a list entitled When We Add or Subtract.

Extension Project

At a center, place file cards, cardboard, file folders, numbered cubes, and blank game boards (Line Master 43). Have the children create a game which involves addition and/or subtraction such as the ones suggested in Find the Solution, pages 154-155 and 165. A child uses many problem-solving skills even if he or she chooses to copy a game you have made for class use. Be sure to give the children many opportunities to teach their games to their friends.

Geometry

Unit Objectives

Section 1

A Manipulating Geometric Solids
B Sorting Geometric Solids
C Relating Real-world Objects to Geometric Solids

Section 2

D Creating and Interpreting a Pictograph

About this Unit

Geometry

Geometry is a part of mathematics that has frequently been neglected in primary programs. Yet, young children need many opportunities to manipulate models of geometric solids if they are to discover their properties and to develop an awareness of spatial relationships. These experiences and discoveries will form a base of understanding on which a more formal study of geometry can later be built. If these early concrete experiences are lacking, children will have a much reduced chance for success when geometric relationships are later presented at a more abstract level.

The study of geometry is, in fact, a study of the child's environment, and is therefore intrinsically interesting and relevant. The activities of this unit offer children opportunities to explore the properties of solids in their world and to be involved in highly motivating problem-solving situations.

Graphing

To date, children have had several opportunities to create and interpret a variety of concrete graphs. Through these experiences the children should have developed an understanding and appreciation of the usefulness and purpose of displaying information on a graph. The concrete graph does, however, have these limitations:

- often the materials can not be displayed permanently;
- frequently the questions do not lead naturally to concrete materials being displayed;
- usually they require a large physical space.

For these reasons, the pictograph is a very useful type of graph. Each picture on a pictograph represents a concrete object. To understand this connection, the children initially participate in creating a pictograph of a concrete graph.

Problem Solving

In addition to the graphing section of this unit, children have several other opportunities to participate in problem-solving activities. They apply and extend their sorting skills in the activities What Will the Solids Do?, page 181 and Sort the Solids, page 182. Through careful observation they identify and sort solids in the room and then display their findings on a graph in Graphing Classroom Solids, page 183. The children are involved in predicting and constructing a model to confirm their predictions in Can You Build It?, page 182. In addition, activities provided in Five Minute Math, page 175 develop these problem-solving skills.

- sorting
- identifying and completing patterns
- creating stories
- developing observation and listening skills

Vocabulary

- Column
- Graph
- Least
- Less
- Model
- More
- Most

- Pictograph
- Roll
- Row
- Slide
- Solid
- Stack

Planning Ahead

The next unit introduces addition and subtraction for 6 through 10. It is recommended that you reassess any children you feel may not have mastered combinations to 5 to determine whether they need more time to internalize those combinations before beginning to explore combinations for 6 to 10.

Ongoing Objectives

- Reading a calendar
- Counting on
- Estimating and comparing length
- Estimating and comparing mass
- Identifying and counting coin collections
- Problem solving
  - Sorting
  - Identifying and completing patterns
  - Creating stories
  - Developing observation and listening skills

Five Minute Math

Calendar Activities

- Take attendance each day and record it on the chart of the days of the week. Ask, **How many days in a school week? What is the first (last) day of a school week?** Have a child point out a school week on the calendar. Ask questions at the end of the week such as these:

  - **How many children were away Monday?**
  - **Were there more than 2 children away Thursday?**
  - **Which day was only 1 child away?**
  - **When were the greatest (least) number of children away?**

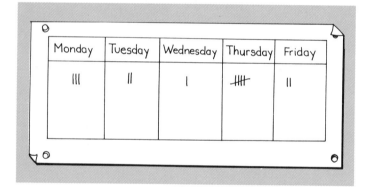

- Post classroom duties on a chart of the days of the week.

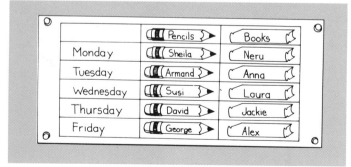

When you introduce the duty chart ask these questions:

- **Who is pencil monitor on Wednesday?**
- **Who is pencil monitor tomorrow?**
- **Who is pencil monitor 2 days after Armand?**
- **Who is pencil monitor on the day before Friday?**

Counting Activities

- Use counting as a means of timing an activity. For example, **Can Dina's group tidy the block center before we count to 100?** Or, **How far can we count before the recess bell rings?**
- As the children walk to the gym, to the door for recess, or to the library, have them count how many steps they take. Repeat the activity, and have them take giant steps or baby steps rather than normal steps.
- Continue to use the cumulative record of days in school as a basis for counting; pointing to the numerals as you proceed.
- Place numeral cards from 1 to 100 in a bag. Invite a volunteer to select, display, and read a card. The children begin their counting from that number.
- Select several minute intervals during the day for counting. Each time, record the last number counted on the board. Count on from that number during the next minute counting session.

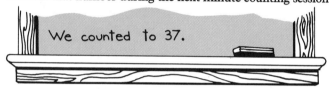

Measurement Activities

- Hold up an object such as a piece of chalk and ask, **What is longer than this piece of chalk?** Display the item identified (a pencil) and ask, **What is longer than this pencil?** Display or point to the item identified (a book shelf) and ask, **What is longer than this book shelf?** Repeat the activity changing longer to shorter.

- Play I Spy with statements such as these:
  I spy with my little eye something that is longer than a piece of chalk but shorter than a pencil, . . . about the same height as the door handle is from the floor, . . . shorter than a paper clip.

- Place an object such as an eraser on a balance. Ask, **What 2 things do you think we could find that together would be lighter than the eraser?** Have the children test the items they identify. Ensure that each time objects are tested, a conclusion is reached as to whether they are lighter or heavier than the eraser.

Money Activities

- Display a nickel and a collection of pennies. Say, **Let's count the money. First we start with the nickel.** Encourage the children to participate as you begin counting the collection. **Five, six, seven, eight, . . .** Each time you count a coin move it to one side. Repeat the process for different collections of coins.
- Provide each child with a nickel, a collection of pennies, and an egg carton cut into 2 sections. Explain that the egg carton is a cash register and have the children place their coins so that the nickels and pennies are in separate sections. Explain that at the end of the day cashiers must count their cash. Have the children count their cash and report to the others how much money is in their till. Have the children exchange their cash registers and repeat the process.

Problem Solving Activities

Sorting

Make a list with sketches such as the ones illustrated.

Read the list aloud with the children and ask, **Which one does not belong? Why? What could we title the list? What else belongs on the list?** Encourage childen to create their own lists by drawing or cutting and pasting pictures from magazines.

Identifying and Completing Patterns

Create a pattern with objects such as the one shown. This could be displayed effectively on the overhead projector.

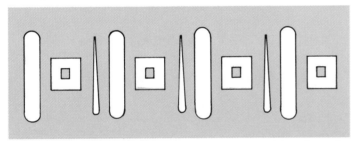

Ask the children to close their eyes. Remove an object from the pattern. Have the children open their eyes and ask, **What did I remove? How do you know?** Display a different pattern and continue the activity.

Creating Stories

- Identify the number of counters you place in a container, e.g., 5. Have the children identify the container and the objects. For example, the container could be a basket and the counters could be 5 puppies. Have a volunteer remove puppies from the basket and tell a story.

  There were 5 puppies sleeping in the basket. 2 puppies woke up and went to play. 3 puppies kept on sleeping.

  Encourage the children to continue telling stories on the same theme as long as interest is maintained. Have them change the identity of the objects when interest appears to diminish.

- Print 2 numerals on the chalk board, e.g., 3 and 2. Have the children make up story problems using the 2 numerals. Have the children demonstrate their story problems with small objects. For example, **There were 3 cars in the parking lot. 2 cars drove away. How many cars are in the lot?** Or, **I have 3 stickers. My friend gave me 2 more stickers. How many do I have now?**

Developing Observation and Listening Skills

- Display 2 items which are different in only one way.

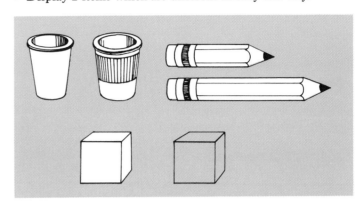

Tell the children you are thinking of one of 2 items. Invite the children to think of a question to ask you that will lead them to discover which of the 2 items you have chosen. For example: If you displayed a long and a short pencil, a child could ask, **Is the pencil long?**

- Display a variety of items and tell the children you are going to think of one of the objects and give them a clue to help them guess what you chose. For example, if you displayed a pencil, book, crayon, glue bottle, and a piece of chalk; this conversation could take place:

Teacher:	**I am thinking of something on the table. You can write with it. What could it be?**
Child:	**The pencil, crayon, or chalk.**
Teacher:	**Why isn't it the book or glue bottle?**
Child:	**You can't write with them.**
Teacher:	**It is made of wood. What could it be?**
Child:	**The pencil.**
Teacher:	**How do you know it is the pencil?**
Child:	**Only the pencil is something you write with that is made of wood.**

Using the Poem

The poem Imps at Play takes place in Ted's cabin. As usual, the imps are playing and having fun while Ted sleeps soundly in his room. The imps have transformed Ted's home into a playground by improvising with his belongings. Boxes, tubes, balls, and cones have come out of the cupboards and drawers to be stacked and arranged into a playground of fun.

The poem provides a basis for discussion and introduces geometric solids in a natural way. The children themselves will be involved in exploring the properties of objects just as the imps are in the poem. The poem initiates the activity Imps at Play, page 180. In this activity, the children are engaged in creating a real playground for the imps. The poem and picture may also motivate discussion when the children are relating real-world objects to geometric solids.

Supplementary Material

Ted is my Friend: Mathematics Activity Book, pages 63-68; and graphing mat, pages 38 and 55.

Imps at Play

Imps at play go round and round,
Sliding and rolling and tumbling down.

Boxes and balls and tubes they've found,
Sliding and rolling and tumbling down.

They're building and stacking without a sound,
Sliding and rolling and tumbling down.

Imps hurry and scurry when Ted's not around,
Sliding and rolling and tumbling down.

What fun for imps in their own playground,
Sliding and rolling and tumbling down!

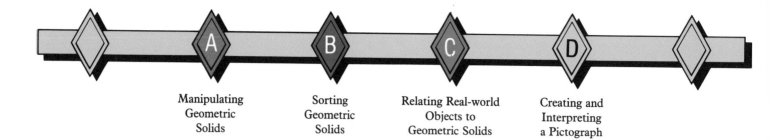

Section 1

Planning the Section

Objective	Level	Activity	Grouping	Program *or* Management Suggestions
A Manipulating Geometric Solids	Concrete	1. Let's Explore 2. Imps at Play 3. Junk Sculpture	👤👤👤👤 👤👤👤👤 👤	In Activities 2 and 3 the children use the materials brought from home to build permanent structures. Before introducing these activities, ensure that there is a variety of materials available. Note that if materials are limited, have the children engage in Activities 2 and 3 after they have completed Activities 4, 5, and 6.
B Sorting Geometric Solids	Concrete	4. What Will the Solids Do? 5. Can You Build It? 6. Sort the Solids	👤👤👤👤 👤👤👤👤 👤👤👤👤	You may wish to introduce Activities 4 to 6 informally as the children engage in exploring materials during Activity 1. Any of Activities 1 to 6 can be set up at different centers. Have small groups visit different centers daily.
C Relating Real-world Objects to Geometric Solids	Concrete Pictorial	7. Solid of the Day 8. Graphing Classroom Solids 9. Focussing on Solids 10. Search, Find, Trace	👤👤👤👤👤👤👤👤 👤👤👤👤👤👤👤👤 👤👤👤👤👤👤👤👤 👤👤👤👤	In Activity 7 children are asked to bring in materials from home for the day. It is recommended that you send a letter home explaining the reason for this request. Activity 9 involves leaving the classroom. You may wish to arrange to have parents or older students accompany you on this outing.

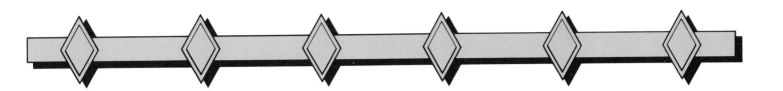

About this Section

This section begins with the activity Let's Explore, page 180. It is important that each child have opportunities to manipulate a variety of geometric solids as they use them in various constructions. To provide children with an interesting collection of materials, you may wish to have the children bring in objects from home. See page 317 for a model of a letter requesting appropriate materials. It is important to recognize a child's contribution to classroom materials. Asking each child to show the items he or she has brought in from home often sparks concerted effort in collecting materials.

These solids are the focus of this section.

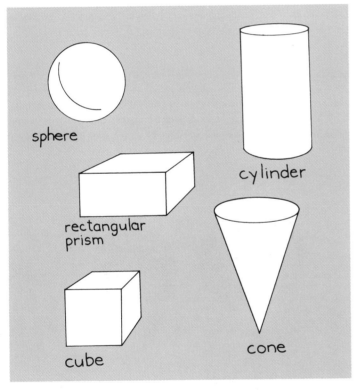

The vocabulary developed to describe the geometric models depends on the children's ability, and the focus of their experiences. It is not expected that children recall the vocabulary: sphere, cylinder, cube, cone, or rectangular prism. However, many children enjoy using new, big words and if you model the language, they will naturally use this vocabulary. The focus of the activities, however, should be on what the children have discovered or created.

Geometric solids will have the most relevance to a child when seen in the context of familiar articles from everyday life such as boxes, balls, ice cream cones, buildings, cans, etc. For this reason it is important to help the child draw as many parallels as possible between geometric solids and the familiar objects which surround her or him.

Observations and Evaluation

These key questions can form the basis of discussion as you rotate among the groups.

- **Does this roll/slide/stack? Show me.**
- **What could you make with this?**
- **How are these alike/different?**
- **What does this look like?**
- **What else has the same shape as this?**

To gather more information about how competently children identify and sort geometric solids, display a collection of solids and ask, **Which of these do you think rolls? Which of these can you stack or slide? Show me.** Hold up a solid and say, **Place all the other things that have the same shape as this together.**

Suggested Materials

- Several bins of models of geometric solids including those available commercially, and materials brought from home such as paper towel rolls, tin cans, spools, or cardboard boxes of different sizes [Activities 1 to 8]
- A piece of wood or a book to form an inclined plane at each work area [Activity 4]
- Hoops or pieces of yarn at each work area [Activity 6]
- A large graphing mat (See page 33 for suggestions.) [Activity 8]
- A toilet paper roll for each child [Activity 9]
- A collection of magazines, brochures, and catalogues [Activity 10]

Line Masters

Line Master **68**
Activity 4
1 per child

Line Master **69**
Activity 5
1 per child

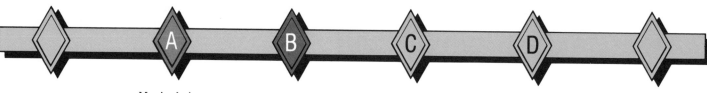

Activities

1. Let's Explore

Provide several bins of geometric solids at different work areas. Invite small groups of children to explore the materials. It is important to observe the kinds of spontaneous building, sorting, ordering, etc., the children engage in with the materials as a focus for following discussions and lessons. At the end of the exploration time, have the children gather together. Encourage them to tell about their activities. Ask, **What did you do with the materials? What did you build? What did you use in your building? What didn't you use? Why? Did you discover anything interesting? What material do you wish we had more of? Why?**

Children may want to know what the commercial geometric solids are called. You may wish to ask the children what their shape reminds them of and then suggest the children use the name which seems most suitable, **Solids shaped like a can.** You may also wish to give the children the correct terminology, i.e., cylinder. If your class is one which enjoys focussing on big words, you might wish to put 1 or 2 of them on a chart as your big words for the week.

2. Imps at Play

Invite the children together and explain that they are going to use some of the materials they brought from home to create a playground for the imps. Lead a discussion on the different things that could be found at such a playground. Provide art materials such as crayons, scissors, glue, construction paper, and paint for the children to use to transform the geometric solids into various pieces of playground equipment and structures. Give the children the opportunity to describe what they have made, which solids they used, and how the imps will use the solids.

You may wish to provide all the materials required at a covered surface such as a table top or a designated region of floor space. Invite the children in small groups to participate in building the site.

Variation

Decide on a few different types of sites to build such as a neighborhood, city, or space station. Place materials at different work areas and identify each construction site. Have the children choose which site they would like to help build.

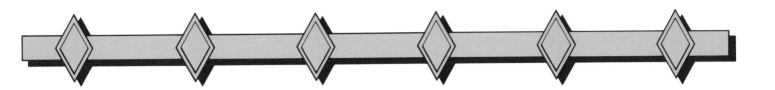

3. Junk Sculpture

Invite the children to choose a number of boxes, paper towel rolls, containers, etc., and take them to a workspace. Provide the children with glue. Tell the children they are going to glue their collection of objects together to make a junk sculpture. Ask the children to suggest what they might make their sculpture look like. Encourage creative problem solving to decide how objects can best be glued together. Invite the children to name and/or describe their sculptures when they are complete.

You may wish to gather the children around a display of junk sculptures to discuss them. Questions such as these could form the basis of a discussion:

- **Are there any of these solids** (hold up a model of a geometric solid) **in this sculpture?**
- **How many of these solids** (point to an example) **are in the sculpture?**
- **Is there a sculpture made of one type of solid?**

4. What Will the Solids Do? PS

At different work areas place bins of geometric solids, and a piece of wood and a book or any other available materials to make a small inclined plane.

Gather a small group of children around you and demonstrate how to set up an inclined plane. Distribute a copy of Line Master 68 to each child. Read the directions aloud with the children. Demonstrate how they can record their discoveries by checking yes or no. Direct the children in small groups to the different work areas. Encourage the children to predict and discuss their discoveries in their groups.

Note that the slope of the incline must be steep enough to allow the solids to roll or slide. Rotate among the groups to ensure that the slope of the plane is appropriate.

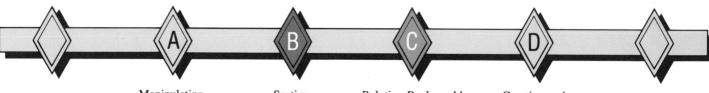

A	B	C	D
Manipulating Geometric Solids	Sorting Geometric Solids	Relating Real-world Objects to Geometric Solids	Creating and Interpreting a Pictograph

5. Can You Build It?　　　　　PS

At different work areas place bins of geometric solids and a copy of Line Master 69 for each child. Gather the children together, display the line master, point to one of the structures, and ask, **Do you think you could build this with the solids?** Encourage the children to explain their predictions. Tell the children that they will have the chance to discover the answer using the materials at the centers. Demonstrate how they can record their discoveries by checking yes or no. Direct the children in groups of 2 or 3 to different work areas to begin building. Encourage the children to predict whether they can build the structure before they attempt to construct it.

6. Sort the Solids　　　　　PS

At different work areas provide a variety of geometric solids and hoops or yarn to mark boundaries of sets. Remind the children how they used hoops/yarn to mark the boundaries of sets. Invite small groups of children to different work areas to sort the solids. Encourage the children to re-sort the collection using different criteria. Circulate and encourage the children to tell their sorting rule and describe their sets. You may wish to have several groups exchange places to see if they can guess each other's sorting rule.

Some children may decide to sort their collection into sets of solids that roll and those that slide or stack. The cylinder, a member of both sets, poses an interesting problem. Ask the children to suggest solutions. If no solution is forthcoming, point out that the hoops are movable and if necessary demonstrate how they can overlap to create a section which is part of both hoops.

After the children have had the opportunity to sort and re-sort their collection a number of times, invite them to gather around a collection. Have the children share different ways they sorted.

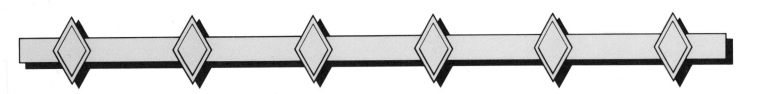

7. Solid of the Day

Gather the children together and display a model of a sphere. Invite them to find objects in the room which are the same shape. As the children identify objects, list them on a chart. Have the children bring the objects they identify to a display area. Encourage the children to bring objects shaped like a sphere from home. These objects can be displayed for the day and recorded on the chart. Also list any objects the children notice in the environment.

On following days focus on different solids so that a list and display are created for the cylinder, cube, rectangular prism, and cone. If you keep these lists displayed, the children will continue to search their environment for objects having the same shape as the solids introduced.

You may wish to store the objects collected and the materials from home in cartons under or by a table. Divide the table top into sections using pieces of yarn or masking tape. Direct the children to the materials and encourage them to sort the collection into sections on the table top. Have the children discuss and label the different sets they create.

8. Graphing Classroom Solids   PS

Set up a graphing mat with a cube, a sphere, a cylinder, and a rectangular prism as concrete labels to indicate the objects to be graphed. Invite the children to find things in the classroom which have the same shape as the geometric solids and place them on the appropriate places on the graph. When the children have found as many objects as they can, have them gather around the graph. Ask questions about each object to determine if it is correctly placed. For example, if something is in the cylinder column, ask, **Does it look like a can? Does it roll and slide?**

When the children have examined all the objects, ask, **Which objects did you find the most of in the classroom? The least? How many more _____ than _____?**

When the children have finished interpreting the graph, have them return the objects to their original place.

Variations

- Use the boxes, cans, cartons, cylindrical potato chip containers, etc., which the children have brought from home to make a concrete graph. Interpret the graph. **Which geometric solids do we have most of? The least of? How many more _____ than _____?**
- Divide the children into small groups. Have each group focus on finding objects having a particular shape.

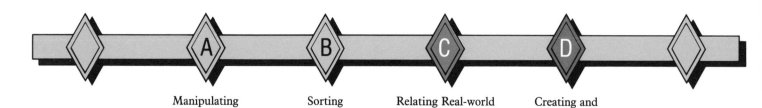

A	B	C	D
Manipulating Geometric Solids	Sorting Geometric Solids	Relating Real-world Objects to Geometric Solids	Creating and Interpreting a Pictorgraph

9. Focussing on Solids

Provide each child with a toilet paper roll or a paper towel roll to act as an imaginary telescope. Tell the children they will be going on a shape walk in the neighborhood (or school-yard) to search for things shaped like the geometric solids they have been working with in class. Explain that they are to use the telescope to search for and focus on appropriate objects. Take a clipboard with you to record the various objects the children see. Alternatively, you may wish to have children record their own observations. This is best done if the children sit in a number of different spots and look around them.

When you arrive back in class there are a variety of ways to summarize the group's observations. For example:

- the children could contribute to a class list of items spotted;
- you could lead a discussion of the children's observations;
- the children could make models of the items spotted;
- each child could draw an item to contribute to a display of the observations;
- each child could draw and record her or his own list of items spotted.

Variation

Enlist the aid of several parents or older children. Divide the children into groups. Have each group look for a different solid. You may wish to have the parents carry a clipboard and list or sketch the solids they find, or you may have them simply make a tally. Discuss with the children the objects they found when you return to the classroom.

10. Search, Find, Trace

Ahead of time, glue lightweight geometric solids on separate large sheets of paper. Post these sheets in a spot where children can easily reach them. At different work areas place markers, magazines, brochures, and catalogues.

Direct the children to the work areas to search for pictures of objects that resemble the geometric solids glued on each posted sheet. Ask the children to cut out the pictures, trace the outline of the solid with their finger, outline the solid with a marker, and then glue it in the appropriate section. Encourage the children to search through a number of different publications for objects that resemble the posted geometric solids. Discuss which solid was the most/least common.

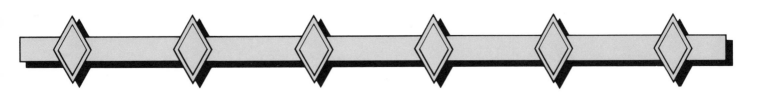

Section 2
Planning the Section

Objective	Level	Activity	Grouping	Program *or* Management Suggestions
 D Creating and Interpreting a Pictograph	Concrete and Pictorial Pictorial	1. A Picture of a Graph 2. All About Us 3. We Prefer 4. I Wonder	♦♦♦♦♦♦♦ ♦♦♦♦♦♦♦ ♦♦♦♦♦♦♦ ♦	Each activity offers a variety of graphing ideas. Activity 1 presents the connection between concrete graphs and pictographs. In Activity 2 children graph information about themselves. The suggestions for Activity 3 involve the children in making choices and stating their preferences. The children decide on their own graphing topic in Activity 4. They collect information independently and present it on a pictograph. It is important to remember that these graphing activities are intended to be carried out over an extended period of time.

About this Section

In this section, the children continue to develop their graphing skills as they create and interpret pictographs. Once again, it is suggested that you involve the students in creating and interpreting a graph on an average of once a week. You may wish to post a question and a graph at the beginning of the day. Children can respond to the question throughout the day. Set aside time at the end of the day to discuss the completed graph.

The first activity involves the children in creating a concrete graph and then graphing the same material pictorially. While many children make the transition to the pictograph easily, others do not see the connection between concrete objects and pictorial representations. It is recommended that you involve the children in creating pictographs of concrete graphs on other occasions as well to firmly establish the link. Continue to intersperse concrete graphs even after children are creating pictographs with confidence. The children will have the opportunity to cement their understanding in light of their additional graphing experience.

Each activity offers suggestions for graphs which compare 2 groups, 3 groups, and more than 3 groups. Begin by posing a question which involves creating a 2-column graph. When the children read these graphs comfortably, introduce questions which result in a 3-column graph. Ensure that each column is labelled with a picture and/or word. Each graph should also have a title.

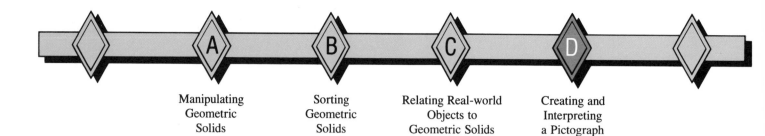

Observations and Evaluation

These key questions can form the basis of a discussion on the various pictographs created in this section.

- **What does this graph tell us?**
- **Which column has more/less/most/least?**
- **Are any columns the same? What does that mean?**
- **Are there more/less _____ than _____?**
- **How many more/less _____ than _____?**
- **How many children have (like) _____?**

You will know that your children appreciate the usefulness of displaying information on a graph when they spontaneously suggest creating a graph to answer a question or to present information.

Suggested Materials

- A pitcher of orange juice [Activity 1]
- A pitcher of apple juice [Activity 1]
- A paper cup for each child [Activity 1]
- A variety of graphing mats such as large divided plastic sheets on mural paper, a region of floor divided into sections, 2-, 3-, or 4-column graphs on large sheets of paper [Activities 1, 2, 3, and 4]

Line Master

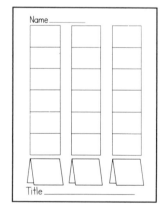

Line Master **70**
Activity 4
1 per child

Activities

1. A Picture of a Graph   PS D

Prepare a picture of apple juice and a pitcher of orange juice. Distribute a paper cup to each child. Explain that today they have a choice of apple juice or orange juice for a snack. Ask the children to decide which kind of juice they would like to have. Have them make a yellow crayon mark on their cup if they want apple juice and an orange crayon mark if they want orange juice. Stand behind a table with both pitchers of juice. Invite all the children who decided on apple juice to stand in a line in front of the pitcher of apple juice and all children who want orange juice to stand in front of the orange juice pitcher. Ask, **Does it look like more children want apple juice or more children want orange juice?**

Pour the juice and have the children sit in a circle to drink it. Place a label for orange juice and a label for apple juice at the end of the 2-column graphing mat as shown. In turn, have each child place her or his empty glass in the appropriate column. Ask questions such as these to interpret the graph created.

- **What did more/less children choose to drink? How do you know?**
- **How many more children chose apple juice than orange juice?**
- **How many children chose to drink apple juice/orange juice?**
- **Can you tell us anything else about this graph?**

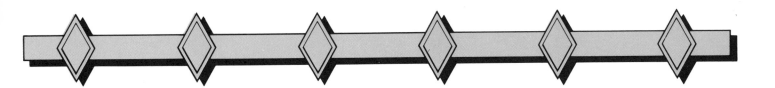

Explain that often it is important to keep a record of a graph. For example, it would help to know how much of each kind of juice to make for a similar snack on another day; you could use it to compare the choices children made on another day; or you could show it to other people who weren't in the room at this particular moment. Ask, **Can anyone think of how we could keep a record of our graph?** Through this discussion establish the convenience of pasting pictures on a graph. Provide each child with a piece of paper. Have them draw a yellow glass if they had apple juice and an orange glass if they had orange juice. Hang a 2-column graph in a spot children can reach. Label the columns and have each child tape her or his picture in the appropriate column. Direct children so that they place their pictures across or up from the label leaving no empty boxes.

Ask the same questions you asked earlier about the concrete graph. In addition, draw the children's attention to the concrete graph and pictograph and ask, **Do these graphs tell us the same information?** If there is a difference, discuss what could have possibly contributed to the discrepancy and, if possible, solve the problem.

On another day prepare the same kind of juice but reverse the process. Have the children first draw a picture of a glass of the juice they want for snack and have them place these pictures appropriately on a 2-column graph. Then pour glasses of juice for each recorded choice and distribute them to the children for a snack. After the snack, compare the pictograph and concrete graph to establish once again, that they show the same information.

At this point, or on another day, post the 2 juice pictographs and ask these questions.

- **How are these graphs the same? How are they different?**
- **Did the same number of children choose apple juice/orange juice each time?**
- **Can we tell from this graph if Linda had the same kind of juice both days?**
- **Can we tell from this graph if everyone had the same kind of juice both days?**

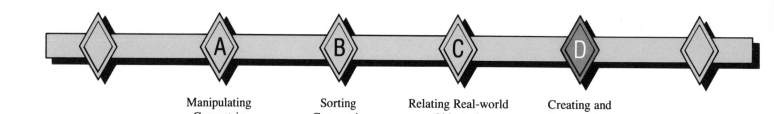

A — Manipulating Geometric Solids

B — Sorting Geometric Solids

C — Relating Real-world Objects to Geometric Solids

D — Creating and Interpreting a Pictograph

2. All About Us PS D

On a large floor graph, have the children sit or stand to form a graph in response to the question, **Are more children right-handed or left-handed?** Discuss the graph and then have the children create a pictograph to show this information. Provide each child with a piece of paper. Divide the children into pairs. Have each child trace the hand with which her or his partner writes, or you may wish to provide finger paint and have the children make a print of the hand with which they write. To eliminate possible confusion, have the children draw fingernails on the back of the hand. When the children have recorded a picture of their hands, gather them together around a 2-column graph as shown. These columns should be divided into sections large enough to accommodate the paper on which the children recorded their hands. Lay this mural paper on the floor. In turn, have the children place their pictures in the appropriate columns. When the graph is complete, have the children interpret it. These questions can form the basis of your discussion.

- **Which column has more?**
- **Which column has less?**
- **Are there more right-handed or left-handed children?**
- **How many right- (left-) handed children are there?**
- **How many more children are right-(left-) handed?**

Note that you may wish to have the children tape or glue their pictures on the graph as they place them, or you can ask a few volunteers to help tape or glue them in place after the discussion. Ensure that they tape all hands with the fingernails (or palms) face up. Post the graph in the classroom or the hallway with an appropriate title. If possible, you might display all graphs in one display area under the heading Read All About Us!

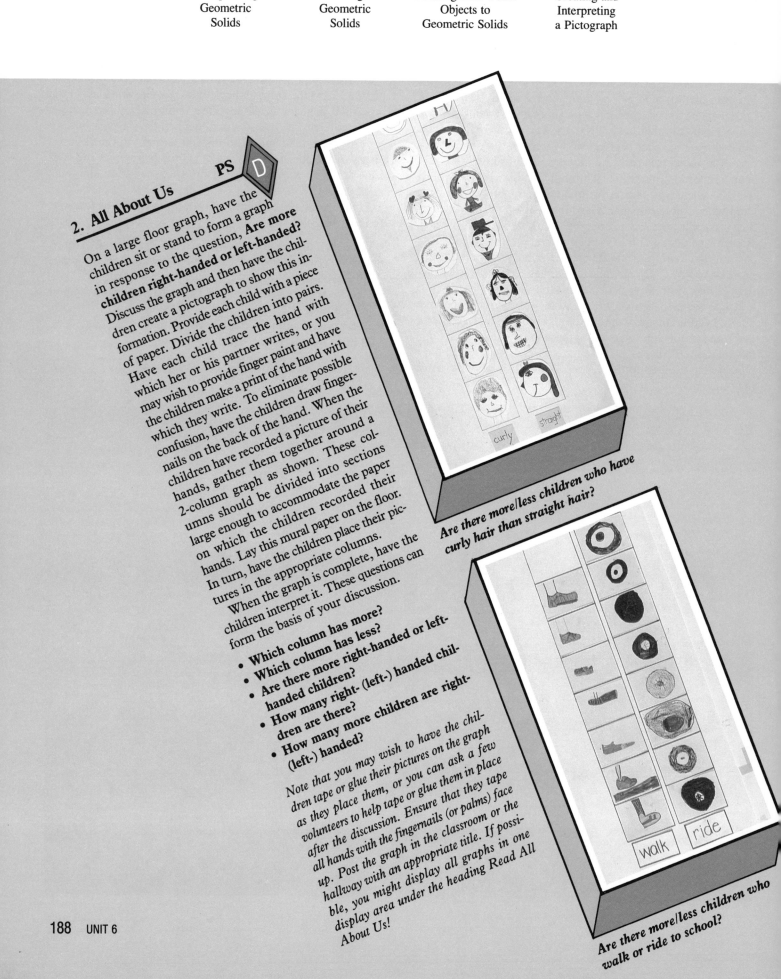

Are there more/less children who have curly hair than straight hair?

Are there more/less children who walk or ride to school?

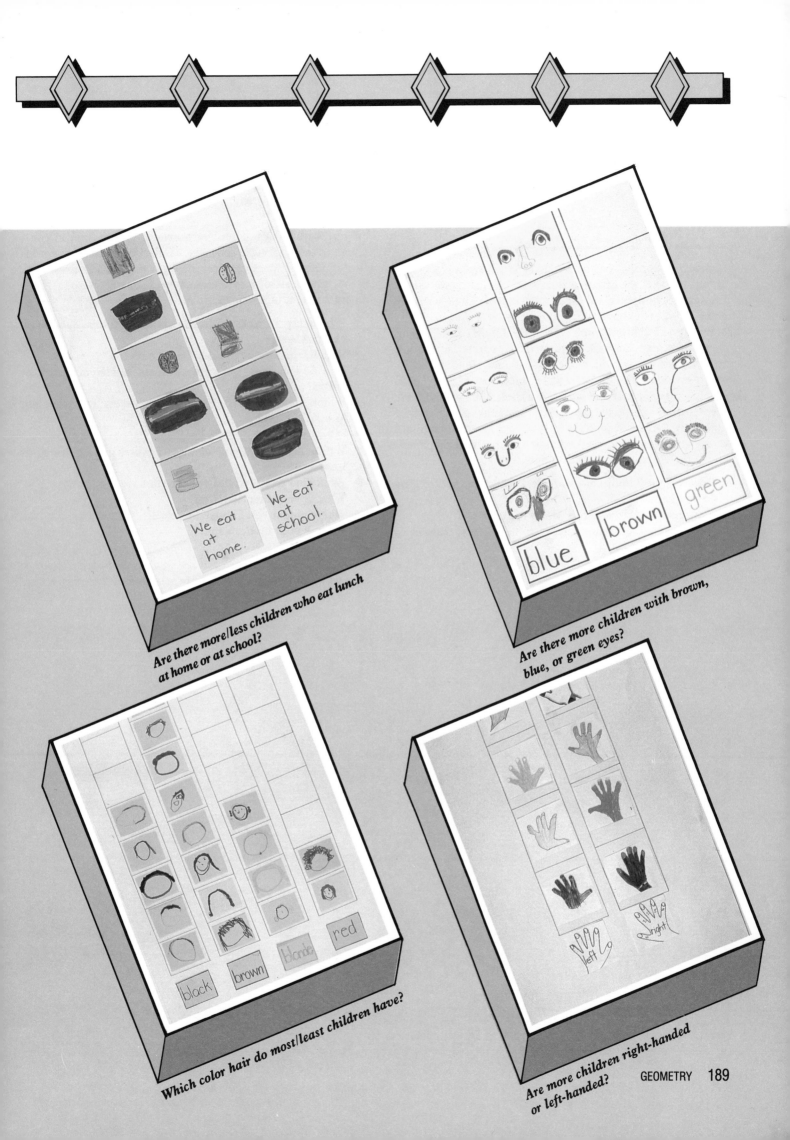

Are there more/less children who eat lunch at home or at school?

Are there more children with brown, blue, or green eyes?

blue   brown   green

Which color hair do most/least children have?

black   brown   blonde   red

Are more children right-handed or left-handed?

left   right

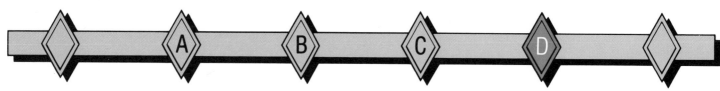

A	B	C	D
Manipulating Geometric Solids	Sorting Geometric Solids	Relating Real-world Objects to Geometric Solids	Creating and Interpreting a Pictograph

3. We Prefer   PS D

Gather the children together around the displayed pictographs to recall the different questions you have graphed. Engage the children's interest by telling them that now they are going to find out about which things they prefer or like best.

Prepare a 2-column graph on a piece of mural or experience chart paper. Explain to the children that you have 2 storybooks and they can choose which one you will read aloud. Label the graph with the titles or, even better, tape book jackets on the graph. Provide each child with half a sheet of paper and invite them to draw a picture of themselves. Have the children tape or glue their completed pictures in the column corresponding to their choice of book. Have the children interpret the graph. Ask any of these questions to initiate discussion.

- **Which of the 2 books did more (less) children choose? How do you know?**
- **How many children chose (name of story)?**
- **How many more children prefer (name of story) than (name of story)?**
- **Did more (less) children choose (name of story) than (name of story)?**

On following days, continue to involve the children in creating and interpreting graphs which reflect their choice or preference. This list suggests preferences you may wish to investigate. Note that you can vary the number of choices offered to compare different numbers of groups.

- **Which flavor ice cream do you like best; vanilla, chocolate, or strawberry?**
- **Which fruit would you like for a snack?**
- **How do you prefer your potatoes; mashed, french fried, or boiled?**
- **Which game would you like to play at recess; tag, skipping, or hide and seek?**
- **Which story did you like best?**
- **Which season do you like best; fall, winter, spring, or summer?**
- **What kind of pet would you like to have?**
- **What is your favorite color?**
- **Where would you choose to travel?**
- **What is your favorite sport?**

To create a pictograph you can have the children draw a response or use photocopies of pictures of children to indicate their personal choice.

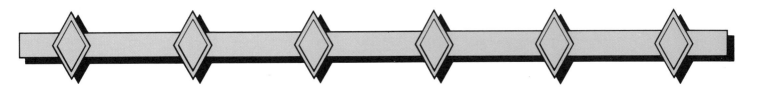

4. I Wonder   PS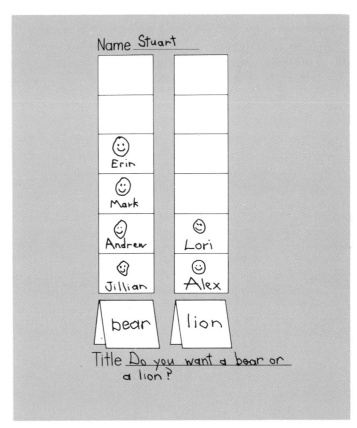

Gather the children together around a recording area. Lead a discussion on what type of questions the children would like to graph. Encourage the children to think of questions which are fanciful as well as realistic.

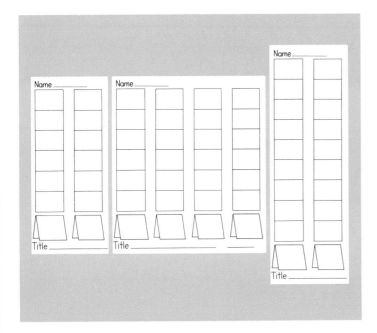

Graphing Ideas

Would you like to come to school in a plane, helicopter, or train?

Would you like an elephant, bear, or lion for a pet?

For your birthday, would you like a bike or a watch?

Would you like to travel to the moon?

Provide each child with a graph (Line Master 70). Explain that they can graph any question they want. Point out the space for the title and labels and have them fill in those sections before they begin. Demonstrate how they can fold or cut off the extra columns or join 2 line masters to make a larger graph.

Explain that they create this graph by asking individual children their question. The child responds verbally and then prints her or his name in a box in the appropriate row. Remind the children to fill in the boxes in sequence and not to skip any of them. After the child is satisfied that he or she has collected enough information, have him or her complete the graph by drawing a response above the names as shown.

Name Stuart

bear   lion

Title Do you want a bear or a lion?

Set aside time on different days to have the children present their graphs. Have them begin by stating what they were interested in finding out. Encourage them to display their graph and then ask the group questions or present their findings.

Note that if you have photocopied pictures of your children, they can be cut and pasted to indicate a response. Children may wish to write out questions to go with their graphs. These graphs can be posted as a bulletin board display. Place copies of Line Master 70 at a center so that the children can pursue graphs of their interest on a continuing basis. You may wish to have the children visit different classrooms to collect information from other children.

Meeting Individual Needs

Guide children who have organizational difficulties to select a question which compares only 2 groups for their first few graphs. Suggest that the children collect information from a small group of children (approximately 8) before they survey a larger sample.

Geometry Across the Curriculum

Language Arts

- Have the children discuss what the world would be like if there were no cylinders, spheres, cubes, etc. Invite them to draw pictures and write a story collectively or individually about the different things one would encounter.
- Ask the children to solve a variety of verbal riddles such as **I roll and roll but you can never stack me. What am I?**
- In conjunction with this unit, you may wish to read any of these books (see page 318 for an annotated bibliography):
  - *Shapes and Things* by Tana Hoban
  - *Changes, Changes* by Pat Hutchins
  - *Round is a Pancake* by Joan Sullivan

Art

- Provide each child with a container such as a tissue box, cereal box, or soup can. Have the children trace a face of the container, design new packaging for the product on the piece of paper, and glue it on the container.

- Have the children make various animals from cylinders and rectangular prisms.

Science

- Provide a variety of interesting molds such as various sizes of cups, plastic food containers, baking pans, ice cube trays, or pails. Fill them with water and place them in the freezer (or outside overnight if it is below 0°C) until frozen. Outside use the ice molds to build an interesting ice sculpture. Discuss the various solids and how long it will take for them to melt.

- If no sand table is available, try to borrow one or use a plastic wading pool. Encourage the children to use various containers as molds. Discuss the different castles, buildings, environments, etc., that they create. Have other children guess which containers were used to form each sand mold.

Extension Project

Social Studies

Collect a variety of pictures of interesting and different buildings such as tepees, igloos, highrise apartments, the Taj Mahal, or the pyramids. Discuss how these buildings compare with the children's own homes and the school. Invite the children to design their own buildings of the future. Provide materials for the children to actually build models of their designs.

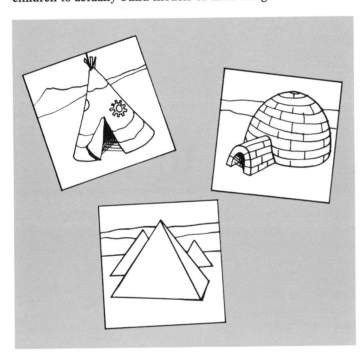

Physical Education

- Have the children move in the gym making their bodies roll or slide.
- Try to play one of the ball games with an object that is a cube or rectangular prism. Have the children suggest a new game using the object.

Have the children build skeletal models of geometric solids. The children can use toothpicks and Plasticine or straws and Plasticine or paper clips. Encourage the children to describe the models they build. Some children will enjoy learning the name of the structures they create. Have the children count and record the number of toothpicks and small balls of Plasticine they used to build their models.

Marshmallows can be substituted for Plasticine. Have the children build the skeletal models on a piece of cardboard so that they can transport them easily. Use pipe cleaners and straws to build an even sturdier skeletal model.

Addition and Subtraction to 10

Unit Objectives

Section 1

A   Combining and Separating Sets to 6, 7, 8, 9, and 10

B   Recording Sums and Differences to 6, 7, 8, 9, and 10

C   Creating and Solving Story Problems

D   Adding with 3 Addends

E   Solving Number Sentences to 10

Section 2

F   Buying Items

G   Making Change

About this Unit

Addition and Subtraction

In Unit 5, children worked through carefully sequenced activities to develop the concepts of addition and then subtraction. They participated in activities to generate the addition and subtraction facts to 5. In this unit, children engage in activities to develop combinations to 10. Various manipulating games and activities are provided to maintain a high level of interest. Since the concepts of addition and subtraction have been firmly established, each activity develops both addition and subtraction facts for a given number. Some activities are structured so that children incidentally generate fact families.

The activities of Section 2 focus around the class store. These situations provide excellent opportunities for children to apply their skills of identifying coins, counting coin collections, counting on, and their understanding of the concepts of addition and subtraction.

Problem Solving

Children have already had many opportunities to create and solve verbal story problems. The activities Chart the Problem, page 207; Solve My Problem and Problem Page, page 208 develop the skills of interpreting, creating and/or solving printed story problems typically referred to as word problems.

Section 2 provides an excellent opportunity to involve the children in situational problem solving. Children consider many factors while making decisions regarding the class store as well as during role play situations (see The Shopping Mall, page 215 and Craft Sale, page 218). In addition, activities provided in Five Minute Math, page 197 develop these problem-solving skills:

- sorting
- creating story problems

Vocabulary

- Addition
- Change
- Dime
- Equals
- Minus
- Nickel

- Number Sentence
- Penny
- Plus
- Sale
- Subtraction

Ongoing Objectives

- Reading the calendar
- Counting by twos
- Estimating and comparing length
- Recognizing time names
- Discussing and recording the weather
- Identifying geometric solids
- Problem solving:
  - Sorting
  - Creating story problems

Five Minute Math

Calendar Activities

- These questions could be included in your calendar time.
  - **What day will it be 3 days from now? What date is that?**
  - **What day was it 4 days ago? What date was that?**
  - **What day was it the day before yesterday? What date was it?**
  - **What day will it be the day after tomorrow?**
  - **How many days are there in a week?**

- Draw the children's attention to the vertical reading of a calendar through questions such as these:
  - **How many Fridays are there this month? Let's count.**
  - **What is the date of the first Monday? The second Monday?**
  - **What is the date 1 week from today? 2 weeks from today?**
  - **How many complete weeks are in this month?**
  - **Is this the first (second, third, or fourth) week of the month?**

- Have the children begin a pictograph of the weather. Pictographs of the weather can be created for past months by referring to the information recorded on past calendars.

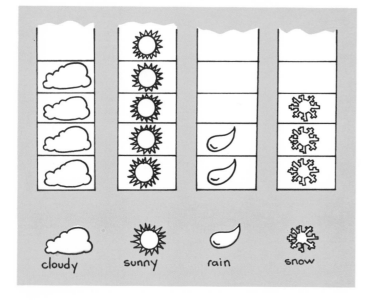

cloudy   sunny   rain   snow

Counting Activities

- Encourage the children to identify things that come in twos. Children might respond, **Ears, eyes, hands, feet, shoes, and socks.** Tell the children that there is an easy, fast way to count these things. Isolate a group of up to 10 children and have them join in as you count their eyes by twos. Repeat this activity for different groups of children so that the children become familiar with the sound and rhythm of counting by twos.
- Count by twos a variety of objects such as pencils, crayons, books, or blocks. Reinforce the importance of shifting 2 objects from one place to another so that the children know which objects have been counted.
- Line up counters in double columns and have the children count by twos.
- Line up the children by twos to go to the gym, outdoors, etc. Have the children count by twos to see if everyone is present.
- Drop 2 counters into a can at the same time and have the children count by twos as you drop the items.
- Ask a group of 10 children to stand at the front of the room. As the children count their legs, arms, hands, eyes, or ears by twos, shade in the numbers on a hundreds chart. Then read the shaded numerals aloud with the children.

1	2	3	4	5	6	7	8	9	10
11	12	13	14	15	16	17	18	19	20
21	22	23	24	25	26	27	28	29	30
31	32	33	34	35	36	37	38	39	40

- Circle all the even numerals to 20 on the cumulative record strip in red. Have the children read these numerals aloud. Continue counting by twos beyond 20 if your children appear ready.

Measurement Activities

- Ask questions such as these:
  - **Do you think the table will fit through the window?**
  - **Do you think the door is wider than the window?**
  - **Do you think the bookcase is taller than the filing cabinet?**

After you ask each question, provide a volunteer with a piece of string to verify the predictions.

- Put a piece of tape on the wall at the eye level of an average height child. Point to the tape and ask, **Do you think you are as tall as this?** Have the children tell whether they think they are the same height, taller, or shorter. Have the children stand by the tape to check their estimates.

On subsequent days, place the tape higher and ask the children to estimate if they could reach the tape by standing on their toes. On another day, place the tape even higher and ask, **Can you reach this piece of tape by jumping?**

- Draw a base line on the chalk board. Then draw a very short line perpendicular to it at one end and a long line perpendicular to it at the other end.

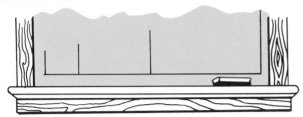

Invite the children, in turn, to draw lines going straight up from the base line in order from the shortest to the longest. When it is no longer possible to add lines (because the differences are minimal), start over with a new base line.

- Post pictures of specific class events and print the time each event takes place under its picture. (Time Clothesline, page 115, would work very well.)

Have the children refer to the display to respond to questions such as these:

- **What time does school start?**
- **When do we break for recess?**
- **What happens at 12 o'clock?**
- **Do we go to the library before 3 o'clock?**

At a later date, you may wish to add clock faces to this display to informally introduce the children to telling time.

- Encourage the children to listen to weather forecasts. Discuss what it means to make a prediction. In the morning, post the predicted weather; in the afternoon, establish if the weather turned out as predicted. Have the children make predictions for the next day's weather. Discuss how one should dress for the predicted weather.

Geometry Activities

- Without letting the children see, place a geometric solid in an opaque bag. Invite a volunteer to determine which solid is in the bag by using only her or his sense of touch. Encourage the child to describe the solid. For example, **It is smooth all over. There are no corners. It is shaped like a ball. It's a sphere.**

- Display a collection of geometric solids. Start a pattern and invite children to extend it. Encourage the children to read the pattern aloud in different ways. For example, **Cube, cube, sphere; box, box, ball; stack, stack, roll; or corners, corners, no corners.**

- Hold up a geometric solid and say, **I spy something that is shaped like this.** Invite the children to find the object you have sighted. Continue to give clues if necessary. For example, **It is bigger than the one I'm showing you. It is red.**

Problem Solving Activities

Sorting

- Post a sign such as the one shown.

Have the children contribute to this display.

At later dates, post signs such as these:

- **In my house, I have things made of wood only. What could I have at home?**
- **At recess, we are going to play with round things only. What could we play with at recess?**

Creating Story Problems

- Print the number sentence 2 + 3 = 5 on the chalk board. Have the children make up puppet plays to illustrate this number sentence. (Puppets can be made from Line Masters 2 to 7 or finger puppets can be made from Line Masters 14 to 16.) Allow time for practice.
- Print a number sentence on the chalk board. Have the children draw a picture during the week to illustrate this sentence. Post these illustrations with the number sentence.

Using the Story

The story The Great Escape details an exciting adventure of the imps at play sliding down Ted's sofa cushions. It provides the basis for the activity Sofa Slide, page 205, where the children manipulate imp cutouts to slide down Ted's sofa. The story can also serve as a basis for creating story problems. The children could dramatize the imps lining up on Ted's sofa. Questions such as these could initiate discussion:

- **How many ways can you group the imps to show 6 (7, 8, 9, and 10)?**
- **There are 10 imps waiting to slide. One slides down. How many imps are left waiting to slide? Another imp slides down. Now how many are on the cushion? How many were there on the top? How many are left waiting to jump?**

The story can also be used as a review of ordinals. The children can state their ordinal position as they pretend to be the imps lining up to jump.

Supplementary Material

Ted is my Friend: Mathematics Activity Book, pages 69-75; and story boards, pages 39-42 and 51-54.

The Great Escape

The warm rays of the late afternoon sun slanted across Ted's kitchen floor. It was very, very quiet. Ted and Troll-teddy were not in the little white cabin. A tiny head popped up through the crack in the floor, then another and another and another. The imps paused to listen carefully.

"I told you he wasn't here," said Ari positively. "I heard him tell Troll-teddy that they were going sledding on the hill all afternoon."

"But you never know when they might come home," said Rumple with a frown. "And if they do, you never know if we'll escape in time."

"We'll hear them coming," said Ari. "Don't worry about escapes — it's time for fun!"

Kalaloo stuck her head back down the crack and called, "Come on out, you sleepy heads! Ted's not here. It's time for fun!" A group of sleepy imps scrambled up to join her and the others.

"Well, what will we do?" asked Rumple nervously. Who knew when Ted might open the cheerful red door and come bouncing in all of a sudden?

Kalaloo put her head to one side. "I feel like having a slide," she announced. "I've wanted to slide for ever so long and I see just the right place for it!"

She ran to Ted's overstuffed sofa and began to climb.

"Me too! Me too! Wait for me, Kalaloo!" shouted little voices as the imps scurried after her. In a moment Kalaloo stood on top of Ted's sofa ready to slide down the back onto the soft cushions.

"I'm first," she called.

"I should be first, because my name is Slider," said Slider.

"All right," responded Kalaloo good-naturedly. "You can be first. Who'll be second?"

"I'll line everyone up," volunteered Ari. "That way we won't all crowd together and fall. Besides, that way everyone will have a turn. You're first, Slider. You're second and you're third," she said pointing to two tiny imps. "I'm fourth; you're fifth, Kalaloo, and you're . . . where's Rumple?"

"Here I am," puffed Rumple crossly. "I don't know why Kalaloo always chooses such high places to start. Climbing is such hard work."

"Never mind, Rumple," said Ari soothingly. "You can be sixth and it's going to be lots of fun. You'll see.

Just be sure to aim for the cushions and not in-between.''

"Why do I have to be sixth?'' grumbled Rumple. "And what if I fall in-between?'' To tell the truth, he was feeling grumpy because the top of that sofa was so very far from the crack in the floor and after all, Ted could walk through the door any minute! But Rumple's grumbling was interrupted by squeals of "Wheeee!'' as one imp after another slid down the sofa and landed with a soft kerplop on Ted's big plump cushions. Soon four laughing imps had taken their turns and were looking back up at Kalaloo and Rumple who teetered on the edge, getting ready to slide.

"Watch out below!'' called Kalaloo to the four imps as she launched herself down the sofa back, closely followed by Rumple. Kerplop! Kalaloo landed with a soft thud and rolled over giggling. Kerplop! Kalaloo sat up and looked for Rumple. He should be sitting beside her on the cushion, but he wasn't. Where was Rumple? Then Kalaloo heard strange muffled noises. She saw strange little things wiggling from in-between the cushions — they were Rumple's toes! In a flash Kalaloo understood! Rumple had slid head first into the space between the sofa cushions. Only his feet were sticking out! And he was stuck!

"Come and help,'' called Kalaloo. "We have to pull Rumple out of the cushions. It Ted sits down on him, he'll squish him flat!''

The imps grabbed Rumple's feet and pulled hard. He only moved a little. Then pulled again; now they could see his knees. Suddenly, there was the sound of snow scrunching on the path outside. "It's Ted,'' shrieked Ari. "Pull *hard*!'' "Oooof!'' Rumple popped out from between the cushions. "No time to sit—run, run, it's Ted!'' Kalaloo and Ari caught Rumple's hands and pulled him to the crack in the floor. Not a second too soon! "Whew,'' breathed Ari as she pushed a breathless Rumple down the crack and the cheerful red door opened to let a snowy Ted and a snowy Troll-teddy come tumbling into the warm kitchen. "That was a close escape!''

"Yes,'' said Rumple,'' but everybody helped. If you have to have an escape, that was the best kind to have . . . a truly great escape! It was even kind of fun. . . .'' And Rumple actually began to smile!

199

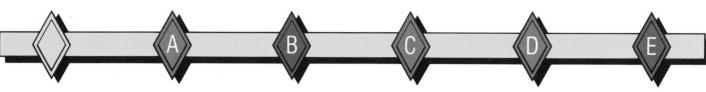

A	B	C	D	E
Combining and Separating Sets to 6, 7, 8, 9, and 10	Recording Sums and Differences to 6, 7, 8, 9, and 10	Creating and Solving Story Problems	Adding with 3 Addends	Solving Number Sentences to 10

Section 1

Planning the Section

Objective	Level	Activity	Grouping	Program *or* Management Suggestions
A Combining and Separating Sets to 6, 7, 8, 9, and 10	Concrete Semi-concrete	1. Six Furry Caterpillars 2. Log Walks 3. Double Scoop 4. Sofa Slide 5. Let's Show Stories	†††† †††† †††† †††† ††††	As you introduce Activities 1 to 5 to small groups, other children can extend the manipulating games they learned in Unit 5 to develop combinations for 6. It is also recommended that you set up the stores described in Activity 1 of the next section and direct children to explore those materials and situations.
B Recording Sums and Differences to 6, 7, 8, 9, and 10	Concrete, Pictorial, and Symbolic Concrete and Symbolic	6. Recording the Games 7. Authors Wanted	† ††††	Begin Activities 6 and 7 only after the children have had many opportunities to participate in Activities 1 to 5. Also remember to have children label the records created at the number centers.
C Creating and Solving Story Problems	Concrete and Symbolic Pictorial and Symbolic	8. Chart the Problem 9. Solve My Problem 10. Problem Page	†††††††† † †	Activity 8 should be repeated frequently before introducing Activities 9 and 10.
D Adding with 3 Addends	Concrete and Symbolic	11. Assorted Packages 12. Triple Scoop 13. What Will it Be?	†††† †††††††† ††††	Children may have already had experiences solving and recording number sentences of more than 2 addends. Introduce Activities 11 to 13 if these experiences have not arisen or for further practice.
E Solving Number Sentences to 10	Concrete, Pictorial, and Symbolic	14. Games Galore	††††	Activity 14 suggests a number of games to reinforce the concepts of this section. Materials should be prepared ahead of time. Direct children to these games for review and reinforcement.

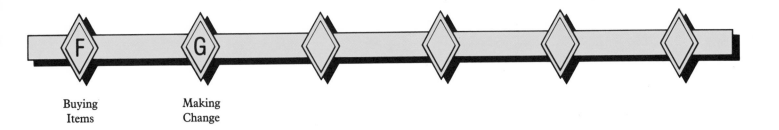

F — Buying Items

G — Making Change

About this Section

Children manipulate concrete materials in Activities 1 to 4 to generate the addition and subtraction facts for numbers 6 to 10 inclusive. After they are familiar with the language and procedure of the actions involved in combining sets to form 6, introduce the children to the procedures for separating a set of 6. These actions are then brought together so that an additive action is followed by a subtractive action and so on. When this process occurs in Activities 1 and 2 (where color defines the sets), children experience the related addition and subtraction facts. For example: **4 green caterpillars and 2 red caterpillars are in bed** (4 + 2 = 6). **6 caterpillars are in bed and the 2 red ones go to play with Ted** (6 − 2 = 4). The children start over placing a different number of green and red caterpillars in the bed.

Activities 3, 4, and 5 (which do not have sets defined by color) provide opportunities for children to experience additive and subtractive actions in a continuous flow while combinations are generated. For example: **5 imps are on the cushion and 1 more imp joins them** (5 + 1 = 6). **6 imps are on the cushion but 2 decide to climb to the top of the sofa to jump** (6 − 2 = 4). **4 imps are on the cushion and 2 jump down** (4 + 2 = 6). **6 imps are on the cushion again, and they all decide to climb to the top of the sofa** (6 − 6 = 0), and so on. Play these games on different days and encourage children to select the ones that appeal to them. Their selection will probably change. It is the practice that is important; not the specific activity.

In addition to these games, you may wish to extend and adapt the manipulating games from Unit 5. Children should also be involved in the activities Lights! Camera! Action!, pages 148 and 161; Let's Show a Story, pages 149 and 162; and Let's Tell Stories, pages 149 and 162 to develop the concept of 6 (and then 7 to 10) at the outset of this section. It is important that children have opportunities to verbalize and hear the various language patterns of addition and subtraction as they relate to facts for 6 through 10.

It is suggested that children first work on combining and separating sets to 6. After many concrete experiences, they should begin to record their actions as described in Activities 6 and 7. Also have children label the combinations and arrangements of 6 they recorded at the number centers in Unit 3. If children's fine motor skills have not yet developed, provide cards cut from Line Master 53 for them to use to form number sentences. Continue to model both the horizontal and vertical notation as you progress through this unit. After this comprehensive study of 6, children should repeat the process for 7, 8, 9, and finally 10.

Activities 8 to 10 involve the children in creating and solving word problems. Keep in mind the reading level of your children and provide pictures to support the print as necessary.

Children may have already recorded number sentences with more than 2 addends as they labelled their records created at number centers and/or generated names for numbers in The Name Game, page 170. Activities 11 to 13 can be presented to introduce number sentences of 3 addends if the situations have not arisen.

Observations and Evaluation

Before beginning this section, children should have a solid understanding of the addition and subtraction facts to 5. Many children may have demonstrated mastery of this material as you worked through Units 5 and 6. At this point, assess children about whom you want more information. Engage these children in the manipulating games of Unit 5 and present them with the step of predicting how many are in the second hand and/or going down the slide as described in the chart on page 144. If a child is successful, continue to check her or his understanding by presenting a larger number (e.g., a set of 5 if successful with a set of 4).

In addition, these key questions and situations will provide you with further information on the child's grasp of the concepts.

- Give the child a set of small concrete objects. Have her or him play any of the manipulating games from Unit 5. Say, **Show me 5. Show me 5 another way. And again. Have you shown me all the ways you can make 5?**
- Provide the child with access to materials of 2 colors (cubes, counters, or beads). Say, **Show me 5 as many ways as you can. Tell me about the different ways you made 5.** If the child is successful, say, **How could you record this way of showing 5 with a number sentence? And this way? Read what you have recorded.** If the child is successful, select a number sentence and say, **Show me this number sentence with these (cubes).**

Children who do not demonstrate a solid understanding of facts to 5 should continue to work with combining and separating sets to 5. Teach them the games in Activities 1 to 4 of this section, but have them work at their own level of understanding. These new activities will help maintain a high level of interest and allow the children to feel that they are keeping pace with the others.

Most of the observations and directions noted in the charts on pages 144 and 157 apply to this section as well. This chart describes situations particular to working with numbers greater than 5.

A	B	C	D	E
Combining and Separating Sets to 6, 7, 8, 9, and 10	Recording Sums and Differences to 6, 7, 8, 9, and 10	Creating and Solving Story Problems	Adding with 3 Addends	Solving Number Sentences to 10

Observations	Teacher Direction
A child places 3 counters and then 4 more counters. The child counts from 1 to 7 to determine the total number of counters.	The child who counts the initial set again may not see the number of a set as constant or may be approaching the problem in an inefficient way. In either case, the child's performance indicates that he or she needs more opportunities at the concrete level. Review and encourage the strategy of counting on.
A child demonstrates a solid grasp of the facts of 6 while recording number sentences which correspond to the actions performed and observed.	Have the child solve the facts to 6 on Line Master 71. Ask the child to also demonstrate a few of them. If successful, direct her or him to begin exploring the facts of 7. The child who has a solid grasp of addition and subtraction facts to 10 can be directed to the Extension Project, page 219

Suggested Materials

- 6 green and 6 red counters or cubes (or any other 2 colors) for each child [Activities 1 and 6]
- A paper towel roll for each child [Activities 2 and 6]
- Small objects such as counters, interlocking cubes, or bread tags [Activities 3, 6, 8, 11, 12, 13, and 14]
- A box or container to make a sofa for each child [Activities 4 and 6]
- A collection of magazines, brochures, or catalogues [Activity 9]
- A large quantity of small, clear plastic bags or envelopes with windows [Activity 11]
- A variety of game boards [Activity 14]
- A collection of bottle caps [Activity 14]
- A collection of number sentence cards [Activity 14]

Line Master **74**
Activities 3, 6, and 12
1 per child

Line Master **79**
Activity 10
1 per child

Line Masters

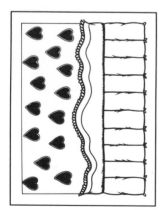

Line Master **73**
Activities 1 and 6
1 per child

Line Masters **14** to **16**
Activities 2, 4, 5, and 7
A large quantity

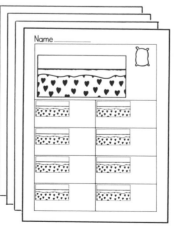

Line Masters **75** to **78**
Activity 6
1 per child

Any of Line Masters **18** to **23**
Activities 5 and 7
1 per child

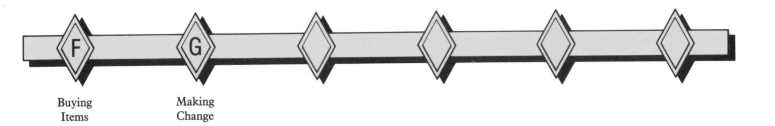

F   Buying
Items

G   Making
Change

Activities

1. Six Furry Caterpillars   A

Invite a small group of children to sit in a circle. Distribute a copy of Line Master 73 and 6 green and 6 red objects such as counters, interlocking cubes, bread tags, beads, or blocks to each child. Explain that the small objects represent caterpillars and the line master shows their beds. Have the children fold the line master so that only 6 beds are showing.

Introduce the poem Six Furry Caterpillars as you demonstrate the actions with your materials.

6 furry caterpillars snuggled in their bed.
3 are green and 3 are red.
"There you are!" their mother said.
6 furry caterpillars snuggled in their bed.

Say, **3 green caterpillars and 3 red caterpillars are in bed. There are 6 caterpillars altogether.** As you point to the red and green caterpillars, say, **3 red caterpillars plus 3 green caterpillars equals 6 caterpillars altogether.** Ask the children to demonstrate the story in the poem while you chant it. Go around the circle having the children read the sets and sums as the child who made them points to each group of caterpillars.

Invite the children to make new combinations of 6 using red and/or green caterpillars. Have children repeat the poem using the new combinations. Reinforce the combinations by having the children verbalize the number sentence. Repeat the procedure until children are familiar with the game. When children are familiar with the poem and are able to describe the actions without hesitation, introduce the subtractive action.

Tell the children that they are going to learn a new verse of the Six Furry Caterpillars poem. This verse deals with taking some of the caterpillars out of their bed.

Introduce the verse to the children as you demonstrate the actions with your materials.

6 furry caterpillars snuggled in their bed.
3 got up to play with Ted.
"Where are you?" their mother said,
How many caterpillars still in bed?

Say, **6 caterpillars were in bed. 3 got out to play. 3 caterpillars are still in bed.** As you point to the caterpillars and remove 3, say, **6 caterpillars minus 3 caterpillars equals 3 caterpillars.** Reinforce this number sentence by having each child perform this operation with their materials as the other children verbalize the actions.

Have the children replace the caterpillars and repeat the procedure, removing a different set of caterpillars. Play this activity with the children until they are familiar enough with the procedures to continue in small groups or with a partner.

The relationship of addition and subtraction facts can be established by chanting the 2 verses together. Establish the 2 sets and their sums in the first verse and take 1 of the sets away in the second verse.

6 furry caterpillars snuggled in their bed.
5 are green and 1 is red.
"There you are!" their mother said.
6 furry caterpillars snuggled in their bed.

6 furry caterpillars snuggled in their bed.
1 got up to play with Ted.
"Where are you?" their mother said.
How many caterpillars still in bed?

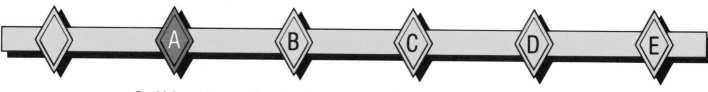

2. Log Walks

Provide each child with a paper towel roll and access to the black and white cats, rabbits, or dogs cut from Line Master 15. Have them roll the cutouts onto the paper towel roll so that this effect is achieved.

Identify the roll as a log and demonstrate how the animals can walk along it. (Place an animal as shown and slide it across the log.) Place 1 black cat on the log and say, **1 black cat was walking on the log.** Put 5 white cats on the log, say, **5 white cats joined the black cat. How many cats are there altogether?** Encourage the children to join you as you describe the number story, **1 cat plus 5 cats equals 6 cats. There are 6 cats altogether on the log.** Invite the children to make new combinations of 6 using black and/or white cats. Have each child, in turn, point to the sets of cats on the log as their classmates describe the situation. When the children are familiar with the language and procedure, introduce the subtractive action. Model the language and process. Remove all cats of one color from the log. Say, **6 cats are walking on a log. The 5 white cats jump off the log.** Remove 5 cats as you say, **6 cats minus 5 cats equals 1 cat.** (Point to the remaining cat as you say, **equals 1.**) Have the children demonstrate a similar process. When they are familiar with the subtraction situation, bring the addition and subtraction together so that cats of one color are joined by cats of another color to form a set of 6. Then have all cats of one color jump off the log. *Note that each time a child begins a new story he or she must change the combination of black and white cats.*

3. Double Scoop

Invite a small group of children to sit in a circle. Distribute 6 small objects and a copy of Line Master 74 to each child. Have the children identify how many objects they received.

Invite the children to suggest what flavor ice cream they could make, e.g., strawberry. Have the children place 4 small objects (strawberries) on the top scoop and 2 strawberries on the bottom scoop. Have them describe their ice cream cones. **There are 4 strawberries on the top scoop and 2 strawberries on the bottom scoop. There are 6 strawberries altogether. 4 strawberries plus 2 strawberries equals 6 strawberries.**

To reinforce the combination, give each child an opportunity to point to her or his sets as the other children say the sets and the sum. Repeat the process a number of times until the children are able to proceed on their own with a partner or in a small group.

When children are comfortable describing their ice cream cones using addition number sentences, explain that they are going to pretend to eat the top scoop. Have the child fold the line master as shown. Demonstrate how to draw a smiling mouth on the folded paper.

Have the children open the line master and build an ice cream cone so that there are 4 strawberries on the top scoop and 2 strawberries on the bottom scoop. Ask, **How many strawberries are there?** Say, **It's time to eat some ice cream.** Fold the paper so that the top scoop is covered and the smile is showing. Say, **6 strawberries. I eat 4 of them. 6 strawberries minus 4 strawberries equals 2 strawberries.** (Point to the remaining strawberries as you say, **equals 2.**) Have all the children repeat the process. Ensure that they describe the actions as they take place. Invite the children to decide individually how many strawberries they are going to put on each scoop. As they build their cones have them describe the process, e.g., **2 strawberries plus 4 strawberries equals 6 strawberries.** In turn, have each child eat the top scoop (fold their paper over it). Encourage all children to describe the process aloud. **6 strawberries minus 2 strawberries equals 4 strawberries.**

To maintain a high level of interest, you may wish to have the children choose different flavors of ice cream. The small objects could represent mint chips, nuts, or cherries.

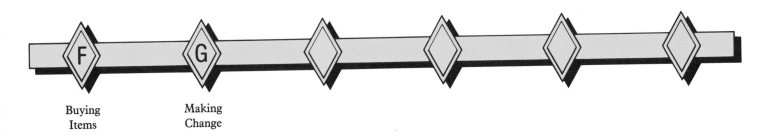
4. Sofa Slide

A

Give each child 6 imp story characters cut from Line Master 14 and have them roll and tape the cutouts as shown.

Gather the children together and recall the unit story The Great Escape. Explain that today the imps are going to slide down Ted's sofa right in the class! Give each child a standard size sheet of paper and a small box or plastic food container. Demonstrate how to fold their paper and set it up to create Ted's sofa. Place 4 imps down below and 2 imps above. Say, **There are 4 imps playing on Ted's cushion. 2 imps are ready to slide down the sofa to the cushion.** Point to the 4 imps as you say, **4 imps plus** (slide the 2 imps down the sofa) **2 imps. How many imps on Ted's cushion altogether?** Encourage the children to respond, **6 imps. 4 imps plus 2 imps equals 6 imps altogether.** Have the children place some of their imps on Ted's cushion and the others above on the sofa. In turn, have each child point to her or his sets and then slide the imps down the sofa. Encourage the

children to describe the situation. For example, if a child placed 3 imps on the cushion and 3 imps on the top of the sofa, he or she would say, **3 imps below, 3 imps above.** The child would slide the 3 imps down the sofa and everyone would continue, **3 imps plus 3 imps equals 6 imps.**

Ensure that each child has an opportunity to demonstrate the process at least twice.

When the children are describing the action and result without hesitation, introduce the subtractive action. After all the imps are on the cushion, say, **There were 6 imps rolling and playing on Ted's sofa. 3 imps wanted to slide again, so they got off the cushion to climb back up to the top.** Remove 3 imps from the cushion as you say, **6 imps minus 3 imps equals 3 imps.** (Point to the 3 imps on Ted's cushion as you say, **equals 3.**) Invite each child, in turn, to place all 6 imps on the cushion and then remove some imps to the top. Each time the action is performed, encourage the children to describe the process, e.g., **6 imps minus 2 imps equals 4 imps.**

Have the children move imps from the cushion to the top until the process and language are familiar. After children demonstrate that they have learned the particulars of the activity, have them integrate the addition and subtraction actions. For example, if you start with 5 imps below and 1 imp above slide the top imp down and, say, **5 imps plus 1 imp equals 6 imps.** Remove 2 to the top and continue, **6 imps minus 2 imps equals 4 imps.**

Continue the process as long as interest is maintained. When children appear comfortable playing the game, remove yourself from the group. Children may enjoy coloring the imps and creating designs on the sheet of paper (Ted's sofa).

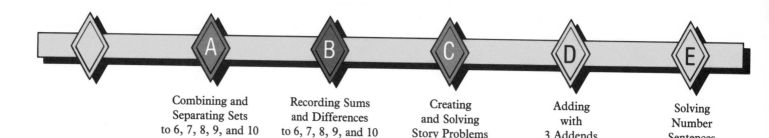

A	**B**	**C**	**D**	**E**
Combining and Separating Sets to 6, 7, 8, 9, and 10	Recording Sums and Differences to 6, 7, 8, 9, and 10	Creating and Solving Story Problems	Adding with 3 Addends	Solving Number Sentences to 10

5. Let's Show Stories

A

This is a story board activity. Provide each child with a story board (Line Masters 18 to 23) and story characters cut from Line Masters 14 to 16. Tell a long story that involves additive and subtractive action. After each action, invite the children to tell a corresponding number sentence. This story, told on the beach story board (Line Master 22) with children cutouts (Line Master 16) is representative of an unlimited number you can have the children act out.

One sunny afternoon 4 children came to the beach to play in the sand. They had played for only a little while when 2 more children came to play with them. How many children were playing in the sand? What number sentence tells this story? (4 plus 2 equals 6.) **They played follow the leader and had lots of fun. 1 child sat down to rest but the others kept on playing. How many children were still playing? What number sentence tells this story?** (6 minus 1 equals 5.) **After a little rest, the child went to find the others. How many children were together now? What number sentence tells this story?** (1 plus 5 equals 6 or 5 plus 1 equals 6.) **There was no one in the water so they all went wading at the edge. How many children went wading? What number sentence tells this story?** (0 plus 6 equals 6 or 6 plus 0 equals 6.) **After a short time, the lifeguard said the waves were getting too big so they all went back to the sand. How many children were in the water? What number sentence tells this story?** (6 minus 6 equals 0.)

When the children have acted out many of this type of addition and subtraction stories, invite a volunteer to take over as storyteller. On other days, encourage children to tell stories in small groups or to a partner.

Variation

Tell stories involving addition and subtraction for the children to act out with their counters. Identify the space in front of them as a specific spot, e.g., a bus and have the counters represent objects, e.g., children.

6. Recording the Games

B

After the children have had many opportunities to play the manipulating games (Activities 1 to 5) and have often observed you model scripts (as described on pages 150 and 163), begin to involve them in keeping a record of the number stories they generate.

Line Masters 75 to 78 are provided for recording purposes. The large top frame is intended to be used as a working space for placing the concrete materials used in the manipulating game. This frame accommodates the first step of transferring the action to the page.

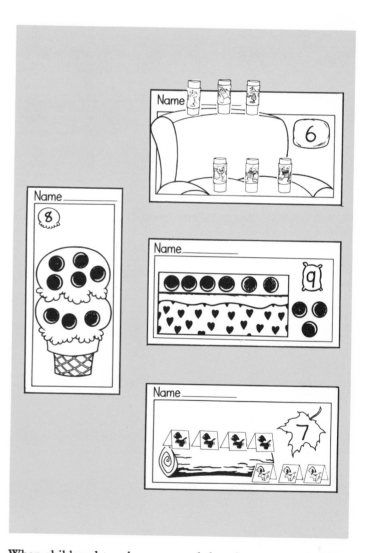

When children have demonstrated that they can successfully transfer their actions to the page with concrete materials, have them begin to keep a more permanent record by drawing a pictorial representation of the action and the corresponding number sentence.

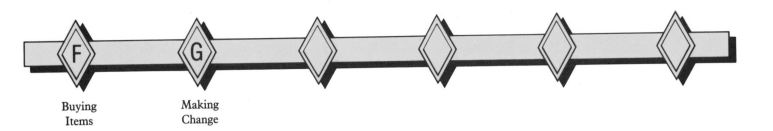
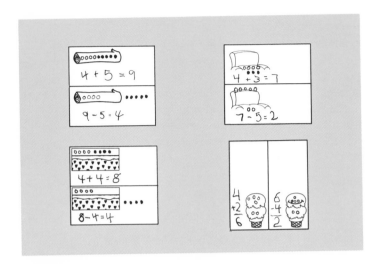

In the final step of recording, children simply record the number sentence that tells their action.

You might consider modelling and discussing different ways children could represent pictorially the animal and imp cutouts. Notice that here circles were simply used to indicate position. Remind children to record the number of objects they are working with in the top corner.

Number sentence strips have not been provided for facts 6 through 10. Those children who continue to require labels can use the numerals and signs from Line Master 53 to create number sentences.

7. Authors Wanted — B

Provide the children with story boards (Line Masters 18 to 23), story characters (Line Masters 14 to 16), paper and pencils. Explain that you are going to tell a story that involves many number stories (see Let's Show Stories for suggestions). To keep a record of the whole story, invite the children to be authors. Explain that they will print each number sentence they say (or build the appropriate number sentence with cards cut from Line Master 53).

At appropriate points in the story, ask, **What is the number sentence?** Have the children say the number sentence and allow time for them to record it as well. Model a record of the number sentence before asking the children to record it if you observe that they need additional direction.

These records can form the basis of further follow-up activities on ensuing days.
- *The children could draw pictures for each number sentence.*
- *The record could be used as a script for a finger puppet play.*
- *A child could select a number sentence and read it aloud for her or his partner to act out with counters.*
- *The children could select a number sentence and tell a corresponding story.*

8. Chart the Problem — PS — C

Gather the children around a recording area such as a chart stand, easel, or chalk board. Display 10 small objects on the surface and begin to manipulate them as you tell a story problem. **There were 5 friends playing on the adventure playground. They were having a wonderful time. 3 more children came to play. How many children were there altogether?**

Encourage the children to respond in a sentence. Print the story you told on the recording area. Have a volunteer manipulate the materials as he or she tells a story problem. Record this story as well while the child is telling it. Continue to invite children to make up story problems. Record each one as the children tell them.

On a following day, gather the children around the recorded story problems. Read the first one aloud with the children and invite them to solve it. They may act it out with concrete materials or simply state their response. Continue this process for each recorded story problem.

You may wish to have the children create new story problems to answer on yet another day. Some children may be interested in printing their own list of problems for the class to solve. Set aside time for these children to present their story problems to the group.

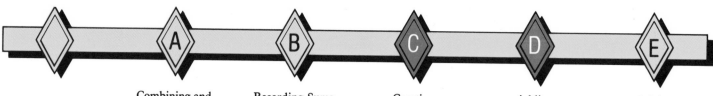

9. Solve My Problem. PS C

At different work areas, place a variety of magazines, brochures, catalogues, drawing materials, and paper. Have the children go to these areas to create their very own story problem. Explain that they should illustrate the problem first. This can be done by cutting and pasting pictures from magazines or drawing the problem freehand. Encourage them to add detail to their illustrations.

When the children have completed their illustration, ask them to print their story problem on a separate sheet of paper. Circulate among the children to provide help. Again, encourage the children to add detail and interesting information to their story problem.

Gather the children together. Invite volunteers to display their illustration and ask their story problem question. Discuss the problem and answer as a group. Ensure that all children have the opportunity to present their problems. These presentations may take place for a few minutes over a period of several days.

You may wish to post these illustrations and accompanying stories as a bulletin board display. You might consider having the children glue their story on the back of the illustration. These problems could be collected and placed at a center for children to solve. Many children will enjoy illustrating and writing story problems. You may wish to set up an area with materials where they could pursue this interest independently.

Meeting Individual Needs

Gather together children who are having difficulty thinking of a story problem. Post a large illustration and lead a brainstorming session on possible related story problems. After many ideas have been suggested, invite the children to write a story for the posted illustration. Children who have difficulty expressing their thoughts in writing may benefit from taping their ideas.

10. Problem Page PS C

Distribute a copy of Line Master 79 to each child and draw their attention to the first frame. Invite a volunteer to read the question aloud. Discuss the question with the children and arrive at a solution as a group. Print the appropriate number sentence on the chalk board and have the children read it aloud. Work through another question if necessary before directing the children to work areas to complete the page.

Note that the line master is open-ended. You can create new problems by substituting different numerals before you make the copies.

Meeting Individual Needs

Children who are ready for a further challenge might enjoy creating their own picture story problems. Provide story character cutouts and paper at work areas for them.

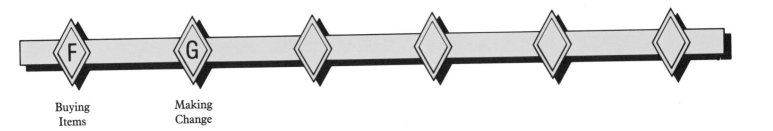

F — Buying Items

G — Making Change

11. Assorted Packages

Invite a small group of children to sit in a circle. Provide each child with paper strips, a small clear plastic bag or an envelope with a window, and a handful of small objects in 3 different colors. (Interlocking cubes, counters, bread tags, or beads could be used.) Explain that the small objects represent marbles and today the children are going to be packers at a marble factory. Ask them to package an assortment of 6 marbles so that each color (kind) is included. In turn, have each child describe her or his package of marbles in terms of the number of each color. **I have 6 marbles. 2 marbles are white, 1 marble is red, and 3 marbles are brown.**

Select a package of marbles and discuss which number sentences would label its contents. Record the responses on the chalk board, e.g., the contents of the described package could have these labels: $2 + 1 + 3 = 6$, $2 + 3 + 1 = 6$ or $1 + 2 + 3 = 6$, etc. Have each child print at least 1 number sentence label for her or his package on a paper strip ($2 + 1 + 3 = 6$). Ask the children to pass their packages to the child on their right. Explain that the packages must go through a shipping check. Have each child open the package, spill the contents, and check them with the label. Repeat the activity until children are familiar with the process and understand that there is more than one possible correct label for a package.

Direct children to work areas where all materials needed to make assorted marble packages have been placed. Post a numeral from 5 to 10 at each work area. This numeral will indicate the number of marbles to be put in the packages made at that work area. Invite the children to assemble and label packages of assorted marbles. Encourage the children to describe the contents of their packages aloud to the other children at the work area. After many packages have been assembled, have the children rotate to another work area to take on the role of shipping clerk. In this role, the child checks the contents with the label of each package.

This activity can be repeated over a number of days. Ensure that children go to a different work area to package a different number of items each time. To maintain a high level of interest you could ask the children to suggest what they would like to package (stickers, jelly beans, or balloons).

Meeting Individual Needs

- Provide a model for those children who are having difficulty with printing the number sentence. Alternatively, you could mark their paper strips as illustrated to provide an additional cue.

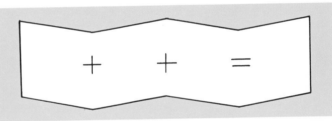

- Children who are ready for a further challenge may be interested in trying to create as many different labels as possible for each package.

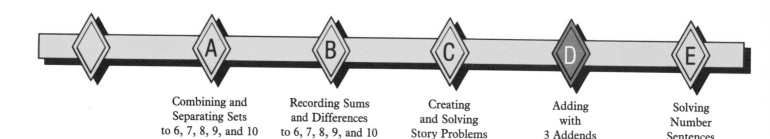

12. Triple Scoop

D

Provide each child with a copy of Line Master 74 and have them create a triple scoop ice cream cone by drawing an additional scoop as shown.

Give each child 6 small objects. Invite the children to suggest what flavor ice cream you should make and identify the objects e.g., chocolate chips for chocolate chip ice cream. Ask them to place the chocolate chips on the scoops so that there are some chips on each scoop. In turn, have children describe the ice cream cones they have created. For example, the ice cream cone shown could be described in this way, **My triple scoop ice cream has 3 chocolate chips on the top scoop, 1 on the middle scoop, and 2 on the bottom scoop.** Ask, **How many chocolate chips are there altogether?** A child might respond, **6 chocolate chips altogether. 3 chips plus 1 chip plus 2 chips equals 6 chips.**

Repeat the process so that children have the opportunity to create and describe another ice cream cone. This time record a number sentence on a display area to correspond to each description. A child could say: **My cone has 2 chips on the top scoop, 2 chips on the middle scoop, and 2 chips on the bottom scoop. There are 6 chips altogether.** You could write

$$\begin{array}{r} 2 \\ 2 \\ +\ 2 \\ \hline 6 \end{array}$$

After you have recorded the descriptions as number sentences, extend the game so that children are matching an ice cream cone to a number sentence. For example, point to a number sentence and say, **I order an ice cream cone that is 4 plus 1 plus 1 equals 6. Who can fill my order?** Several children may respond with different cones. Discuss why a cone that has 4 chips on the top scoop, 1 on the middle scoop, and 1 on the bottom scoop fits the same number sentence as a cone that has 1 chip on the top scoop, 1 on the middle scoop and 4 on the bottom scoop. Choose other number sentences for children to match with ice cream cones. When children are familiar with the process and language, distribute a copy of Line Master 77. Have the children add a third scoop to each cone. Invite the children to continue to play the game to discover how many different types of cones they can create. Explain that they should record each cone to keep track of the different cones they could offer for sale.

On another day, have the children use their recording skills to play a partner game. One child orders a cone by pointing to and reading a number sentence from a record sheet. The partner creates that cone.

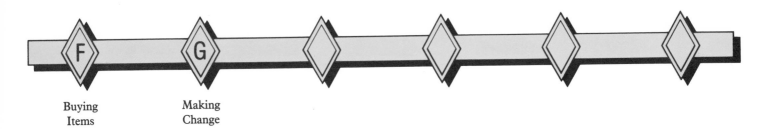

13. What Will it Be?

D

Invite the children to sit in a circle and distribute up to 10 small objects and a sheet of paper. Help the children to fold the sheet of paper into 3 sections and decide what it will be. For example, they could choose to identify it as 3 shelves in Ted's cupboard, 3 windowpanes, or a 3-drawer chest. (Note that the story board can be turned vertically or horizontally.) Print a number sentence on the chalk board, e.g., $5 + 1 + 1 = \quad$. Have the children demonstrate the story to find the sum and then have them tell you their story as they point to each set and the result.

There were 5 raindrops sliding down a windowpane. There was 1 raindrop on another windowpane and yet another one on a different windowpane. 5 plus 1 plus 1 equals 7 raindrops altogether.

Repeat the process with different number sentences of 3 addends. Ensure that all children demonstrate the number sentence with concrete materials and that each child has the opportunity to tell a story. When children are familiar with the process of working with 3 addends, direct them to continue individually or with a partner. Have them record the number sentences they create and solve.

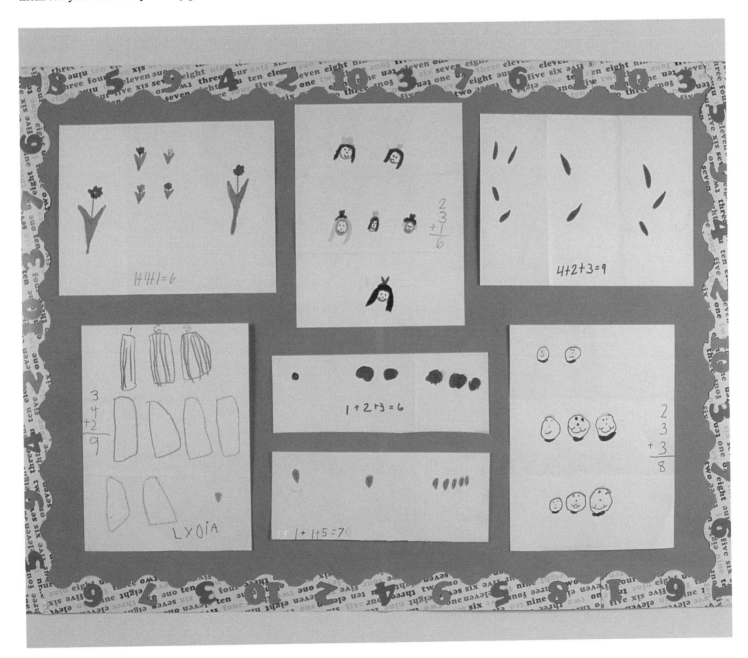

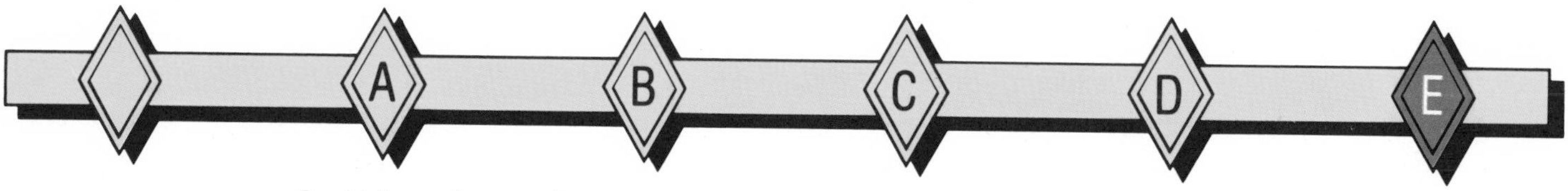

14. Games Galore

At a center, provide any or all of the reinforcement games suggested here. These games provide children with the opportunity to recall the number sentences explored in Section 1 of this unit as well as those developed in Unit 5. It is important to remember that these games are intended to reinforce the concepts, not teach them. You can also extend the games of Unit 5, pages 154-155 and 165 to include number sentences to 10. Provide small objects to be used as counters if necessary.

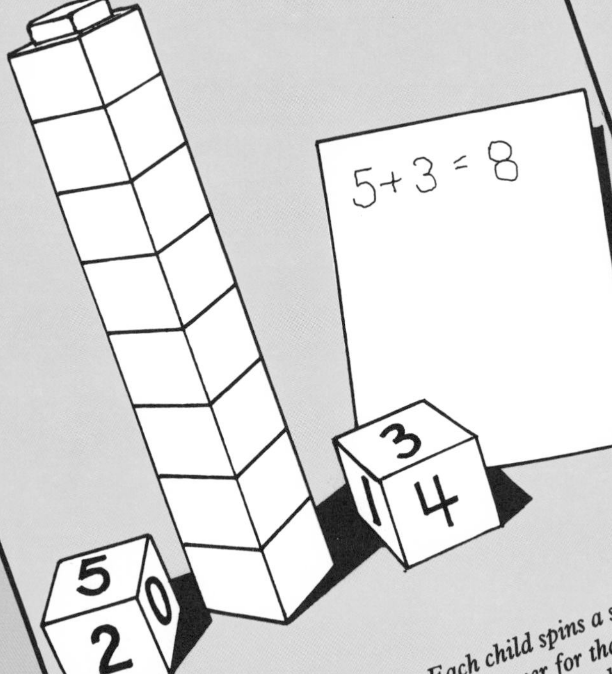

$5 + 3 = 8$

Children play this game in pairs. Each child spins a spinner or rolls a cube numbered 0 to 5, and builds a tower for that number from interlocking cubes of one color. Children place both towers together and record a corresponding number sentence. After they have constructed several towers, the children spin to find out how many cubes to snap off the tower. They then record the appropriate number sentence.

Show This

7

$4 + 3 =$

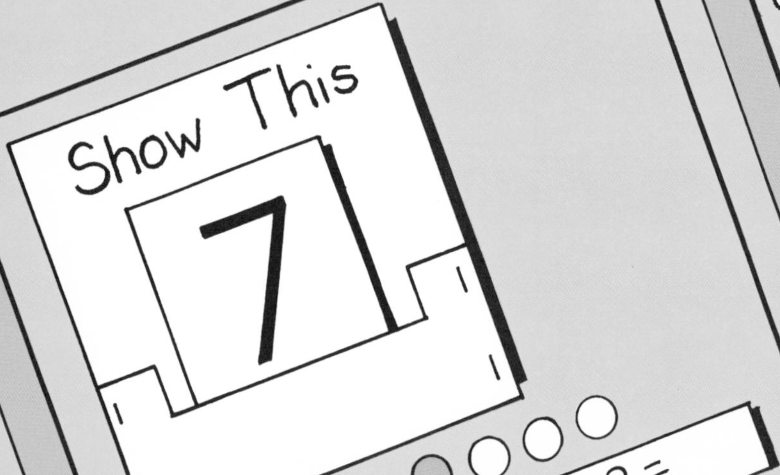

One child places a numeral card in the Show This folder and displays it. Her or his partner searches for a number sentence that equals the displayed numeral and uses counters to show that number sentence. The card is selected and removed from the collection of cards. The children reverse roles and continue until all number sentence cards have been removed.

Children (at least 3) gather around the game board with a piece of paper and crayons. Each child, in turn, selects a number sentence card from the pile and answers the question. The child moves her or his marker along the game board the number of spaces equivalent to the answer. The child then draws the part of the monster indicated. Play continues until the children are satisfied their monster is complete.

Make a Monster

Start | mouth | eye | head | tail | hand | leg | nose | antennae | ear | arm | eye | mouth | tail | head | hand | foot | ear

8 - 2

Bottle caps
4 + 5 = 9

The child chooses up to 10 bottle caps and places them in a cup. He or she holds the cup a reasonable distance from a surface, shakes the cup, and empties its contents. The child records a number sentence to describe how many bottle caps landed face up and how many landed face down. It is interesting for the child to also keep a tally of how many times each combination appeared.

Circle names for 8

3	4	0	7	1	8	1
6	3	5	3	2	5	2
3	2	0	4	5	9	6
1	1	4	2	0	9	5
5	0	8	7	2	8	4
2	1	4	0	5	3	2
3	5	4	2	6	0	7

The child circles the addends that equal the numeral indicated at the top of the laminated sheet. The children can record their name, the date, and the number of circled addends they discovered on the back of the sheet.

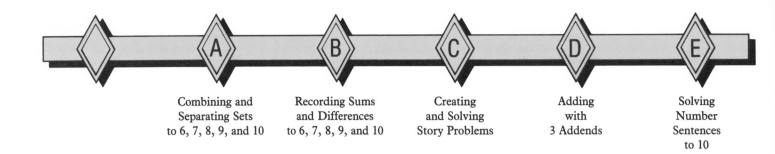

Section 2

Planning the Section

Objective	Level	Activity	Grouping	Program *or* Management Suggestions
F Buying Items	Concrete Pictorial and Symbolic	1. The Shopping Mall 2. Let's Shop! 3. Shopping Bags 4. The Bill, Please	♦♦♦♦ ♦♦♦♦♦♦♦♦ ♦ ♦♦♦♦	Children should have many opportunities to visit the stores described in Activity 1 before continuing with this section. Activity 2 should also be presented frequently. Ensure that each child has the chance to role play.
G Making Change	Concrete	5. Your Change Is . . . 6. Craft Sale 7. At the Restaurant	♦♦♦♦♦♦♦ ♦♦♦♦♦♦♦ ♦♦♦♦	In Activity 5, the teacher models the process of counting on to make change. It is recommended that children have several opportunities to observe and participate in this process before engaging in Activities 6 and 7.

About this Section

Activity 1 suggests how to set up a variety of storefronts and mini–centers. It is important that the children have many opportunities to visit these centers before you introduce any of the other activities formally. These visits to the stores are, in fact, an opportunity for children to explore materials before they are directed to them for a specific purpose.

Setting up stores presents an opportunity to involve the children in situational problem solving. Consider these questions with the children:

- **Where should we put the store(s)?**
- **What kinds of things could we make? What materials do we need? Where can we get them?**
- **How can we keep the store organized?**
- **How many people should be allowed in the store(s) at one time?**
- **How can we keep track of the money?**

Use real money or play money in these activities. (Line Master 41 may be useful as well.) Develop a system with the children to ensure that all money is accounted for. You could store coin collections in envelopes (wallets) that have the total recorded on them and have the children responsible for returning the wallet with the amount indicated. These wallets could be checked at the end of the day by a "banker".

This section was developed assuming that children have been involved in Money Activities from Five Minute Math sections of previous units and the activities One More Penny and Penny Sale, page 87; and The Treasure Hunt, page 88, of Unit 3. Therefore, to date, these skills have been introduced and reinforced:

- counting coin collections
- counting on
- matching a coin collection to a price.

If possible, keep the stores set up as you engage in the next unit. As children continue to role play situations at the stores, they apply and reinforce the skills developed in this unit.

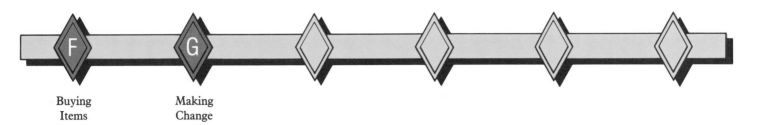

Buying
Items

Making
Change

Observations and Evaluation

The objectives of this section are best assessed in context. It is important to know not only if the child has acquired the specific skills of finding total cost and making change but also whether he or she knows when and how to apply these skills. It is, therefore, recommended that you observe the children informally as they visit the stores. Keep in mind these questions:

- Does the child comfortably take on the role of customer and storekeeper?
- When told the cost, can the child give exact change or select an appropriate coin, e.g., a dime for something that costs 8 cents?
- When given change can a child identify whether it is correct?
- As a storekeeper, does the child count to make change?

If you are unsure of a child's understanding, you may decide to role play a situation with her or him. These key questions can be worked into the role playing situations:

- **How much money do you have to spend?**
- **What would you like to buy? Tell me how much it costs. That's right, you owe me 9 cents. Should you get change? Why?**
- **Count your change. Is it right? Let's check, 9 cents, 10 cents.**

Suggested Materials

- A large collection of coins [Activities 1, 2, 4, 5, 6, and 7]
- A variety of storefronts and/or mini-centers [Activities 1, 2, and 5]
- A variety of materials to make those crafts the group chooses [Activity 6]

Line Masters

Line Master **80**
Activities 1 to 4
A large quantity

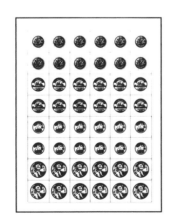

Line Master **41**
Activities 1 to 7
A large quantity

Activities

1. The Shopping Mall   PS   F

Set up as many of the storefronts and/or mini-centers illustrated as possible in different areas of the classroom. Enlist the children's help in collecting and making materials, pricing items, and making decorative signs and props. Provide many opportunities for the children to visit these different storefronts. Encourage them to participate as customer and clerk.

These portable mini-centers are readily stored in a container the size of a shoe box. Place all boxes on a shelf labelled "A Small Mall".

Note that egg cartons make good cash registers. To keep track of the money you may wish to have a central container to store envelopes (wallets). In each wallet, place a different number of coins and record the total on the outside. Remind the children that it is their responsibility to check that they return the wallet with the appropriate change.

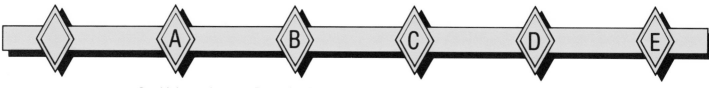

A	B	C	D	E
Combining and Separating Sets to 6, 7, 8, 9, and 10	Recording Sums and Differences to 6, 7, 8, 9, and 10	Creating and Solving Story Problems	Adding with 3 Addends	Solving Number Sentences to 10

2. Let's Shop!
F

Gather the children around a storefront or mini-center, e.g., the post office (illustrated in the previous activity). Hold up a penny, a nickel, and a dime for the children to identify. Review the value of each coin if necessary. Invite a volunteer to be a clerk and position her or him on one side of the table. Ask another volunteer to take the role of customer. Have the customer select a stamp that he or she would like to buy and the appropriate coin(s) (exact change) from the coin container. Have the customer and clerk act out the situation. Ask the audience to describe the scene after it has been performed. For example: **Mary went to the post office to mail a post card. She wanted to buy a 10 cent stamp. She gave the clerk a dime. The clerk gave her a stamp and Mary mailed the post card.**

Continue to have volunteers act out situations where one item is purchased at a time. When children are comfortable acting out these situations, increase the number of items to 2. In these situations a bill showing the total of the 2 purchases should be recorded. Provide bills from Line Master 80 for this purpose. Demonstrate how to record the total of the 2 items. Involve the children in helping the clerk determine the total cost as children role play the situation. Remember to involve the audience in describing the play.

Paul went to the post office to buy a post card and a stamp. The post card cost 5 cents and the stamp cost 3 cents. The clerk made up a bill and asked for 8 cents. Paul gave the clerk 1 nickel and 3 pennies.

If you have a calculator, make it available to the clerk. It can be used to check that the total cost is correct.

Frequently involve the children in a variety of role playing situations. Encourage small groups of children to engage in the activity without you.

3. Shopping Bags
F

At different work areas, place pictures and bills cut from copies of Line Master 80, paper, pencils, and glue. Direct the children to these work areas to select and cost the items they would like to buy. Have the children select 2 or 3 items, paste them on a sheet of paper, draw a shopping bag around their selection, and then print a corresponding number sentence on a bill to indicate the total cost. The bill should be pasted beside the bag. Encourage the children to pack and total the cost of several shopping bags.

Note that some children will create a problem which involves a sum greater than 10. However, since the children have actually created the situation, they will bring a high level of motivation and commitment to solving the problem. Have coins available for children who require concrete materials to solve the number sentences they create. If possible, provide the children with access to calculators to check their bills.

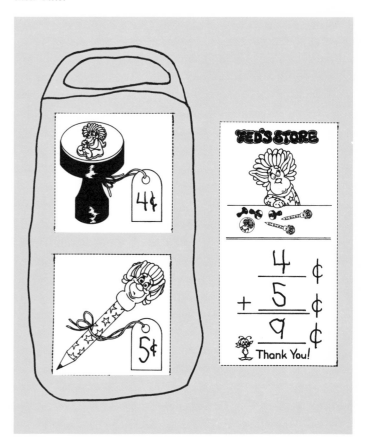

Meeting Individual Needs

Give the child who is ready for a further challenge a set amount of money to spend, e.g., 10 cents. Have her or him record as many combinations of items (pictures cut from Line Master 80 or ones displayed) as possible that would cost 10 cents.

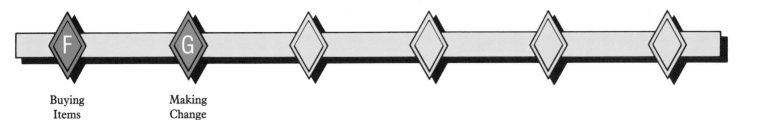

Buying
Items

Making
Change

4. The Bill, Please

Divide the children into pairs and provide each pair with bills and pictures (or small priced items) cut from Line Master 80 and access to collections of coins. Have each child select 2 items for purchase. Tell the children to present the items they selected to their partners as they say, **The bill, please.** Explain that the partner should then make a bill to correspond to the items selected. Encourage the children to always check their bills very carefully before counting out the money owed.

You may wish to have children keep a record of their purchases. To keep a record they can glue their choices and bill on a sheet of paper.

5. Your Change Is ...

Extend the role playing at the storefronts and/or mini-centers to introduce the children to making change. Gather around a store, e.g., a variety store and give each child a nickel and a dime. In turn, have each child select an item he or she would like to purchase. First, the customer must decide which coin to give you (the storekeeper). **I'd like to buy a package of hockey cards. It costs 7 cents. Here's a dime.** Respond, **It costs 7 cents, 8 cents** (give a penny) **9 cents** (give a penny) **10 cents** (give a penny). **Your change is 3 cents.**

Ask the customer to count her or his change before leaving the store. Encourage the children to count on with you as you give the customer her or his change. When children have observed and participated in several situations involving making change, select a volunteer to take over your role as storekeeper.
Frequently involve the children in these role playing situations. Encourage children to practice making change when they are in the stores.

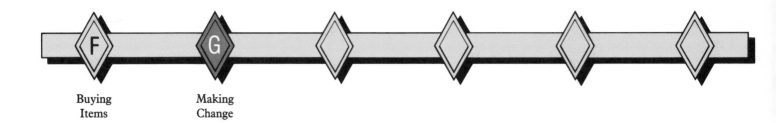
6. Craft Sale   PS G

Plan a craft sale with the children. Involve them in deciding what items would be reasonable to make, what materials are needed, where materials should be placed, when the craft sale will take place, and what the different items will cost (from 1 cent to 10 cents).

On the day of the craft sale, enlist the children's help in sorting the items into pricing groups e.g., the 4 cent table, the 7 cent table, etc. Signs with the item for sale and price should be placed at the table.

Give each child a dime and place pennies at each table. Set up a rotation system so that every child has the opportunity to buy an item and also to act as the clerk who counts out a customer's change.

This activity can be extended even further as a problem-solving situation if you ask each child to bring in a dime from home. The children could then be involved in deciding how to use the money collected, e.g., donate it to charity, buy a book for the library, or buy a special treat.

7. At the Restaurant   G

Ahead of time, set up a restaurant with tables, chairs, plastic dish sets, etc. Develop a menu with the children which includes a selection of foods and prices. Duplicate the menu and place it at the restaurant.

Have a child assume the role of waiter or waitress and take the orders of the patrons. Once the role playing is complete, the patrons must pay the bill the waiter or waitress presents. The waiter or waitress should take the payment and count out the appropriate change.

Repeat the activity until children are familiar with different roles and the process. Have them continue in small groups.

Addition and Subtraction Across the Curriculum

Language Arts

- Create couplets about facts with your children.

  1 plus 1 equals two
  Now there is some for you.

  3 plus 1 equals four
  Now we need no more.

- In conjunction with this unit you may wish to read any of these books (see page 318 for an annotated bibliography);
  - *The Great Big Enormous Turnip* by Alexei Tolstoi
  - *There Were Ten in the Bed* by Pam Adams
  - *Mr. Gumpy's Outing* by John Burningham

Science

Have children plant fast growing plants such as beans. Have them record the growth of leaves in a plant diary. Once a week, children record the number of leaves and the date. Discuss the growth of leaves with the children. **Last week there were 6 leaves. This week there are 2 more leaves. There are 8 leaves.**

Social Studies

Lead a discussion on different types of machines that add and subtract, e.g., calculators, adding machines, cash registers, or counters. Collect as many of these machines as possible for further discussion and exploration. Have the children draw designs of their own adding-subtracting machines.

Physical Education

Scatter hoops around the gym floor. In each hoop place a card with a numeral from 1 to 5. Give a signal such as a word, music, or a clap to start children walking. On a second signal children should stand in the hoops to create a set that corresponds to the numeral in the hoop. Call out a number from 7 to 10 and have children find and move to hoop(s) to create a set to correspond to the number called. Have each group tell how they made the number. **A hoop of 4 and a hoop of 3 make 7.**

Extension Project

Establish a center for making filmstrips in your classroom and have the childen make filmstrips of continuing addition and subtraction stories. These filmstrips can be drawn on long strips of paper (cut to size). Alternatively, the children could tape or glue story boards together in a long strip and draw the action on this strip. The children can make a tape of their story to accompany the filmstrip, print a script or a number sentence caption on each frame of the filmstrip, or simply tell the story as they show the filmstrip. You may wish to provide a couple of filmstrip projectors as shown for all the children to use, or have the children build their own projectors.

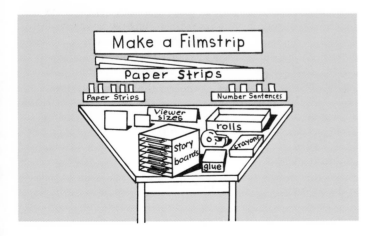

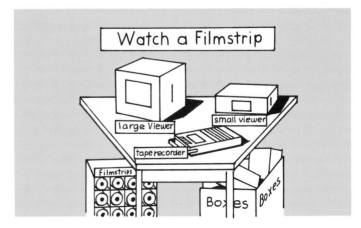

Geometry and Fractions

Unit Objectives

Section 1

A Relating Faces of Geometric Solids to Geometric Figures
B Sorting and Identifying Geometric Figures
C Relating Real-world Objects to Geometric Figures
D Patterning with Geometric Figures
E Identifying Sides and Corners
F Tiling a Surface

Section 2

G Creating and Recognizing Symmetrical Figures
H Identifying Fair Shares
I Identifying Halves, Fourths, and Tenths

About this Unit

Geometry

By the time a child enters grade 1, he or she has already observed and discovered a great deal about the properties and relationships of different geometric figures. The young child learns that only certain puzzle pieces fit together, that her or his footprints are smaller than an adult's and have a shape very different from a dog's, or that most coins are round; whereas book pages are usually rectangular. While children manipulate the geometric figures and discuss their actions, observations, and discoveries, they develop a solid foun-

dation for later instruction in geometry.

This unit deals with 2-dimensional figures. Mathematically, a 2-dimensional figure has no depth. Since even this page has 3 dimensions (albeit a very small third dimension), it is not, strictly speaking, a rectangle but a rectangular prism. However, it is still a good model of a rectangle. The thinner the object, the better the model. In this unit, a variety of materials are suggested as models of 2-dimensional figures. These include Pattern Blocks and Attribute Blocks as well as paper models.

Fractions

The word "half" is often present in children's vocabulary, although their use of the word typically reveals a misconception of its true meaning. As children discuss the larger (or smaller) half, we become aware that they understand that a half is part of something but not that it also implies an equal part. In Section 2 of this unit, the children first explore the concept of symmetry. They have opportunities to test for symmetry by folding and matching. The discussion of fair shares and equal parts is a natural outgrowth of the experiences of creating and recognizing symmetry in figures.

Problem Solving

In this unit, children have the opportunity to further develop their sorting and patterning skills. They sort geometric figures in the activity Face Families, page 229 and create patterns using geometric

figures in Figure Patterns, page 231 and Patterns for Ted's House, page 232.

As children participate in the activities which involve tiling surfaces, they develop their organizational and spatial perceptual abilities. During these tiling activities, some children may spontaneously apply their patterning skills as well. In addition, activities provided in Five Minute Math, page 223 develop these problem-solving skills:

- sorting
- identifying, extending, and creating patterns
- identifying likenesses and differences
- creating story problems

Planning Ahead

The next unit focusses on numbers to 99. To develop the concept of place value, each child must have access to a substantial collection of materials. Interlocking cubes and/or base 10 materials are suggested as valuable materials. In addition, you can engage your children in making materials as described in The Ten Pack, page 255. Consider collecting the materials suggested for that activity as you progress through this unit.

Vocabulary

- Circle
- Face
- Fair Share
- Fourth
- Half

- Rectangle
- Square
- Symmetry
- Tenth
- Triangle

Ongoing Objectives

- Reading the calendar
- Ordering the months of the year
- Counting by tens
- Estimating and measuring length
- Identifying and counting coin collections
- Problem Solving
  - Sorting
  - Identifying, extending, and creating patterns
  - Identifying likenesses and differences
  - Creating story problems

Five Minute Math

Calendar Activities

- Post a sign with the months listed in order, and have the children chant them in order. Ask, **What month is this? What was last month? What is next month? What month comes before June? After September?**
- Have the months posted on separate strips in random order. As a group, put the months in order. Direct the children's attention by asking these questions:

  - **What is the first month of the year?**
  - **January, February, _____. What month comes next?**

When the months are in order, ask questions such as these:

  - **What month comes before June?**
  - **What month comes after October?**
  - **What month comes between May and July?**
  - **What month comes before (after) your birthday?**
  - **How many months are there in a year?**

- Post last month's calendar. Ask, **What was the weather like last month on this date? What do you think the weather will be like next month? Why do you think the weather will be different?** Have the children refer to the calendars of other months to answer these questions:

  - **What was the weather like in November?**
  - **Did it rain in October? How many days did it rain?**
  - **Have we gone to the library every week?**
  - **Was Ryan's birthday in September or October?**

Counting Activities

- Ask a group of 5 children to stand at the front holding both hands in front of them. Encourage the children to count the displayed fingers by tens. Repeat this activity a number of times so that the children can become familiar with the sound and the rhythm of counting by tens. Increase the number of children in the group to be counted as the children develop the skill of counting by tens.

- The children place 10 counters in each of several containers. Count by tens, moving a container to one side each time a multiple of 10 is said aloud. You may wish to check the result by counting again by ones or twos.
- Have the children count aloud by tens. Circle the numbers they say in a different color on the cumulative record strip than was used previously for twos. Have the children read these circled numbers aloud.

Measurement Activity

All the children stand and stretch their arms at shoulder height as far as possible. Ask 3 children to join hands to show the class how far a chain of 3 children reaches. Ask, **How many children do you think it will take to make a chain that goes from one end of the room to the other?** After everyone has estimated, involve the children in determining how many children are needed to make a chain as long as the room. The children who form the chain count themselves, in turn, aloud. Say, **Raise your hand if your guess was high. Just right. Low.**

On succeeding days, the children make and test other estimations for children chains. For example, they could estimate and measure the width of the room, the width of the hall, the length of the hall etc.

Money Activities

- Display a dime and ask the children to identify the coin and its value. Distribute dimes and have the children describe them. Print 10 cents and dime on the board. Have 3 children place their dimes on a display area. Ask, **What is a fast way to count the money?** If necessary, suggest counting by tens. As you move each dime aside, have the children count aloud by tens. Ensure that the children use the word "cents" as they count, e.g., **10 cents, 20 cents, 30 cents.** Continue the process using various collections of dimes.
- Show the children a dime and have them identify its value. Cover the dime with a container and slide another dime under it. Ask, **How much money is under the container now?** After the children respond, **20 cents,** slide another dime under the container and repeat the question. Continue this process as long as it is appropriate for your children.
- Invite the children to sit in a circle and give each child a dime. Pass a tin can and have each child drop their dime into it. Before 9 children have dropped their coins into the can say, **Stop. How much money do you think is in the can?** Encourage the children to predict. Empty the can and, as a group, count the collection of dimes by tens. Place those dimes aside and begin passing the can from the point where you stopped.

Problem Solving Activities

Sorting

Draw illustrations such as these on the chalk board.

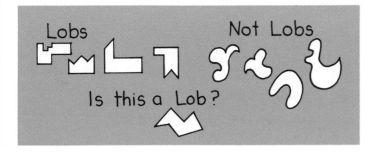

Encourage the children to explain why the figure is or is not a Lob. Have them draw a figure for each set.

Identifying, Extending, and Creating Patterns

Create patterns with Pattern Blocks such as the one shown. Place Pattern Blocks within reach of each child and invite her or him to make the figure that would come next in the pattern.

Identifying Likenesses and Differences

- Display Attribute Blocks or figures cut from Line Master 81. Select one figure such as the large blue thick square. As you hold it up, say, **Show me a figure that is different from this one.** When a child has selected a figure, say, **How is it different?** If a child chooses a figure that is different in more than one way, ask, **How else is it different?** If the child has selected a figure that is like the one selected initially in any way, ask, **How is it the same?** Display a different figure and repeat the process.
- Display Attribute Blocks or figures cut from Line Master 81. (The collection of figures from the line master should be in at least 2 colors. Note that there can be no discussion of the attribute of thickness when using cutouts.) Choose 2 figures that differ from each other in only one way, e.g., a large, red, thin circle and a large, blue, thin circle. Ask, **Are these figures different or the same?** Follow up the children's responses with the question, **How are they the same (different)?** Display 2 other figures and repeat the process. Do not expect the children to recognize more than 1 similarity or difference at a time. However, if they are frequently engaged in the activity, they will eventually be able to describe how the figures are similar and different in respect to the 4 attributes of color, size, thickness, and shape.

Creating Story Problems

Tell story problems that involve more than 1 step. The children should have access to concrete materials so that they can show the problems as you tell the story. Begin with story problems that involve 2 steps. When children are able to answer these story problems with confidence, increase the number of steps. For example,

- **There were 4 birds sitting on a branch. 3 birds flew away. Later, 2 more birds landed on the branch. How many birds are sitting on the branch?**

Using the Poem

The poem What Can You See? introduces children to geometric figures in their world. It can become the focus of a search for shape among the familiar objects in the home, the classroom (a basis for the activity Classroom Search, page 230), and the neighborhood.

You may wish to display the accompanying illustration again when you introduce the activity Patterns for Ted's House, page 232. The children will think of a variety of ideas for patterns as they look closely at the illustration.

The poem may be performed with one group saying or singing the question, the second group saying or singing the answer, while everyone joins in the final verse. The poem could be used for a short performance with the children singing the question and answers while displaying appropriate shapes discovered in the environment.

Supplementary Material

Ted is my Friend: Mathematics Activity Book, pages 76-79.

What Can You See?

What can you see
That's a circle for me?
What can you see out there?

A clock and a plate,
And the cookies I ate,
That's what I see out there!

What can you see
That's a square for me?
What can you see out there?

A cracker or two,
And the picture Ted drew,
That's what I see out there!

What can you see
That's a rectangle for me?
What can you see out there?

A window, a door,
And a dozen things more,
That's what I see out there!

What can you see
That's a triangle for me?
What can you see out there?

A pixie paper hat,
And a design on one mat,
That's what I see out there!

Look all around,
There are shapes to be found.
What can you see out there?
Let's look! What can you see out there?

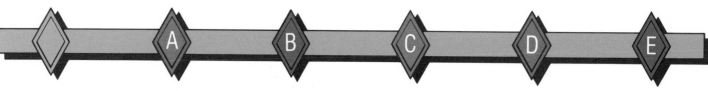

A	B	C	D	E
Relating Faces of Geometric Solids to Geometric Figures	Sorting and Identifying Geometric Figures	Relating Real-world Objects to Geometric Figures	Patterning with Geometric Figures	Identifying Sides and Corners

Section 1

Planning the Section

Objective	Level	Activity	Grouping	Program *or* Management Suggestions
A Relating Faces of Geometric Solids to Geometric Figures	Concrete	1. Trace a Face 2. Mystery Maps	👤👤👤👤👤👤👤 👤👤👤👤	Activity 1 introduces the vocabulary for the Unit. Mystery maps must be prepared ahead of time for Activity 2.
B Sorting and Identifying Geometric Figures	Concrete	3. Face Families 4. I Made…	👤👤👤👤👤👤👤 👤👤👤👤	The faces made in Activity 1 are used in Activity 3.
C Relating Real-world Objects to Geometric Figures	Concrete	5. Classroom Search 6. Search and Capture	👤👤👤👤 👤👤👤👤	Small groups of children can be involved in Activities 5 through 8 at the same time. Circulate among the groups to encourage discussion.
D Patterning with Geometric Figures	Concrete	7. Figure Patterns 8. Patterns for Ted's House	👤👤👤👤 👤👤👤👤	You may wish to take children on a search for patterns of geometric figures in their environment before they begin to create their own as suggested in Activity 7.
E Identifying Sides and Corners	Concrete	9. Side and Corner Count 10. Make and Count	👤👤👤👤 👤👤👤👤	Sides and corners are discovered and defined in Activity 9. This activity should take place over a few days to ensure that the children create many different kinds of geometric figures.
F Tiling a Surface	Concrete	11. Cover the Block 12. Cover It Up 13. Cover and Paste	👤 👤👤👤👤 👤	Children learn tiling fundamentals in Activity 11. Have the children tile with a variety of materials over a few days.
E - **F**	Concrete	14. Figure Fun	👤👤👤👤	Activity 14 suggests several ways to further reinforce the concepts presented in this section.

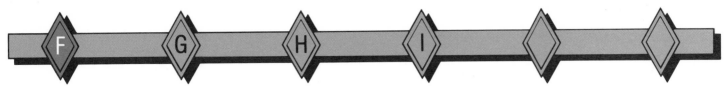

About this Section

Some of the materials used in this section may not be familiar to all your children. It is important that all children have opportunities to explore the materials freely before they are directed to use them for a specific purpose.

The activities in this section are all designed to give children first-hand experiences with 2-dimensional geometric figures. Initially, children engage in activities in which they relate the familiar 3-dimensional solids to 2-dimensional figures. The flat faces of geometric solids are traced to form geometric figures. Children continue to explore the properties of the 2-dimensional figures throughout the section. While it is necessary for children to manipulate many models of these figures and to talk about them if they are to understand them, many of the concepts may be reinforced incidentally in the Geometry Across the Curriculum. Shape walks, shape searches at home and at school, shape riddles, and shape art all help to extend the children's awareness of shape in the environment.

The activity of tiling a surface is best done with a variety of materials of different sizes. By tiling the same surface with materials of several different sizes, the children begin to grasp the concept that the smaller the tile, the more tiles it takes to cover a given surface. They also learn that certain objects are therefore not appropriate to tile some surfaces.

Observations and Evaluation

Evaluation may be accomplished largely by observing and listening to the children as they manipulate the materials. These key questions can form the basis of discussions.

- **Which solid could you trace to get a figure like this one?**
- **Why do these figures belong in the same group? What else belongs?**
- **How are these figures the same? How are they different?**
- **What can you find in our room that has the same shape as this?**
- **Find a figure which has the same number of sides (corners) as this one.**
- **Could you cover the table with those tiles? Is there a better material to cover the table with? Why?**

If you want to gather more information about how some children identify 2-dimensional geometric figures, engage them (individually or as a small group) in these tasks.

- Scatter a collection of 2-dimensional geometric figures on a display area. Invite a child to select a figure and, say, **Tell me about the figure.** If necessary, help initiate the description by asking, **What shape/color/size is it? How many sides/corners does it have? What in the room has the same shape?**
- Select a figure, e.g., a triangle, and say, **What am I holding? Show me another triangle. Show me a larger/ smaller triangle. Find a circle (square, rectangle).**

Suggested Materials

- A variety of 3-dimensional geometric solids such as commercial sets and/or a collection of cans and boxes [Activities 1, 2, and 8]
- Maps created by tracing geometric solids [Activity 2]
- Geoboard and elastics or a peg board and pegs for each pair of children [Activities 4 and 10]
- A variety of magazines, brochures, and catalogues [Activity 6]
- A collection of Pattern Blocks, Parquetry Tiles, or Attribute Blocks [Activities 7 and 8]
- An assortment of items for printing geometric figures such as spools, blocks, vegetables, or pieces of sponge or rubber [Activity 8]
- Templates of geometric figures cut from plastic lids [Activity 8]
- A small lump of Plasticine for each child [Activity 9]
- Straws cut to different sizes [Activity 9]
- A variety of material to use for tiling such as index cards, paint chips, Pattern Blocks, ceramic tiles, paper of different sizes, or newspaper pages [Activities 11 and 12]

Line Masters

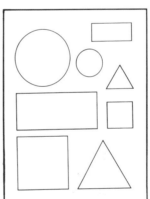

Line Master **81**
Activities 5, 7, 12, and 14
A large quantity

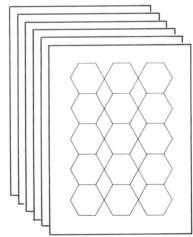

Line Masters **30** to **35**
Activities 7, 11, 12, 13, and 14
A large quantity

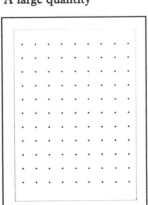

Line Master **27**
Activity 10
1 per child

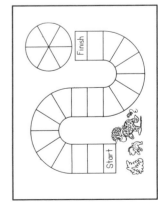

Line Master **43**
Activity 14
1 copy

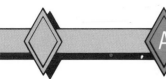

Activities

1. Trace a Face

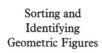

Gather the children around a work area where a variety of geometric solids are displayed. Select a cylinder, place it on a sheet of paper, and trace the face with a pencil. Ask, **What do you think you'll see when I move the cylinder? Do you see something else that you could trace to get a circle? Show me.** Each time a child identifies an object, have her or him trace it to confirm the prediction. Ask, **Is it a circle?** Repeat this process. Trace a cube to introduce the square, a rectangular prism to introduce the rectangle, and a pyramid or triangular prism to introduce the triangle. Encourage the children to use the vocabulary circle, square, rectangle, and triangle as they describe the different tracings.

Provide the children with opportunities to trace the faces of the solids. Some children may need a partner to hold the solid as they trace it. Encourage them to describe their discoveries to their classmates. On another day, have the children select a geometric solid, trace it, and create a funny face on their shape tracings. Store these completed faces for future use. (They form the basis for Activity 3.)

Some children may want to make a variety of faces. Provide time for them to pursue this interest. You may wish to post labelled geometric figures for the children's future reference.

2. Mystery Maps

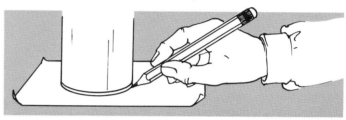

To prepare mystery maps, trace different geometric solids on a piece of cardboard. Trace only one face of each solid.

Distribute the maps and the collection of geometric solids used to create them. Have the children identify each figure. **This is a triangle. This one is a square.** Challenge them to discover which geometric solid you traced to make each outline or map. You may wish to have the children work in small groups, with a partner, or individually. Have the children exchange maps after they have matched a solid to each figure.

You may wish to have the children help prepare these maps or create additional ones for their classmates to solve. Note that some of the solids generate more than 1 shape. Using the process of elimination and focussing on the size of the figures, the children should be able to match 1 solid to each figure.

Meeting Individual Needs

- If a child is having difficulty matching the solids to traced faces, it might be beneficial to have her or him match familiar objects to traced outlines. Matching on a board such as the one illustrated may be a more appropriate exercise.

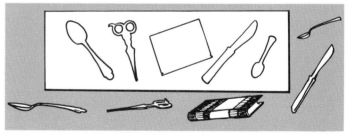

- If a child is ready for a further challenge, provide a map with all the faces of one solid. Have the child try to determine which solid (from a collection of solids) was used to create the map.

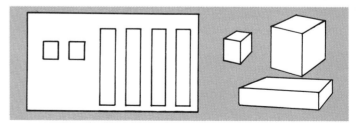

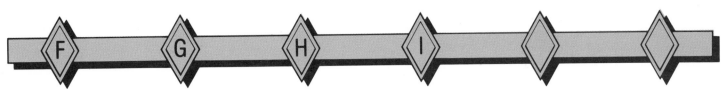

F — Tiling a Surface

G — Creating and Recognizing Symmetrical Figures

H — Identifying Fair Shares

I — Identifying Halves, Fourths, and Tenths

3. Face Families   PS   B

Invite the children to sit in a circle. Distribute the faces they created in Activity 1. Tell the children to place these faces in front of them so that everyone can see each face. Ask, **If we were to place these faces in families, which would go together?** Invite a volunteer to select a few faces that would be in the same family as her or his own. Encourage the child to explain why they are members of the same group. For example: **All these faces are squares.** Continue to choose volunteers to sort the faces into families. After all appropriate faces have been placed in a family, have the children label the set: the little triangle family, the large circle family, the square family, etc. If there is an interesting way to re-sort the faces, repeat the process.

You may wish to have the children arrange these sets on a graphing mat. Lead a discussion on which family has the most/least members.

Meeting Individual Needs

Children who appear confused during this activity may benefit from further sorting with less distracting geometric figures. Provide them with opportunities to sort gummed stickers, Pattern Blocks, or figures cut from Line Master 81.

4. I Made...   B

For this activity, each child will need a geoboard and elastics or a peg board and pegs. Divide the children into pairs. Invite the children, in turn, to make a geometric figure on their board. Have the children tell their partner what they made and state a challenge to make a larger or smaller one on their board. **I made a triangle. I want you to make a larger triangle than mine on your board.** When the child is satisfied that the challenge has been met, the children can reverse roles. Continue this activity as long as interest is maintained. Circulate from pair to pair, modelling appropriate vocabulary when necessary.

Children may give challenges which cannot be met. For example, a child could make the smallest possible triangle and ask her or his partner to make a smaller one. Explain that before issuing a challenge the child must be sure it can be met.

If there is a shortage of geoboards, divide each geoboard in half with masking tape or an elastic. A pair of children can then share a board.

Variation

Have the children sit around a collection of geometric figures. Invite a volunteer to choose a figure and challenge the group to find one that is larger/smaller than or the same size as the one selected.

A	B	C	D	E
Relating Faces of Geometric Solids to Geometric Figures	Sorting and Identifying Geometric Figures	Relating Real-world Objects to Geometric Figures	Patterning with Geometric Figures	Identifying Sides and Corners

5. Classroom Search

Cut geometric figures from Line Master 81 and place at least 1 per child in a paper bag or container. Invite each child to choose a figure from the bag. Challenge the children to search the room for objects with the same shape as their selected figures. Provide drawing materials for the children to record their observations. After the children have finished their recording, gather them together. Have them present the figures they chose and the observations they recorded. For example: **I chose a circle. This is what I found in class: a counter, an earring, a clock, and a happy face.**

You might wish to have all observations recorded on pages cut in the shape under consideration. For example, a record of all objects found in the room with the same shape as a circle would be listed on a sheet of paper cut in a circle. The pages could then be assembled to form a booklet.

6. Search and Capture

At different work areas, provide a variety of magazines, brochures, and catalogues. Direct the children to these areas to search for pictures of objects that have the same shape as squares, rectangles, triangles, and circles. Have the children trace each object they find with a marker and then cut it out.

These pictures can be displayed in a variety of ways. You may wish to have the children post them in a collage, assemble them in a class book, or graph them on a pictograph. You might consider leaving the materials at a work area so that children can continue to search for appropriate pictures to add to the display.

Meeting Individual Needs

Some children may impulsively trace objects and later realize that the pictures are inappropriate. Encourage these children to first trace the outline of the object with their finger a few times before they create the more permanent record with a marker.

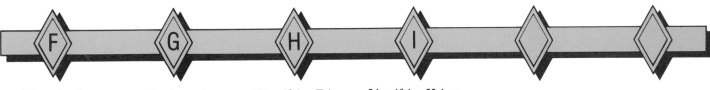
7. Figure Patterns   PS D

At different centers, place geometric figures such as Pattern Blocks, Attribute Blocks, Parquetry Tiles, or figures cut from construction paper (Line Masters 30 to 35 and 81 may be useful). Direct small groups of children to each center to create patterns with these materials. Depending on the materials, children can create patterns by either laying the pieces flat or placing them in an upright position. Have the children describe their patterns in terms of size, color, and shape. **Large red triangle, small blue circle, small blue circle, large red triangle, small blue circle, small blue circle. . . .**

If a permanent record is desired, these patterns may be recorded by tracing the figures, using templates, or cutting and pasting figures cut from Line Masters 30 to 35 and 81.

Time may not permit all children to complete their patterns. If patterns are created on an art easel or stiff cardboard, they can easily be carried to a storage spot. Children can then continue them in another session. You may wish to post recorded patterns as a bulletin board display. Some children may enjoy labelling their patterns.

Meeting Individual Needs

- Children who have difficulty creating their own pattern may require some additional direction. Consider providing them with a pattern to extend.
- Children who are ready for a further challenge can work in pairs. Each child begins a pattern for her or his partner to extend. After the children extend each other's pattern, they read the patterns aloud.

8. Patterns for Ted's House

PS **D**

Lead a discussion on how often geometric figures are found in patterns in our homes. Have the children identify patterns in the classroom. Explain that today they are going to make geometric patterns for Ted's house. Begin a list of the various things which could have geometric patterns such as wallpaper, towels, rugs, sheets, quilts, kitchen floor, dishes, curtains, or furniture. Discuss how the children might combine geometric figures to make a pattern. They could choose to create a pattern in a row, in a circle, with figures on top of one another, etc. You may wish to demonstrate how a shift in a repeated pattern creates another kind of pattern.

At different work areas, provide a variety of materials for the children to make geometric patterns. Before directing children to these centers, have them decide what they are going to make for Ted's house.

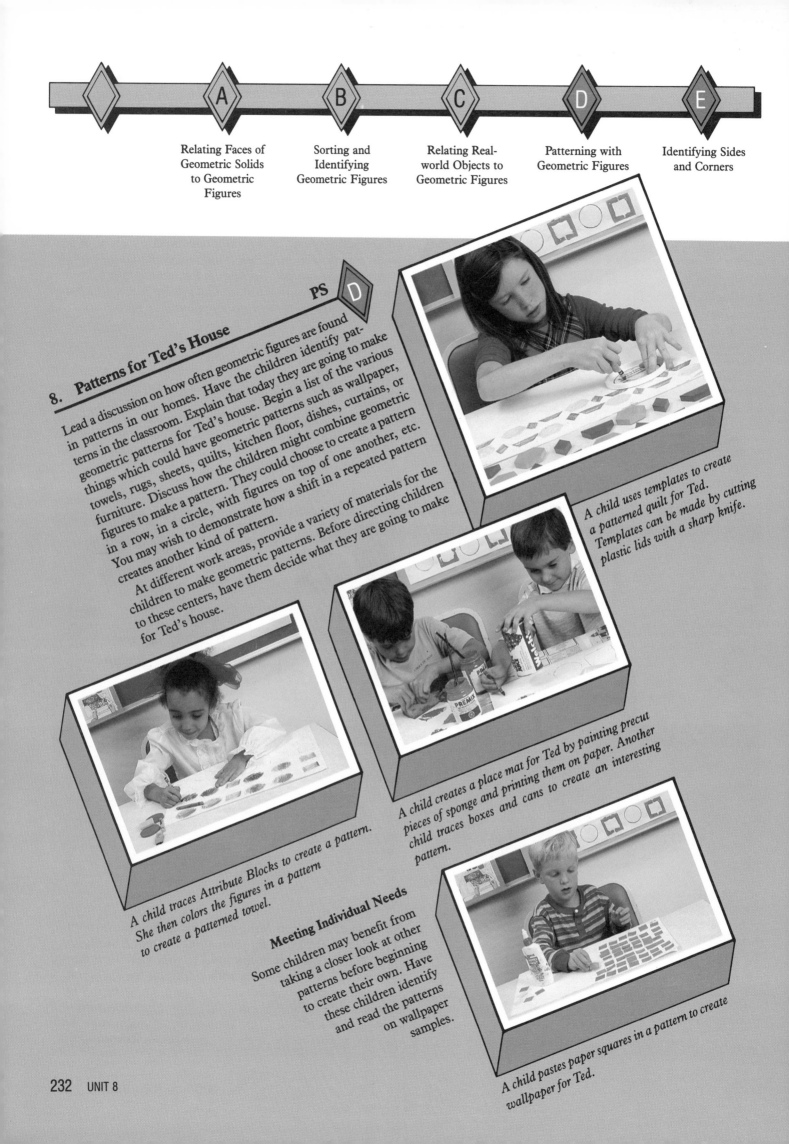

A child uses templates to create a patterned quilt for Ted. Templates can be made by cutting plastic lids with a sharp knife.

A child traces Attribute Blocks to create a pattern. She then colors the figures in a pattern to create a patterned towel.

A child creates a place mat for Ted by painting precut pieces of sponge and printing them on paper. Another child traces boxes and cans to create an interesting pattern.

Meeting Individual Needs

Some children may benefit from taking a closer look at other patterns before beginning to create their own. Have these children identify and read the patterns on wallpaper samples.

A child pastes paper squares in a pattern to create wallpaper for Ted.

9. Side and Corner Count E

At a work area, provide Plasticine and straws cut to different sizes. Invite the children to make triangles using the straws and Plasticine.

Ask each child, in turn, **How many straws are in your triangle? How many pieces of Plasticine are in your triangle?** After the children have responded, discuss what they have discovered about triangles. Through this discussion, establish that every triangle has 3 sides (the straws) and 3 corners (the Plasticine). To convince the children of this rule, you may wish to challenge them to try to make a triangle with a different number of sides and corners. (Plasticine can only be used at a corner.) Repeat this procedure for squares and rectangles.

You may wish to record the rules discovered and post them in the classroom for future reference.

10. Make and Count E

Provide the children with geoboards and elastics and have them create different geometric figures. After they make each figure, ask, **How many sides are there? How many corners are there?** Also, challenge the children to make figures with a specific number of sides and corners, **Make a figure that has 4 sides and 4 corners.** You may wish to have the children sort and graph their geoboard creations as a group. Possible sorting criteria include type of figure, size, number of sides, number of corners, position.

On another day, you might have the children make figures on a geoboard and then draw these figures on dot paper (Line Master 27). This will create a permanent record.

Variation

Have the children play Make and Count at the pictorial level. Provide each child with dot paper (Line Master 27) and invite the children to draw a geometric figure on their sheet. Have them number each side and corner with a different colored pencil. Gather the children together and have them sort the figures according to the number of sides and corners. You may wish to post these as a bulletin board display, or you might store the pages in a folder so that children can sort them independently on other occasions.

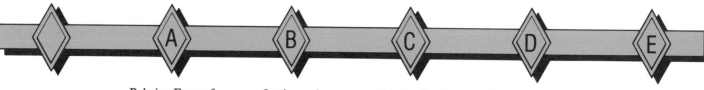

11. Cover the Block   PS   F

Direct small groups of children to work areas with buckets of Pattern Blocks. Tell them their job is to find as many different ways as possible to cover the big yellow block (the hexagon). Stress that the block must be completely covered. When the children have found as many different ways to cover the hexagon block as they can, have them record their discoveries. They could trace or paste hexagons cut from Line Master 30 on a sheet of paper. Pattern Block shapes cut from colored paper (Line Masters 30 to 35) can then be glued on top of the hexagon outlines.

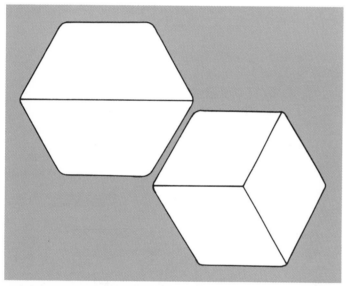

12. Cover It Up   F

At different work areas, provide a variety of materials for tiling such as index cards, paint chips, Pattern Blocks, ceramic tiles, paper sheets of different sizes, newspaper pages, or construction paper figures (Line Masters 30 to 35 or 81 may be useful). Direct the children to these areas to tile various surfaces, such as a piece of paper, a book, a chair seat, a table top, an empty shelf, or an art easel. Remind the children that they must cover the entire surface and that the items should not overlap.

As the children are tiling surfaces, circulate among them to observe how individuals approach the task. Watch for children who approach the task in an organized fashion, placing the tiling material in rows and columns. Note which children begin to tile a surface by placing the items randomly. These observations will tell you a great deal about a child's organizational, perceptual, and problem-solving skills, and whether these skills need considerable practice and reinforcement.

Initiate discussion as the children tile surfaces asking questions such as these:

- **Why did you choose to use the tiles to cover the book?**
- **If you were covering the gym floor, would it be easier to use newspaper pages or index cards? Why?**
- **I see that you covered the book with cards. Do you think it would take more/less cards to cover the chair seat?**

You may wish to group children who used the same tiling material together. Have them estimate which surface required more/less tiles. They can compare the number used by removing the tiles and placing them on a graphing mat or by counting the tiles used.

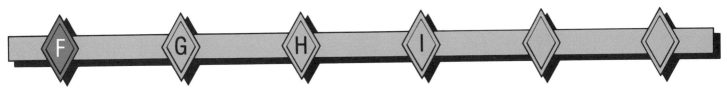

F	G	H	I
Tiling a Surface	Creating and Recognizing Symmetrical Figures	Identifying Fair Shares	Identifying Halves, Fourths, and Tenths

13. Cover and Paste

At different work areas, place a large quantity of figures cut from Line Masters 30 to 35. Provide each child with a sheet of paper to tile. Direct the children to the work areas to tile their paper with the figures provided. Encourage the children to tile the sheet a number of different ways until they discover one that they would like to keep. Tell the children to glue the figures in place. Discuss which figures were easiest to use, which they could not use at all, e.g., circles and why.

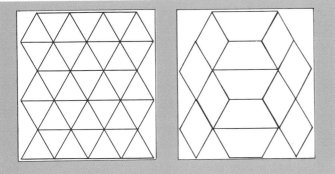

14. Figure Fun

The activities suggested here provide the children with further opportunities to reinforce the concepts of 2-dimensional geometric figures presented in this section. These games and puzzles can be placed at a center for children to pursue independently.

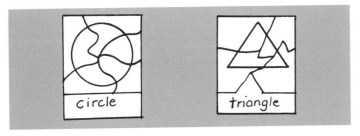

Children match cards to complete the puzzles. Note that there should be a number of puzzles for each figure.

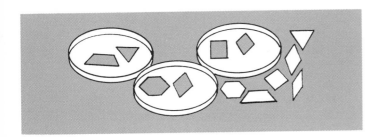

Children match the templates to the cut out figures.

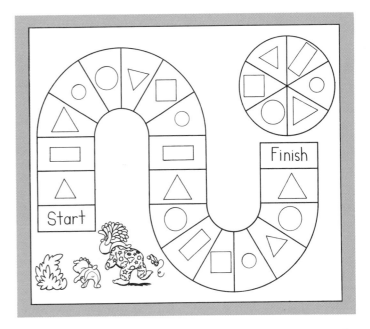

Line Master 43 is used to create a game board. The children spin the spinner and move to a space with the same figure. Have the children count to see how many spins it takes to reach the final space.

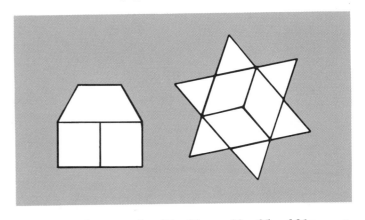

Children use figures cut from Line Masters 30 to 35 and 81 to create pictures.

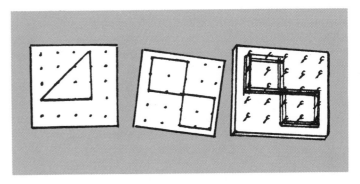

Children use geoboards and elastics to copy the figures drawn on cards.

GEOMETRY AND FRACTIONS   **235**

A	B	C	D	E
Relating Faces of Geometric Solids to Geometric Figures	Sorting and Identifying Geometric Figures	Relating Real-world Objects to Geometric Figures	Patterning with Geometric Figures	Identifying Sides and Corners

Section 2

Planning the Section

Objective	Level	Activity	Grouping	Program *or* Management Suggestions
G Creating and Recognizing Symmetrical Figures	Concrete	1. Fold and Cut 2. Finish My Necklace 3. Block Pictures	♦♦♦♦♦♦ ♦♦♦♦ ♦	In Activity 1 the concept of symmetry is introduced. Collect as many sets of beads and Pattern Blocks as possible for Activities 2 and 3.
H Identifying Fair Shares	Concrete	4. A Shared Snack	♦♦♦♦♦♦♦♦	If possible, share snacks on several occasions. These experiences provide the children with real-life situations in which to consider fair shares.
I Identifying Halves, Fourths, and Tenths	Pictorial	5. Friendly Shares 6. Imp Birthday Party 7. Fraction Fun	♦ ♦ ♦♦♦♦	Activity 7 suggests a variety of ways to reinforce the concept of fractions. Some materials must be prepared ahead of time.

About this Section

Children will enjoy exploring the concept of symmetry through folding and cutting. Developing block pictures along a line of symmetry is also an interesting activity. It requires a more sophisticated grasp of the concept of symmetry. Children with poor visual organization or perceptual problems will probably find this difficult. The use of a mirror helps a child to see what must appear on the other side of the line of symmetry.

Fractions are introduced in the context of fair shares, i.e., equal parts. While the concept that an object may be divided into any number of equal parts may be explored, only halves, fourths and tenths are referenced in this section. You may wish to extend the discussion of fractions.

Observations and Evaluation

As you circulate among the groups, look for children who make the same pattern on the other side of a line of symmetry, rather than a mirror image of the pattern. Double a bead necklace back on itself, use a mirror, or use one-to-one correspondence, working back from the middle, to develop the concept of symmetry with bead necklaces or pictures. Activities 1 or 4 may be used to assess a child's grasp of the concept of symmetry.

These key questions could form the basis of discussions.

- **Is your picture (necklace, pattern) exactly the same on this side as on that side?**
- **If we folded your picture (necklace, pattern), would all the parts match exactly?**
- **Let's try matching all the parts. There's a blue bead beside the knot; show me the blue bead on the other side. There's a red cube beside the blue bead; show me the other red cube. There's a yellow sparkly bead beside the red cube; show me the other yellow sparkly bead.**

When discussing fair shares, ensure that the children understand that there is no such thing as a big or small half. Encourage the children to make fair shares as fair as possible.

- **Are your 2 (4, 10) parts the same size? Are they really halves? (fourths, tenths)? How could we make sure that they're really halves (fourths, tenths)?**
- **Why will you have to cut the pizza (cake) very carefully on the line?**

Suggested Materials

- A large quantity of beads for stringing necklaces [Activity 2]
- Pieces of string for necklaces [Activity 2]
- A bin of Pattern Blocks, Parquetry Tiles, or Attribute Blocks for each work area [Activity 3]
- A snack such as a cracker, cheese slice, cookie, or apple for each pair of children [Activity 4]
- Fraction cards [Activity 7]
- Domino cards [Activity 7]
- A game board [Activity 7]

Line Masters

Line Masters **30** to **35**
Activity 3
A large quantity

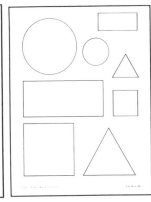

Line Master **81**
Activity 7
Several copies

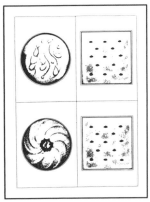

Line Master **82**
Activities 5 and 7
1 per child

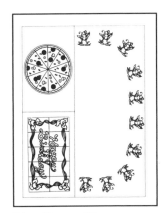

Line Master **83**
Activities 6 and 7
1 per child

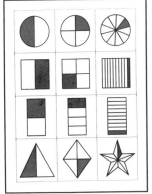

Line Master **84**
Activity 7
A large quantity

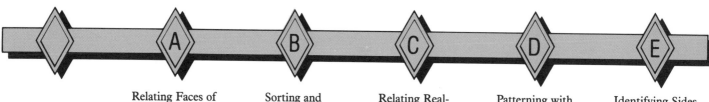

A	B	C	D	E
Relating Faces of Geometric Solids to Geometric Figures	Sorting and Identifying Geometric Figures	Relating Real-world Objects to Geometric Figures	Patterning with Geometric Figures	Identifying Sides and Corners

Activities

1. Fold and Cut

G

Gather the children together around a work area. Provide each child with a piece of paper, a pencil, and a pair of scissors. Invite them to copy what you do with your paper. Fold a sheet of paper in half. Draw a figure along the folded edge. Cut the picture along the pencil line and unfold the paper.

Encourage the children to describe what happened. Have them describe the cut out figure. Ask them if there is anything special about the figure, if they have ever used this technique of folding and cutting before (making Valentine cards, snowflakes, pumpkins, etc.,) and if they were surprised at what they saw when you unfolded the paper. In the course of this discussion, introduce the word "symmetry", explaining that figures that match along a fold line have symmetry.

At different work areas, place paper, pencils, and scissors. (This is an excellent opportunity to use scrap paper.) Direct the children to these work areas to create more symmetrical figures by folding and cutting. After the children have made a number of symmetrical figures, invite them to choose one of their cutouts, fold it along the fold line, and bring it to the circle. In turn, have the children display their figures and, ask, **What do you think this will look like when it is open?** Encourage the others to describe their predictions or sketch them on the board.

Meeting Individual Needs

Invite children who are ready for a further challenge to color their figures so that both sides are identical.

2. Finish My Necklace

G

Provide each child with a string knotted in the middle and a large quantity of beads. Invite the children to string beads in any pattern or color combination they wish on one side of the knot. When the children have finished this, they knot the end so that the beads will not fall off. Divide the children into pairs and have the children exchange their necklaces. Each child then continues the necklace on the other side of the knot so that it has symmetry. When this part of the necklace is complete, the children tie a knot at the end. Have the children check for symmetry by folding the string at the middle knot.

Note that if beads are in short supply, you may substitute cut straws, macaroni, paper squares, circles, triangles, etc.

Meeting Individual Needs

If a child is having difficulty continuing her or his partner's necklace, have her or him hold a small mirror at the middle knot. The child will be able to see what the other side should look like. Alternatively, have the child fold the necklace at the knot and have her or him match the beads one to one.

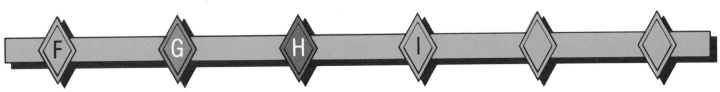
3. Block Pictures — G

At different work areas, place pieces of paper divided in half by a straight line and bins of Pattern Blocks, Parquetry Tiles, or Attribute Blocks. Direct small groups of children to the work areas to create symmetrical designs. Ask the children to choose a block or tile, and place it on a piece of paper so that one edge is adjacent to the dividing line. Invite the children to continue to make a design with the blocks on one half of the paper. Remind them to create the design so that no blocks cross the fold line. After they have completed this design, challenge them to position blocks on the opposite side of the dividing line to create a symmetrical picture.

Note that if the suggested materials are not available, you can provide figures cut from construction paper. (Line Masters 30 to 35 are useful.) These designs can be recorded by copying the design with figures cut from Line Masters 30 to 35 and gluing them down or by tracing the blocks in position.

Meeting Individual Needs

If a child is having difficulty creating a symmetrical design, he or she may benefit from a different approach. Instruct the children to build a symmetrical picture, block by block. Each time the child places a block on one side of the dividing line, he or she should place a matching one on the other side.

4. A Shared Snack — H

Divide the children into pairs. Give each pair a cracker, a slice of cheese, a cookie, or an apple. Lead a discussion on how they could share their snack fairly. Invite the children to relate their personal experiences of sharing things fairly. Explore the meaning of having a fair share of something, i.e., each child has the same amount. Have one child divide the snack into fair shares. If the children are sharing an apple, help one to cut it. The other child chooses a piece. (This system encourages both children to focus on equal shares.) Have each pair of children display their pieces of the snack, and ask, **Are these fair shares?** Discuss why it is so difficult to share these snacks fairly.

You may wish to involve the children in actually making the snack to be shared. For example, as a class you could bake cookies, assemble sandwiches, make toast, or fry pancakes. These snacks could then be cut into fair shares.

5. Friendly Shares

Provide each child with a sheet of paper, scissors, a pencil, glue, and the top half of Line Master 82. Have the children fold the sheet of paper in half and draw a picture of themselves on one half of the paper and a picture of a friend on the other half. (They could print their name and the friend's name on each half.) Ask the children to cut out the cookie and cracker from the line master. Challenge the children to fold and cut the cookie and then the cracker so that they could be shared fairly with a friend. Encourage the children to fold carefully to make sure the shares are fair before they cut the cookie and cracker. Have them paste half the cookie and half the cracker beside each picture on their sheet of paper as shown.

Introduce the word "half" during the discussion of these pictures. **I see you have half a cookie and your friend has half a cookie. Does your friend have half a cracker? How much of the cracker do you have?** Encourage each child to describe her or his picture using the term "half."

On another day, repeat this process to introduce the concept of one fourth. Have the children fold their sheet of paper into fourths and draw a picture of themselves and 3 friends in each section created. Have them fold and cut the other cookie and cracker from Line Master 82 into fourths and paste the fourths as they did for the halves. Lead a discussion to introduce the term "fourth."

6. Imp Birthday Party

Provide each child with a copy of Line Master 83, scissors, and glue. Lead a discussion on what the children think they are supposed to do on the sheet. Establish that the imps are having a birthday party and that each imp should receive a fair share of pizza and cake. Ask, **How many imps are there? How many pieces of pizza will we need? How many pieces of cake? Each imp will have one tenth of the pizza and one tenth of the cake.** Direct the children to work areas to cut the pizza and cake into tenths, and to paste a piece of each for every imp. Encourage the children to describe the process using the term tenth. For example, **This imp has one tenth of the pizza and one tenth of the cake. This imp has....**

7. Fraction Fun

Line Masters 81 to 84 can be used to make a number of interesting reinforcement puzzles and games. It is suggested that you prepare a few of the ideas presented here and place these activities at a center for the children to enjoy. Only through frequent exposure to fractions will children develop a firm grasp of the concepts.

Line Masters 81 and 82 can be reproduced on construction paper to illustrate the puzzles. In each envelope place a copy of an uncut line master. The child can form the puzzles directly on top of the figures.

Children play a matching game such as fish with these fraction cards (Line Master 84). They must ask for the card using the words half, fourth, or tenth, e.g., **Do you have any fourths?**

Line Master 84 can be used to create a domino game.

Children play this game in pairs. Each child turns over a card (cut from Line Master 84) from her or his pile. If both cards depict the same fraction, the children say, **Match**, and place the pair to the side. Play continues until all cards are matched.

Geometry Across the Curriculum

Language Arts

- Display a variety of models of traffic and municipal signs and have the children identify each one. Turn each sign over and invite the children to identify the sign by its shape. Distribute construction paper and have the children create personal signs for their bedrooms, the classroom, the kindergarten room, their bicycles, or their favorite words.

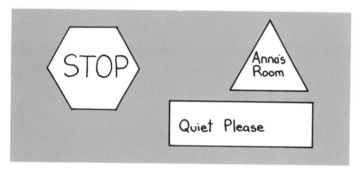

- Invite the children to create and solve riddles focussing on the different geometric figures.
  - **I have 3 corners and 3 sides. What am I?**
  - **I am a circle. I am usually black and go round and round. You listen to me. What am I?**
- Have the children determine which letters of the alphabet are symmetrical. Place a copy of the alphabet and/or cutouts of the letters, and small mirrors at a center for children to investigate.

- In conjunction with this unit, you may wish to read any of these books (see page 318 for an annotated bibliography):
  - *A-Apple Pie* by Kate Greenaway
  - *Circles, Triangles, and Squares* by Tana Hoban
  - *Shapes* by Jan Pienkowski

Art

- Invite the children to investigate symmetry through ink or paint blocks. Have the children fold a piece of paper in half, open the paper, put several drops of ink or paint on one side, fold the paper again, smooth the sheet with their hands, open the sheet, and allow it to dry. The children may wish to add detail with crayon or paint to this design.

- Have the children design pumpkin faces, Christmas trees, valentines, snowflakes, or masks by cutting a folded sheet of paper.

Physical Education

- Make a maze of figures using masking tape on a gym floor or chalk on asphalt outside. Instruct the children to move on these figures in specific ways.
  - **Everyone stand on the triangle. Hop along the sides of the triangle on 1 foot.**
  - **Move very slowly to a 4-sided figure. Sit down and slide into the figure.**
  - **Stand up and jump to the outside of the square.**

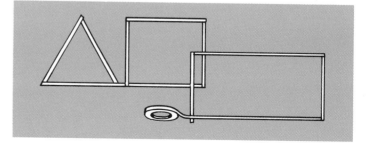

Extension Project

- Provide each child with a long loop of rope or yarn. Have the children use their bodies to form different figures. You may also wish to have the children work with a partner or in a small group.

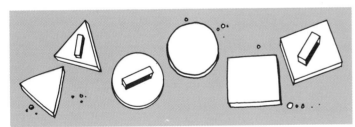

Science

- Have the children contribute to a display of objects with symmetry. Take the children on a walk outdoors to search for symmetry in nature. On this walk, they may find items for the symmetry display. Point out the various flowers, leaves, or blades of grass that may have symmetry and are easy to collect.

- Make cookie dough with the children. Encourage them to form the dough into geometric figures, then bake them, and eat.

- On a sunny day, take the children outside to investigate symmetrical shadows. Invite them to position their bodies in ways to create symmetrical shadows. You may also wish to encourage the children to work in pairs.

Social Studies

- Take the children on a walk through the school, playground, or neighborhood to search for objects which resemble the different geometric shapes studied. Record, tally, and graph your group's findings.
- Encourage the children to trace objects at home. Have them present these Mystery Maps to their classmates.

Place Pattern Blocks at a center, or figures cut from Line Masters 30 to 35. It is recommended that you reproduce these line masters on colored construction paper and laminate all the pieces. Use a different color for each figure. Have the children create pictures with the blocks. When they have completed their picture, have them trace the outline of the picture. These outlines can be filed in a folder entitled, How Did We Make These? Children select an outline and try to place blocks to show how the outline was created.

You may wish to create a few outlines initially as an example. Laminate these outlines and store them at a center in a folder titled Picture Challenges. If possible, laminate the challenges the children create.

Number to 99

Unit Objectives

Section 1

A   Grouping by Fours and Fives
B   Grouping by Tens
C   Trading Pennies for a Coin

Section 2

D   Recording a Ten and Ones
E   Counting and Recording Groups of 10
F   Counting sets to 50 or 100
G   Recording a 2-digit Number

Section 3

H   Identifying the Greater/Lesser Number
I   Identifying the Number Before/ After/Between
J   Creating and Recording Number Patterns

About this Unit

Place Value

The concepts related to place value are very abstract and difficult for young children to grasp. The notion that our number system is based on the formation of groups of tens, i.e., 10 items can be grouped into one group of 10, and ten groups of 10 can be grouped into one group of 100, etc., is extremely complex. This idea also requires the children to count groups as if they were individual objects. Once 10 items have been grouped, the child is expected to conceive of it as a separate entity or one 10. It is extremely important to provide many concrete experiences with the counting, grouping and trading process so that an understanding of the place value procedures can be fostered.

Children should begin by grouping single objects into a group of 10. This will allow the original 10 items to remain visible if counting and checking are necessary to determine how many are in the group. This also helps to establish that one 10 is the same as 10 ones because the children can easily build and separate the group. The use of the grouping mat in the introductory activities helps the children develop this understanding by structuring the process visually so that steps are easily determined.

Once the children begin to predict and verbalize the grouping process, they may trade the 10 objects for one object which represents the 10 single items, e.g., a dime or a block. This is a convenient step when dealing with large numbers as it limits the vast quantities of materials required for the activity. This step, however, does not allow the children to verify that they have the same number of items with which they began. Therefore, do not rush the children into this trading process until they are ready.

The recording of numerals is carefully modelled by the teacher and read aloud once the grouping process has been introduced and reinforced. This delay allows the children the opportunity to connect the symbols to familiar actions and verbal descriptions. Children begin to keep their own records only after they have had opportunities to work extensively with concrete materials and observed the teacher model the corresponding symbols.

Money concepts are developed in conjunction with place value in this unit. The exchange of groups of pennies for nickels and dimes is used to reinforce the trading process. Although coins are more abstract than the bundles and groups used in the activities, they are equally effective in reinforcing the concepts because of their relevance in the children's lives.

Having developed the concept of place value, the unit focusses on number sequence by ensuring that the children work with number before, after, and in between. The final activities in the unit give children a chance to apply the concept of place value when identifying the greater/lesser numeral.

Problem Solving

In this unit, children have the opportunity to extend and create number patterns as they engage in the activities Growing Patterns, pages 276-277 and Hundreds of Patterns, page 277. They sort numerals in the activity Number Sort, page 273. In addition, activities provided in Five Minute Math, page 247 develop these problem-solving skills:

- sorting
- identifying, extending, and creating patterns
- developing observation and listening skills

Vocabulary

- Ones
- Tens

We took only photographs and left only footprints.

The TEN Pack Factory

Ongoing Objectives

- Ordering months of the year
- Counting by fives
- Recognizing time names
- Discussing weather and temperature
- Counting coin collections
- Identifying geometric figures
- Problem solving
  - Sorting
  - Identifying, extending, and creating patterns
  - Creating story problems
  - Developing observation and listening skills

Five Minute Math

Calendar Activities

- Display in random order all the calendars made to date. Have the children place them in order to show the sequence for a school year. Begin by asking, **What month did we start school?** Post the September calendar and ask, **What special things happened in September? What month comes after September?** Have a child find and post the October calendar. Continue the questioning until all calendars are posted in order.

- Post next month's calendar (even though the present month is not over) and start to record special events. Ask, **Does anyone have a birthday next month? Are there any other special things happening next month?** After a few dates have been recorded, ask questions such as these:

  - **How many more weeks until Leah's birthday next month?**
  - **What day of the week is the first day of next month?**
  - **How many days are there in next month?**
  - **What date is our class trip next month?**

Counting Activities

- Ask a group of 5 children to stand at the front holding a hand out in front of them. Encourage the children to count the displayed fingers by fives. Repeat this activity a number of times so that children become familiar with the sound and rhythm of counting by fives. Increase the number of children in the group as they develop their skill of counting by fives.
- The children place 5 counters in each of several containers. Count by fives, moving a container to one side each time a multiple of 5 is said aloud.
- Have the children count aloud by fives. Circle the number they say in a different color (than you have already used) on the cumulative record strip.

Measurement Activities

- Develop the children's awareness of the passage of time by posing questions such as these:
  - **Can you clap twice in a second?**
  - **Can you print your name in a second?**
  - **Can you draw a picture in a minute?**
  - **Can you tie your shoe in a minute?**
  - **Can you tidy the blocks in a minute?**

  When appropriate, have the children participate in the activity to actually determine if it can be completed in a given time period.

- Make lists with the children of the types of activities they engage in during each season.

Summer
We go swimming.
We ride our bikes.

  Discuss how they dress in winter, spring, summer, and fall. Encourage predictions about the weather for each season, e.g., **Summer is hot. We can go swimming.**

- Through discussion and questioning the children become aware of dressing for the weather.

  - **Today it's 0°C outside. What did you wear to school?**
  - **How do we dress if the temperature is 24°C?**
  - **Is it ever 0°C in the summer?**
  - **Is it ever 30°C in the winter?**

Money Activities

- Display a collection of up to 9 nickels. Ask, **What would be a fast way to count these nickels?** If necessary, suggest counting by fives. Have the children count aloud as you drop each coin onto a display area. Ask, **How much money is there?** Ensure that the children use the word cents in their response, e.g., **45 cents.**

- Show the children a nickel and have them identify its value. Cover the nickel with a container and slide another nickel under it. Ask, **How much money is under the container now?** After the children respond, **10 cents,** slide another nickel under the container and repeat the question. Continue this process as long as it is appropriate for your children.

- Have each child prepare a wallet of money by placing a dime or a nickel and pennies in an envelope. Ask the children to pass the wallet they prepared to their right. Have the children count the change in the wallet they received. Encourage them to begin with the nickel or the dime. In turn, have the children tell how much money is in their wallets. Collect the wallets, redistribute them, and repeat the process.

- Display a quarter and ask the children to identify the coin and its value. Introduce the word quarter and its value as 25 cents. Ask, **How many pennies would you get if you traded a quarter for pennies?** Print 25¢ and quarter on the board. Have each child take a close look at a quarter and encourage them to describe its appearance. Display a quarter and a collection of pennies. As a group, count the collection aloud. Repeat the process with different collections.
- Place a quarter and a collection of pennies in various containers. Label each container with a letter or symbol. Give each child in the circle a container, a pencil, and piece of paper. Have each child count the collection and record the amount on the paper with the corresponding symbol. Ask the children to pass the collection and continue the activity.

Geometry Activities

- Distribute a collection of geometric figures (in various sizes and colors) so that each child has one. Ensure that there is at least one identical match for each figure. Invite the children to find their matching partner. Have the children sit in pairs when they find their partner.
- Place a collection of geometric figures (preferably Attribute Blocks of figures cut from cardboard) in an opaque bag or box. Display a similar set of figures. Have a volunteer stand with her or his hands behind her or his back. Place a figure from the bag in the child's hands without letting her or him see it. Encourage the child to describe the figure and select the matching one from the displayed collection.
- Give each child a piece of paper and crayons. Have them draw geometric figures according to your directions. For example: **Draw a green triangle in the top right corner. Draw a red square under the green triangle.**

Problem Solving Activities

Sorting

- Display a collection of coins, sort them according to type, and ask, **What's my rule for sorting these coins?** Re-sort the collection according to color (copper and silver) and repeat the question. Re-sort the collection according to the year of the coin, the pictures on a side, the words, or the type of edge. Place the sorted coins in a spot where children can examine them at their leisure. At a later time, ask, **Who can tell me how I sorted the coins?**
- Have the children sort Pattern Blocks, Attribute Blocks, or cardboard 2-dimensional figures with their eyes closed, using only their sense of touch. After the children have completed their sorting, lead a discussion on what they experienced.

Identifying, Extending, and Creating Patterns

- Print patterns of numbers and/or letters on the chalk board such as the ones shown. Have the children read and extend them.

```
1 3 5 1 3 5 1 3 5
2 4 4 2 4 4 2 4 4
5 5 4 5 5 4 5 5 4
```

- Have the children create patterns on a calculator display. Invite each child to read her or his pattern aloud and ask, **If I could put in more numbers, how would my pattern continue?**

Creating Story Problems

Tell the children that they are going to make up and demonstrate questions for an answer. For example, as you print 3 apples on the chalk board, say, **The answer is 3 apples. What could the question be?** Have each child who offers a question, demonstrate it with small objects. Record the questions on a chart.

> ### 3 apples
>
> I ate 2 apples Monday and 1 apple today. How many apples did I eat?
>
> I had 6 apples. I gave 3 apples to my sister. How many apples do I have left?
>
> I have 1 green apple, 1 red apple, and 1 yellow apple. How many apples do I have?

Developing Observation and Listening Skills

Select 4 objects such as a book, a piece of paper, a pencil, and a chalk brush. Tell the children that you are thinking of one of the displayed objects. Invite them to ask you questions which can only be answered with a yes or a no to discover which object you have selected. Count the number of questions the children must ask to discover the object. Have the children play this game in pairs with 4 objects of their choice.

Using the Story

In the story Raindrops Make Puddles, Ted discovers that his teacup can hold only a certain number of raindrops before the contents overflow and create a puddle. He enjoys repeatedly collecting 10 raindrops in his teacup (making a group of ten) and then emptying (regrouping) it to create a puddle. As children participate in the activities Shift Them Next Door, page 252; Raindrops Make Puddles, page 253; and Off We'll Go, page 254, they engage in a similar activity of grouping and regrouping objects by fours, fives, and then tens.

References to time have also been made in the story. You may wish to use these suggested problems to review time vocabulary and concepts.

- If the story took place on a (Thursday), when did the rain begin?
- If it was four o'clock when Ted cleaned his toes, how many hours had he been outside?
- In which season did the story take place? What season was it before that? What season comes next?

Supplementary Material

Ted is my Friend: Mathematics Activity Book, pages 80-88, and hundreds chart, pages 37 and 56.

Raindrops Make Puddles

For several days it had rained and rained; so for several days Ted had stayed inside his little white cabin. There hadn't been a trip to the meadow. There hadn't even been a trip to the garden or to the giant ginkgo tree. There hadn't been a trip for days and days because it had just rained and rained.

It was about two o'clock on the fourth rainy day when Ted slumped into his soft cosy chair to drink his peppermint tea. One by one, little balls of sunlight began to grow on the far wall and dance up and down. Ted watched in delight as they grew bigger and bigger.

"Sun!" he said to himself as he went to the front door just to make sure.

With his teacup still in his hand, Ted stepped outside into the fresh spring air.

"Oh!" he said as brown mucky mud oozed around his slippers. Ted tried to pick his foot up out of the sticky mud. "Oh!" Ted said as his toes popped out of his slipper and plopped back down into the mud. "Oh!" he said again as he wiggled his toes in the goo. Ted smiled a big smile and he stood there and wiggled and giggled for quite some time. Ted's toes were getting so muddy — it might take an ocean to clean off the mud! But Ted didn't have an ocean. How would he get the mud off before he went back inside?

Then Ted felt a drip on his head. He felt it again. And again. He bent his head back and splash! Right on his nose fell a great big raindrop.

"Raindrops! Raindrops falling from the roof right onto my head!" Then Ted smiled. "Raindrops make puddles and puddles clean toes!" Ted thought to himself, and he muddled the idea of puddles and more puddles over in his mind.

Then out went Ted's teacup and in went the raindrops, one by one. And Ted made up a song:

"Nine little raindrops in my cup,
Ten will make it fill right up.
Tip it, pour it, and out it goes,
Out of my tea cup a puddle grows!"

Puddles grew all over the garden as Ted filled his cup and sang his song. And when all the raindrops had dropped from the top of the roof and the well and the mailbox and from the leaves of the giant ginkgo tree, Ted looked at his empty cup and his muddy toes and the trail of puddles that led back to the little white cabin and he smiled. And as he made his way back to the little white cabin, Ted splished and splashed and sang his tune:

"Nine little raindrops in my cup,
Ten has made it fill right up.
Out of my tea cup the puddles grew,
To clean my toes so they look like new!"

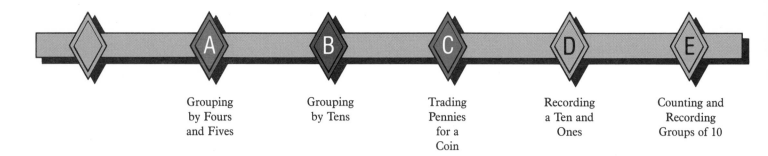

A — Grouping by Fours and Fives

B — Grouping by Tens

C — Trading Pennies for a Coin

D — Recording a Ten and Ones

E — Counting and Recording Groups of 10

Section 1

Planning the Section

Objective	Level	Activity	Grouping	Program *or* Management Suggestions
A — Grouping by Fours and Fives	Concrete	1. Shift Them Next Door 2. Raindrops Make Puddles	♦♦♦♦ ♦♦♦♦	Play Activity 1 (grouping by fours) frequently with the children so that they have many opportunities to form groups. Introduce Activity 2 which involves grouping by fives only after children are comfortable grouping by fours.
B — Grouping by Tens	Concrete	3. Off We'll Go 4. The Ten Pack	♦♦♦♦ ♦♦♦♦	Activity 3 follows the same procedure as Activities 1 and 2. Small groups can make materials in Activity 4 as you engage children in Activity 3. In Activity 4, the children create materials which are used frequently in later counting and place value activities.
C — Trading Pennies for a Coin	Concrete	5. Penny Exchange 6. Fair Exchange	♦♦♦♦ ♦♦♦♦	In Activities 5 and 6, the children apply the concept of grouping to money. You can introduce a small group of children to these activities as other children participate in making the ten packs outlined in Activity 4.

About this Section

The activities in this section are designed to introduce the process of grouping and regrouping. Activities 1 and 2 deal with small groups of 4 or 5. This initial work with small numbers allows for quick verification of quantity and easy handling of materials. Working with these small numbers forces frequent regrouping which results in more experience with the process. Verbal descriptions of the actions are encouraged so that children can check their actions and hear the patterns as they develop. Once the children understand the grouping process, they can begin to group and regroup materials by tens. A grouping mat (Line Master 85) is used in these introductory activities to structure the process and define the steps.

In Activity 4, children make materials which will be used in many later activities. The classroom-made materials should supplement the commercial materials, i.e., interlocking cubes and/or

any base 10 materials typically used to develop place value concepts. Making any or all of the ten packs suggested in Activity 4 ensures that there will be enough materials for each child. Children will also have the opportunity to manipulate many different types of materials as they engage in the activities of the unit. This variety helps maintain a high level of interest.

The concept of grouping and trading is applied to money in Activities 5 and 6 when children exchange pennies for a coin of corresponding value. It is recommended that you keep the coin exchange office established in Activity 6 operating for the course of the entire unit. Children will discover many other interesting exchanges if they are able to visit this office frequently. For example, a child may discover that 20 pennies can be exchanged for 2 dimes, 4 nickels, or 1 dime and 2 nickels.

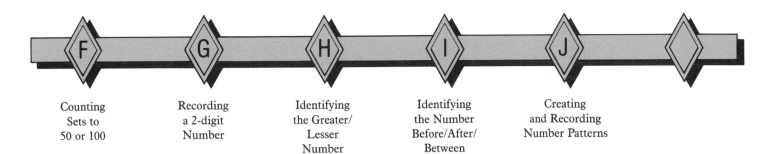

F	**G**	**H**	**I**	**J**
Counting Sets to 50 or 100	Recording a 2-digit Number	Identifying the Greater/ Lesser Number	Identifying the Number Before/After/ Between	Creating and Recording Number Patterns

Observations and Evaluation

The grouping games are structured so that children are placing objects and reading their mats in unison. Keep a careful watch to ensure that each child is adding or removing an object at the appropriate times. Allow time for all children to form or break apart a group before continuing with your direction of, **And one more.** Or, **One less.**

Keep these key questions in mind as children engage in Activity 4.

- **How many packages of 10 did you make? Show me.**
- **How many beads are on the bracelet you made? Show me 5 bracelets of 10 beads. If you made 1 more, how many would you have?**

Observations	**Teacher Direction**
The child is often a step behind the group, watching other children place objects and make groups before doing the same.	The child probably requires additional cues because he or she does not yet see a pattern to the grouping process. Continue to engage her or him in grouping by fours.
A child comments appropriately, **One more and we'll make a lid. We're going to have to dump a lid to take the next one off the mat.**	The child who anticipates when groups are to be formed and taken apart demonstrates a solid grasp of the grouping process. Engage her or him in grouping by fives (or tens if this observation took place as you grouped by fives).

Suggested Materials

- A large quantity of small objects such as kernels, beans, pieces of paper, or counters [Activities 1, 2, and 3]
- 3 lids per child [Activity 1]
- 4 paper muffin cups per child [Activity 2]
- Up to 10 pots (Styrofoam cups cut down) per child [Activity 3]
- A large quantity of beans [Activity 4]
- A large quantity of popsicle sticks or tongue depressors [Activity 4]
- A large quantity of toothpicks [Activity 4]
- A large quantity of straws [Activity 4]
- A large quantity of baggies [Activity 4]
- A large collection of pennies, nickels, and dimes [Activities 5 and 6]

Line Masters

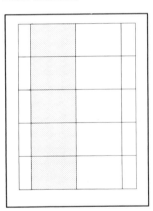

Line Master **85**
Activities 1, 2, 3, and 5
1 per child

Line Master **86**
Activity 4
A large quantity

Line Master **87**
Activity 6
1 per child

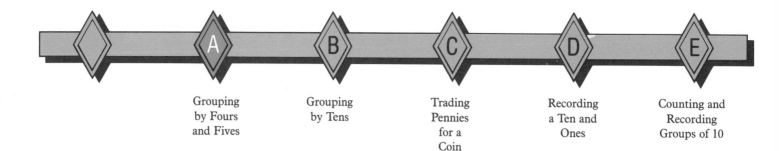

Activities

1. Shift Them Next Door

A

Distribute a grouping mat (Line Master 85), a container of small objects (kernels, or beans) and 3 lids to each child. Tell the children that you are going to show them a special counting game that Ted likes to play. Explain that in this game there is a secret number you never say. Print the numeral 4 on the board. Say, **This will be the secret number for the game today. We do not say this number out loud.** Explain that Ted calls a group of 4 a lid because he stores the fours in lids on his game board (the grouping mat).

Have the children prepare their grouping mats by folding under the bottom 2 sections so only 3 sections show.

Ask, **How many beans are on the shaded side of your mat? How many beans are on the white side of your mat?** Guide them to put their hand on the shaded side and slide it to the white side, while saying, **Zero lids and zero.**

Have the children place one item on the white side of the mat in the top right hand section as you say, **And one more.** Ask, **How many beans are on the mat?** Encourage the children to respond, **Zero lids and 1** as they slide their hands from the shaded side to the white side. Have the children continue to add one object at a time in response to your direction, **And one more.** They should read the mat after each addition, **Zero lids and 2. Zero lids and three. . . .**

When the children are ready to place the fourth item, discuss the fact that there is no place for it on the white side (which is good because you never want to say, **Shshsh**). Have the children collect all the objects from the white side and place them in a lid with the fourth object on the top section of the shaded side. Have the children chant Ted's verse as they collect the objects and place them in a lid.

If it's one, two, three,
That's all right with me.
But when it comes to one more,
Collect them! Pack them! And shift them next door!

Have the children read the board together as, **1 lid and zero.** Continue to direct the children to place objects, one at a time as you say, **And one more,** until the board is complete, with **3 lids and 3.**

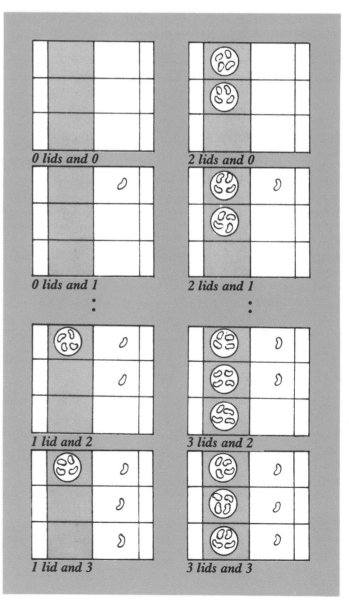

0 lids and 0

2 lids and 0

0 lids and 1

2 lids and 1

⋮

⋮

1 lid and 2

3 lids and 2

1 lid and 3

3 lids and 3

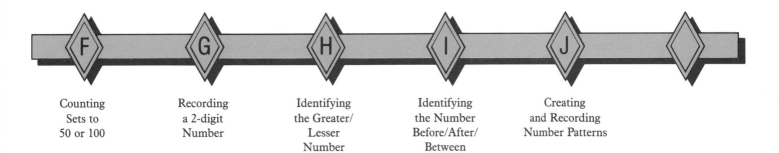

F	G	H	I	J	
Counting Sets to 50 or 100	Recording a 2-digit Number	Identifying the Greater/ Lesser Number	Identifying the Number Before/After/ Between	Creating and Recording Number Patterns	

The next step in the game is to begin the process of clearing the grouping mat. This is accomplished by having the children remove one object at a time after you say, **One less.** Ask the children to remove one object (the last one they placed) and read the board, **3 lids and 2.** Have the children continue to take one object off the mat at a time and describe the mat after each object is removed. You say, **One less.** They remove 1 object and say, **3 lids and 1.** You say, **One less.** They remove 1 object and say, **3 lids and 0.** When the children must take one object off a mat that has 3 lids and 0, discussion will begin. If children suggest taking an object out of the lid, remind them that a lid must always have 4 objects or else it is no longer a lid. Have the children dump a lid; take an object away; place the other 3 objects so that there is one in each white section; and have them read the board as, **2 lids and 3.** Have the children continue to remove objects one at a time until the mat is clear.

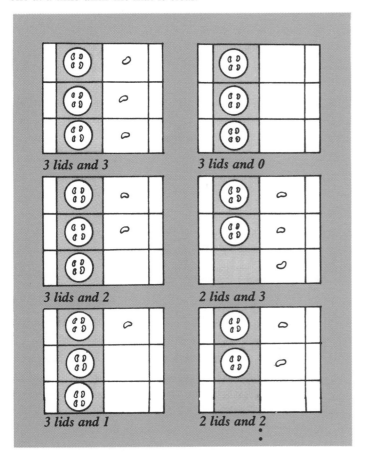

3 lids and 3   *3 lids and 0*

3 lids and 2   *2 lids and 3*

3 lids and 1   *2 lids and 2*

It is very important that the children read the board each time they add or remove an object. The children should move their hand from the shaded side to the white side as they say each statement aloud. When the game is being introduced, you should check each child's work to ensure that he or she is placing the items correctly on the board. Always encourage the children to verbalize what they are doing. If necessary, show the actions using a demonstration grouping mat.

2. Raindrops Make Puddles

Gather the children together to play another of Ted's favorite counting games. Explain that in this counting game 5 cannot be said and all groups of five are placed in paper muffin cups. (It is important to change the container so that children clearly understand that these groups are different from groups of 4.)

Provide each child with a collection of small objects, paper muffin cups, and a copy of the grouping mat (Line Master 85). Tell them to fold their mats so that 4 sections are showing. You may wish to use a different verse to reinforce the grouping process.

4 little raindrops all in a row,
5 won't fit, that I know.
Catch them all and over they go,
Into my cup so that a puddle grows.

Follow the same procedures for adding and removing objects as you did for grouping by fours in Activity 1, Shift Them Next Door.

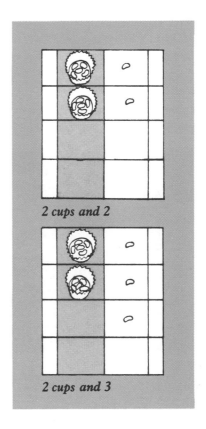

2 cups and 2

2 cups and 3

Reinforce the reading process by having the children verbalize their actions each time they add or remove an object.

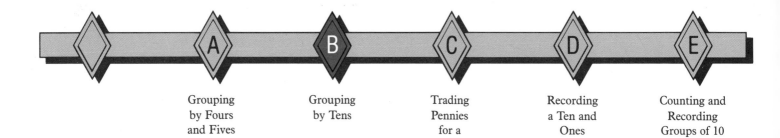

A	B	C	D	E
Grouping by Fours and Fives	Grouping by Tens	Trading Pennies for a Coin	Recording a Ten and Ones	Counting and Recording Groups of 10

3. Off We'll Go
B

Provide each child with 2 copies of Line Master 85 which they glue together and fold so that there are 9 sections. This grouping mat will be used for grouping by tens.

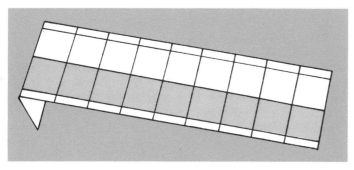

Distribute pots (Styrofoam cups cut down as shown) and a large quantity of small objects such as beans or counters to each child. Follow the same procedure for placing items on and removing items from the grouping mat as outlined in Shift Them Next Door, page 252. Direct the children to add one item at a time and read the grouping mats aloud after each addition, until the tenth item is to be placed. Remind the children that when there is no space they must shift all items to a pot. As the children shift these items to a pot, you can encourage them to chant the verse:

9 little bean seeds all in a row,
10 won't fit, that I know.
Time to plant them, here they go,
Into my pot so that a garden grows!

Once the children are familiar with grouping by tens and can read the grouping mat without hesitation, have them open the mat to 10 sections, print tens and ones at the top of the appropriate columns, and print numerals down each side of the mat as shown. Note that the game should continue so that children have the opportunity to regroup several times. However, when interest begins to wane, stop the activity and repeat it on following days.

o	Tens	Ones	o	o	Tens	Ones	o
1	🫘	ଚ	1	1	🫘	ଚ	1
2	🫘	ଚ	2	2	🫘	ଚ	2
3		ଚ	3	3	🫘	ଚ	3
4		ଚ	4	4	🫘	ଚ	4
5		ଚ	5	5	🫘		5
6			6	6	🫘	ଚ	6
7			7	7	🫘	ଚ	7
8			8	8		ଚ	8
9			9	9			9

2 tens and 5   *7 tens and 8*

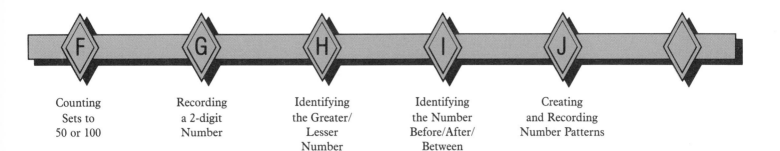

F	G	H	I	J	
Counting Sets to 50 or 100	Recording a 2-digit Number	Identifying the Greater/ Lesser Number	Identifying the Number Before/After/ Between	Creating and Recording Number Patterns	

4. The Ten Pack   ◆ B

In this activity, the children package materials in groups of 10. These packages will be used extensively in many later counting and place value activities. At different work areas (factories), place any or all of the materials listed on the chart. Direct small groups of children to each factory to begin packaging materials.

Have the children share what they made. Ask them to count how many groups of 10 they made altogether. Store these groups of 10 for later use in counting and place value activities. It is also necessary to keep a collection of the single items used to make a group of 10.

Materials	Procedures	Product
• Beans, popsicle sticks, and glue	• Glue 10 beans on a stick	• A bean stick
• Toothpicks and Plasticine	• Stick 10 toothpicks into a piece of Plasticine	• A porcupine
• Line Master 86 and a stapler	• Staple 10 sheets together to form a booklet	• Order booklets
• Line Master 86 and a stapler	• Staple 10 sheets together to form a booklet	• Inventory booklets
• Beads or straw pieces and string	• String 10 beads on a string	• A bracelet
• Raindrops cut from blue paper	• Glue 10 raindrops on each circle to make a puddle	• A puddle
• Popsicle sticks and an elastic	• Bundle 10 sticks together	• A log
• Small items and baggies	• Place 10 items in a baggie	• Items in a bag! (a bag of 10)

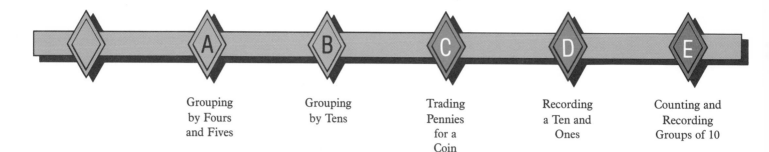

A	B	C	D	E
Grouping by Fours and Fives	Grouping by Tens	Trading Pennies for a Coin	Recording a Ten and Ones	Counting and Recording Groups of 10

5. Penny Exchange

C

Distribute a grouping mat (Line Master 85), 5 pennies and 4 nickels to each child. Explain that 5 is going to be the secret number for this game as well and that the grouping mat must be folded so that 4 sections are showing.

Follow the same procedures for adding and removing objects as you did when grouping by fives in Raindrops Make Puddles. You may wish the children to chant this verse.

Pennies drop, one, two, three, four
Oh what to do with one more!
Gather 'em up and trade 'em for free
5 pennies make a nickel you see.

Have the children read the mat after each addition or removal, e.g., 2 nickels and 3. Do not refer to the total sum of the coins as it will distract from the grouping and trading process. The total may be confusing while working in base five. The children can play Penny Exchange with partners.

On another day, after children have had several opportunities trading 5 pennies for a nickel adapt the game so that they are trading 10 pennies for a dime. Have the children use the same grouping mat used in Activity 3.

6. Fair Exchange

C

Set up a coin exchange office in the classroom. Place a collection of pennies, nickels, and dimes in this office. The coins should be in separate labelled containers. At the entrance to this work area, place a large collection of pennies, and copies of Line Master 87. Encourage students to take turns working in this office.

The children who enter the exchange office (the customers) must bring a collection of pennies. They should fill in their coin exchange sheet and take it to the child working (the teller).

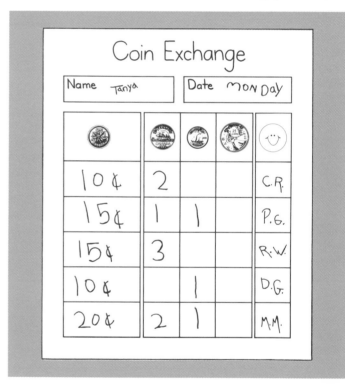

The customers present their collection of pennies and their coin exchange sheet to the teller. The teller counts the collection and checks the sheet. If the figures recorded are accurate, the exchange is made. To confirm that the exchange has been made, the teller records her or his initials in the last column of the exchange sheet. Encourage the children to continue to return with a new collection of pennies so that the process is repeated a number of times.

The children should take turns assuming the 2 roles. Before switching roles, the children must return the coins to their containers. You may wish to have a large collection of pennies at this center from which the children can take pennies for trading. Some children will be able to combine several coins to match their penny collection. Paper coins cut from Line Master 41 can be substituted for real money.

Later when children are comfortable counting collections of 25 cents, have them exchange a quarter for 25 pennies.

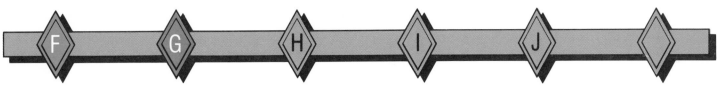

Section 2

Planning the Section

Objective	Level	Activity	Grouping	Program *or* Management Suggestions
D Recording a Ten and Ones	Concrete Concrete and Pictorial	1. Stocking the Shelf 2. What's in the Factory? 3. Catalogue Pages		Activities 1 and 2 should be played a number of times to ensure that every number from 10 to 19 has been formed in and out of sequence concretely and pictorially.
E Counting and Recording Groups of 10	Concrete	4. Trays 5. Fill the Order 6. Deliver the Order 7. Revising the Catalogue		Activities 4 to 7 should be played a number of times to ensure that every multiple of 10 to 90 has been formed in and out of sequence.
F Counting Sets to 50 or 100	Concrete	8. How Many? 9. Choose a Number		Activity 8 must be repeated a number of times to ensure that children experience building a variety of sets to 50. When children have successfully created and counted sets to 50, extend the activities to include sets to 100.
G Recording a 2-digit Number	Concrete and Symbolic Pictorial and Symbolic Concrete, Pictorial, and Symbolic	10. Taking Inventory 11. Filling Orders Again 12. Weekly Count 13. Shipping Yard 14. What Did I Make? 15. Ideas that Count		Activities 10 and 11 must be repeated frequently to ensure that the children have the opportunity to focus on each number. Activity 12 should be continued for the remainder of the year. You may choose a monitor each week to take responsibility for setting up the container. The record created in Activity 14 should be stored as it forms an integral part of Activity 2 in Section 3. Activity 15 suggests a number of activities to reinforce counting sets to 100. Some materials must be prepared ahead of time.

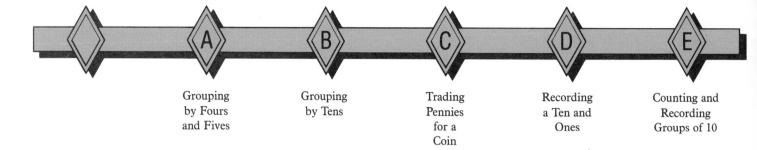

About this Section

Many of the activities in this section are based on a make-believe factory situation which provides the children with a reason for counting sets and recording the corresponding numerals. The materials made in The Ten Pack, page 255 form the basis of many of these activities. You may substitute these materials with interlocking cubes and/or any base 10 materials. However, using the ten packs as stock makes the factory situations more realistic. There should be an order and inventory booklet as described in The Ten Pack for each child. Have the children print their names on these booklets. These booklets will serve as recording sheets for the children's activities. Have extra order and inventory sheets available so that children can make another booklet when necessary.

Children begin by building sets to 19 (Activity 1) and then sets to 50 (Activity 8) on grouping mats made from Line Master 85.

In the last section children displayed sets on these mats and described them as **1 ten and 3**. In this section, the description is extended to include the number e.g., **1 ten and 3 or 13**. Building sets on these grouping mats enables the children to clearly see the sets. The numerals on the sides of the mat also provide a connection between the set displayed and the verbal description. These mats also allow you to check at a glance whether children have displayed the appropriate set. Place value mats (Line Master 88) are introduced after the children have

had opportunities to build and describe sets on the labelled, structured grouping mat.

It is suggested that initially you engage the children in creating, counting, and recording sets to 50. When children demonstrate a solid grasp of number to 50, repeat and extend the activities to include number to 100.

Observations and Evaluation

As you circulate among the children, ensure that they are placing objects appropriately in the tens and ones columns. Listen carefully to how they read their place value mats and model appropriate language whenever necessary.

These key questions can form the basis of assessment as you meet with individuals and small groups of children.

- **How many cubes do you have? Show them to me as tens and ones. Tell me again how many cubes you have.**
- **Show me (4) tens and (3). What is another name for (4) tens and (3)?**
- **Show me (28) cubes. Can you show them to me as tens and ones? How many tens and how many ones make (28)?**
- **Look at your place value mat. How many tens are there? How many ones? What is another name for (2) tens and (1)?**
- **Print a number to show how many bean sticks and beans there are on your mat. Read the number to me. What does the (3) mean in your number? And the (7)?**
- **Print the number that means (6) tens and (5). Read it to me. Could you show it to me with these materials?**

Observations	Teacher Direction
A child places 2 tens and 4 ones in response to your direction, **Show me 2 tens and 4 ones.** When you ask, **How many objects have you placed?**, the child counts the objects one by one.	The child has not yet discovered that 2 tens and 4 ones is related to 24. Continue to engage the child in activities at the concrete level modelling the language patterns, **2 tens and 4 or 24.**
A child counts tens as, **10, 20, 30, 40,** and concludes there are 40 tens rather than 4 tens. Or, a child counts 3 tens and 2 ones as, **1, 2, 3, 4, 5.**	Have the child participate frequently in building and counting sets with concrete materials (Activities 1, 2, 4, 5, 8, and 10 are appropriate) to develop the appropriate language patterns.
A child places 8 single objects on a place value mat to illustrate the numeral 35.	Engage the child frequently in activities where concrete sets are created to show a selected numeral (Activities 1, 4, 5, 6, 8, 9, and 10).
A child responds appropriately to the key questions suggested and has successfully completed activities at the pictorial level.	The child demonstrates a solid understanding of the place value concepts introduced in this section. Engage her or him in the activities of the next section. The Extension Project, page 279 and many of the ideas in Number Across the Curriculum may also be appropriate.

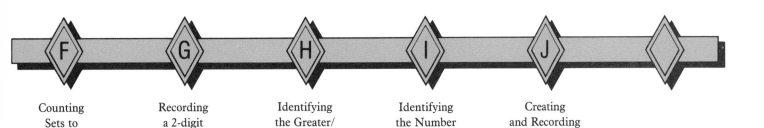

F	G	H	I	J	
Counting Sets to 50 or 100	Recording a 2-digit Number	Identifying the Greater/ Lesser Number	Identifying the Number Before/After/ Between	Creating and Recording Number Patterns	

Activity 8 is a useful assessment activity to determine if a child can build a set to illustrate a numeral you point to or say. This can be extended to assess whether a child can move from the concrete to the symbolic level by asking the child to record numerals on slips of paper or on a personal hundreds square as he or she builds concrete sets.

Suggested Materials

- Ten packs (made in Activity 4 of Section 1) [Activities 1, 2, 4, 5, and 6]
- An inventory booklet (made in Activity 4 of Section 1) for each child [Activities 1, 2, and 10]
- 9 single small items for each child [Activities 1 and 2]
- A deck of numeral cards from 1 to 19 for each work area [Activity 3]
- Cards from 1 ten and 0 to 1 ten and 9 for each work area [Activity 3]
- At least 9 trays or containers [Activity 4]
- Cards from 1 ten to 9 tens for each work area [Activity 7]
- An order booklet (made in Activity 4 of Section 1) for each child [Activities 5, 6, and 13]
- Bean sticks and beans or any other base 10 materials [Activities 8, 9, 10, 11, and 12]
- A large blank hundreds square for demonstration [Activities 8 and 9]
- A set of numeral cards ranging from 1 to 50 for each work area [Activities 10, 11, and 13]
- A container of small objects such as peanuts in a shell, marbles, small cubes, or bottle caps [Activity 12]
- An assortment of packages (labelled with a numeral) and small objects to fill them [Activity 15]
- Inventory sheets [Activity 15]
- Building toys [Activity 15]
- Interlocking cubes [Activity 15]
- Houses drawn on individual sheets [Activity 15]
- Several containers with slits cut in the lids (to act as piggy banks) [Activity 15]
- Collections of pennies, nickels, dimes, and quarters [Activity 15]

Line Masters

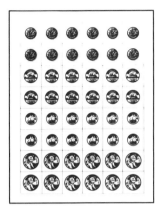

Line Master **41**
Activity 15
A large quantity

Line Master **86**
Activities 1, 5, 11, and 13
1 per child

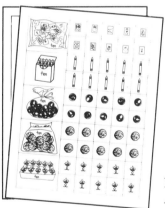

Line Masters **89** and **90**
Activities 3, 7, 13, and 14
1 per child

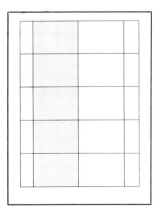

Line Master **85**
Activities 1 and 8
2 per child

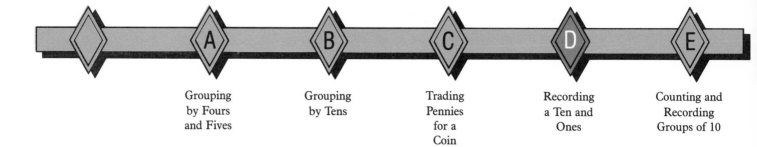

A	B	C	D	E
Grouping by Fours and Fives	Grouping by Tens	Trading Pennies for a Coin	Recording a Ten and Ones	Counting and Recording Groups of 10

Activities

1. Stocking the Shelf

D

Provide each child with a grouping mat (Line Master 85), a ten pack (see page 255) and 10 single items. Have the children place the ten pack on the grouping mat as shown.

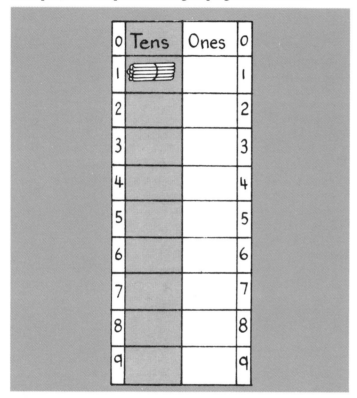

Ask, **How many tens on your mat?** Encourage them to respond, **1 ten is 10.** Say, **And one more. How many then?** The children place one more item on the ones side of the mat and say, **1 ten and 1 is 11.** Have the children continue to add objects one by one, and describe their grouping mats until a set of 19 is created. Have the children clear their mats removing one object at a time as you say, **One less.** Have the children describe their mats after they remove each object, e.g., **1 ten and 8 is 18. 1 ten and 7 is 17,** etc. When children are faced with removing an object from a mat with 1 ten pack, discussion will begin. If necessary, guide them in trading a ten pack for 10 single items and discuss how to remove 1 object and place the other 9 on the ones side of the mat.

Have the children build sets to 19 out of sequence. For example, say, **Show 1 ten and 4. How many are on your mat?** Continue as long as interest is sustained.

On a subsequent day, discuss the purpose of taking inventory in a factory. Tell the children that they are going to fill in a form to identify the number of materials they have. Identify the different sections on the posted inventory form. Have the children place their ten pack on the grouping mat. Ask, **Where do you put a ten on your mat? How many tens are there? Where would you print that 1 ten on your inventory sheet?** Print the 1 ten on your form to model the appropriate procedure.

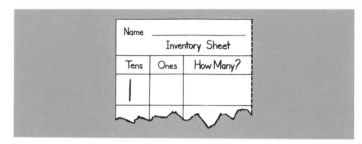

Ask, **How many ones are on your mat? Where do you print zero ones on your inventory sheet?** Print the model on the demonstration form.

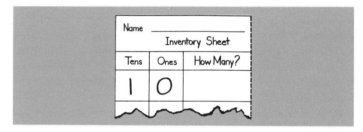

Ask the children to read their mat as, **1 ten and zero.** Ask, **How many items are in the store if you have 1 ten and zero? Where would you print the 10 on your inventory sheet?**

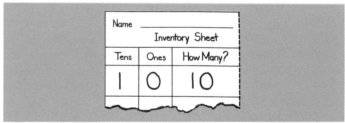

Have the children read the completed inventory statement for the first item. **One ten and zero is 10. 10 in the store.** Follow the same procedure adding one item at a time until all 19 items have been placed and recorded.

Variation

Once the children are familiar with the recording procedure, they can play Stocking the Shelf by themselves or with a partner. They will require 19 single items, a cup, a plastic container, their grouping mat, and their inventory booklet. The child begins by placing the 19 items in the container. One child gently shakes some out. The items are grouped as a ten and ones and placed on the grouping mat. The total is recorded on the inventory sheet.

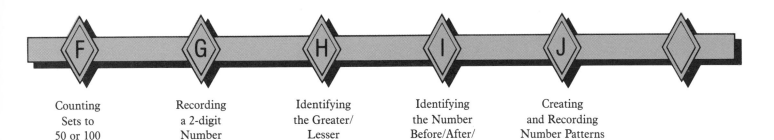

F	G	H	I	J	
Counting Sets to 50 or 100	Recording a 2-digit Number	Identifying the Greater/ Lesser Number	Identifying the Number Before/After/ Between	Creating and Recording Number Patterns	

2. What's in the Factory?

D

Provide each child with a place value mat (Line Master 88), an inventory booklet, a ten pack and 9 single items. Remind the children why people take inventory in a factory. Identify a flat surface (table top or floor space) as the factory and have the children group around it. Have the children place as many items as they wish on their shelf (the place value mat). Explain that now they must take inventory of what is in the factory. To do so, they record the number of objects on each shelf in their inventory booklet. Have the children move, in turn, to each shelf (place value mat), and record the number of items in their inventory booklet.

The number of children who can gather around the factory depends on the size of the flat surface. Since the children will have to actually move around the space, it would probably be best to have a small group of children approach the factory at any one time to complete the inventory.

3. Catalogue Pages

D

Provide each child with a copy of Line Masters 89 and 90. Explain that today they are going to create pages for a catalogue to show the different items found in the factory. At each work area, place blank sheets of paper, a deck of numeral cards from 1 to 19, and cards such as the ones illustrated.

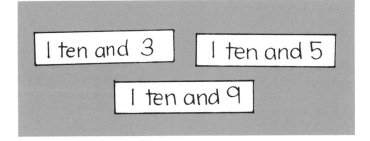

Combine the 2 types of cards and have the children select a card, cut the appropriate number of items from the line master, paste them on a sheet of paper, and label the sheet. After the children have completed a page, encourage them to select other cards to illustrate. These pages can be collected and assembled in a class catalogue or as individual books.

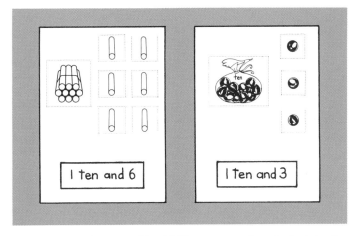

Keep these catalogues on file. Children can use them in Activity 5 to order items.

Variation

Have the children create their own pictures to match the selected cards. These pictures can be assembled to create individual booklets entitled My Own Catalogue or the child's name could be incorporated into the title, e.g., Kiki's Catalogue.

Meeting Individual Needs

Children who are ready for a further challenge may enjoy taking an inventory of classroom materials.

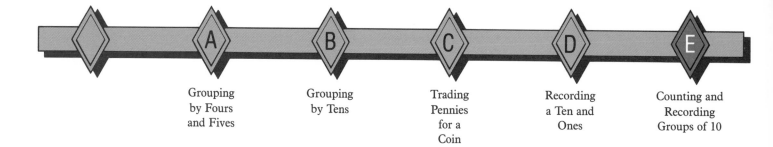

A	B	C	D	E
Grouping by Fours and Fives	Grouping by Tens	Trading Pennies for a Coin	Recording a Ten and Ones	Counting and Recording Groups of 10

4. Trays

Ahead of time, prepare trays (or containers) of ten packs. Place from 1 to 9 ten packs on each tray. Invite the children to sit in a circle around these materials, and tell them that they are going to take an inventory of ten packs. Select one set of materials at a time. Have a child take 1 ten pack at a time from a tray and place it on the floor. Encourage the others to count aloud, **1 ten, 2 tens, 3 tens,** etc. After the children have counted the number of tens, have them count the set another way **10, 20, 30,** etc. Ask, **How many tens?** On a label print the appropriate response, e.g., 8 tens. Ask, **How many?** Complete the label as 8 tens is 80. Continue this procedure for each prepared tray.

Enlist the children's help in making the labels. Alter the procedures by handing a set of tens to different students to count, or place the tray or bin in the center of the circle. Each child takes a ten and places it in the center while saying the total number, 8 tens equals 80.

On another day, place the empty labelled trays at a work area. Direct a small group of children to this area to fill the tray with the appropriate number of ten packs.

5. Fill the Order

Gather the children around a recording area. Provide each child with ten packs and an order booklet made during The Ten Pack, page 255.

Explain to the children that when someone wants to order something from a factory, they send in an order form. Then the shipping clerks go around and collect the items to prepare them for shipping. Tell the children that today they are going to be shipping clerks in the pretend factory. Explain that they will notice items have been placed in packages of 10 to facilitate easy shipping.

Print 10 on a demonstration order form (Line Master 86). Tell the children that this is their first order of the day. Direct their attention to the order form and ask, **Where do you print the order on your form? How many tens in this numeral? Where do you print the number of tens on the form? How many ones are in the number? Where do you print the number of ones on the form?** Have the children fill the first order by picking up a 10 and delivering it to someone else in the group. Have the receiver check the order by counting, **10.** Continue the procedure; increasing the orders by 10 until 90 has been reached. Have the children read down their list of orders. Discuss the pattern they have made. Repeat this activity several times presenting multiples of 10 in random order.

Children can also fill out order forms as they read through the class catalogue created in Activity 3.

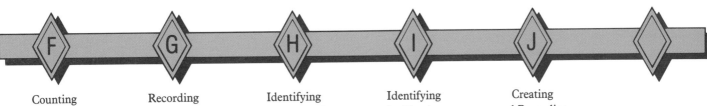

F	G	H	I	J	
Counting Sets to 50 or 100	Recording a 2-digit Number	Identifying the Greater/ Lesser Number	Identifying the Number Before/After/ Between	Creating and Recording Number Patterns	

6. Deliver the Order

E

This is a partner activity. Provide each pair of children with 9 ten packs and an order booklet. One child is the buyer while the other child is the shipping clerk. The buyer fills in an order on the order form and presents it to the shipping clerk. The shipping clerk fills the order by collecting the appropriate number of items and delivering them to the buyer. The order is checked by the buyer, the tens are returned to the larger collection, and roles are reversed.

7. Revising the Catalogue

E

Explain to the children that the catalogue must be revised to include other items now offered for sale in groups of 10. Provide each child with a copy of Line Master 89 or 90. At each work area, place blank sheets of paper, a deck of cards (the multiples of 10 to 90), as well as cards such as the ones shown. Have the children follow the same procedure as they did to create the initial catalogue pages (see page 261).

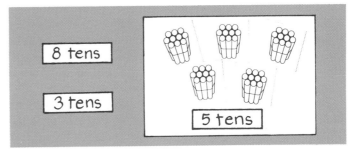

The children can read through the catalogue and decide which items they would like to order. They could fill out their orders in their order booklets.

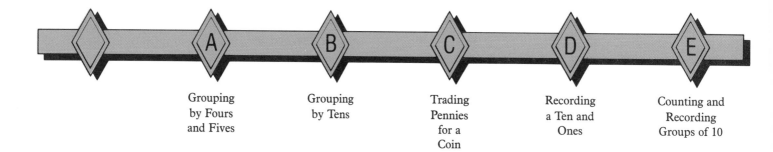

8. How Many? F

Invite a small group of children to gather around a work area. Provide each child with a grouping mat (Line Master 85), bean sticks, and beans. Post a large blank hundreds square. Review number to 19 and multiples of 10 by asking the children to show and name a variety of sets on the grouping mats. **Place a bean stick on your mat in the tens place. How many tens are there? What do we call 1 ten?** Record the numeral 10 on the hundreds square, **Add 3 beans in the ones place. How many tens are there? How many ones are there? What is another name for 1 ten and 3?** Record 13 on the hundreds square, **Take away the 3 beans. Put 3 more bean sticks in the tens place. How many tens are there? What is another name for 4 tens?** Record 40 on the hundreds square. **Take away 2 tens, . . .**

After a comprehensive review of number to 19 and multiples of 10 has taken place, create a situation so that each child has 1 bean stick and 9 beans on the grouping mat. Invite the children to place another bean on their mats. Ask, **What must we do now?** Give the children time to think of solutions to this question. If no one suggests trading 10 beans for a bean stick, guide them to do so. Ask, **How many tens are there? How many ones are**

there? **What is another name for 2 tens?** Record 20 on the hundreds square.

Continue to guide the children to add beans one at a time and regroup with bean sticks when necessary in the same manner until you reach 31 or until interest wanes. On another day, begin the activity by calling out numbers at random (up to 31 and include any multiple of 10) for the children to illustrate with their materials on the grouping mat. Once children are working with these numbers comfortably, start to introduce numbers by having the children build the number you left off at in the previous session. The children add one bean at a time, identify the number of tens and ones, and the number name. Remember to record each number on the demonstration hundreds square. Continue this procedure over a few sessions, to introduce the numbers to 50.

Do not rush to introduce numbers to the children. It is important to develop the concept at a level of comfort and understanding. You may wish to substitute bean sticks and beans with any of the materials created in The Ten Pack, page 255, interlocking cubes or any other base 10 materials. As children become familiar with the procedures of this activity, they might enjoy taking the role of leader.

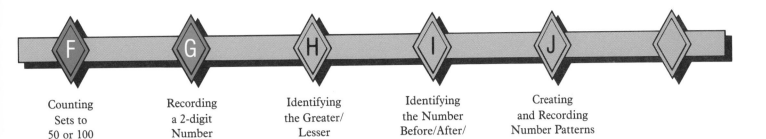

F	G	H	I	J	
Counting Sets to 50 or 100	Recording a 2-digit Number	Identifying the Greater/ Lesser Number	Identifying the Number Before/After/ Between	Creating and Recording Number Patterns	

9. Choose a Number ◆ F

Gather a small group of children around the demonstration hundreds chart created in Activity 8. Provide each child with a place value mat (Line Master 88), bean sticks and beans. Invite a volunteer to choose a number from the chart, e.g., 38. Have the child point to the number and say, **I choose this number. Show it to me please.** Each child, then places materials on the place value mat to illustrate the number requested. Invite the children to describe the materials. **I used 3 tens and 8 to make 38.** Continue to invite the volunteers to choose a number for their classmates to display and describe.

Give the children the opportunity to play this game using several different materials to provide variety and maintain a high level of interest. Any of these materials is appropriate: bundled coffee stirrers and single stirrers, bundled toothpicks and single toothpicks, 10 trains and interlocking cubes, any ten pack and single items.

Variation

Have the children play in pairs. One child chooses a number for her or his partner to create on a place value mat. The number can be selected as described or children can turn over numeral cards in turn. Encourage children to describe the sets they create. **You asked me to make 42. Here it is; 4 tens and 2, 42.**

Meeting Individual Needs

A child who has difficulty with the amount of materials on her or his place value mat should continue to use the grouping mat (Line Master 85) to display sets.

10. Taking Inventory ◆ G

Provide each child with bean sticks, 10 beans, an inventory booklet, and a place value mat (Line Master 88). Remind the children about taking inventory in the factory. Tell them that the owners of the factory need to know how much stock they have, so that they will know how many trucks to send out to the stores. Select a numeral card (23) so that the children cannot see it and, say, **The first shelf has 2 tens and 3. Show it on your place value mat. Now we need to record it on our inventory sheet.** Guide the children to identify again the number of tens and ones on their place value mat and to print the numerals on the appropriate spaces on their inventory sheets. Ask, **What is another name for 2 tens and 3? How do we print 23?** Guide the children to print 23 in the total column. Display the numeral card you initially turned up so that the children can check the numeral they printed against it. Turn over another numeral card and repeat the process. **The second shelf has 4 tens and 2. Show it on your place value mat.** Continue until the children have completed their inventory sheet. Have the children join you in interpreting the inventory sheet aloud. **The first shelf has 2 tens and 3 or 23. The second shelf has 4 tens and 2 or 42.**

Tens	Ones

Name		
		Inventory Sheet
Tens	Ones	How Many?
2	3	23
4	2	42

When the children appear comfortable with this activity, divide them into pairs and direct them to a work area where they can continue to record inventory on a new sheet.

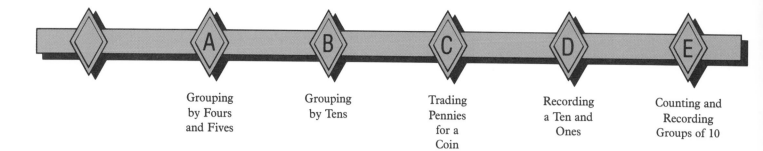

11. Filling Orders Again

For this activity, you will need a set of randomly ordered numeral cards from 1 to 50, an order form (Line Master 86), bean sticks and beans. Gather the children together and remind them of how they filled orders during previous activities. Turn over a card from the pile of numeral cards. Have the children read the order, e.g., **47**. Say, **47 is your first order.** Have the children record 47 as the first order on their forms. Model this procedure on a demonstration form. Ask, **How many tens in 47? Where do we print the 4? How many ones are there? Where do we print the 7? Who can show us how many bean sticks and beans we need to fill the order? Look at the numeral card. Is that how many we were supposed to have in the order?** Turn over another numeral card for the next order and repeat the process just described. Continue filling orders in a group until children are thoroughly familiar with the procedures. Provide each child with an order booklet. Guide small groups of children to work areas where a set of numeral cards from 1 to 50, bean sticks, and beans have been placed. Have the children take turns selecting a numeral card to determine the order everyone should record and fill.

12. Weekly Count

Fill a clear container with a large quantity of a material such as peanuts in the shell, marbles, small cubes, or bottle caps. At the beginning of the week, place this container and paper slips for recording in a spot within easy reach of the children. Explain that during the week they should examine the container, guess how many (bottle caps) are in it, and record their name and estimate on a slip of paper. Establish where these slips should be placed. (A library pocket on a file folder is convenient.) At the end of the week, gather the children around the container and cards indicating the decades as shown. Read the name and number on each strip and ask the child to place it under the appropriate decade card. After all strips have been sorted, empty the contents of the jar. Invite the children to count aloud as you move each item to one side. Group tens in a cup, lid, or baggie. Have a volunteer record the number of items on a slip of paper and place it under the appropriate heading.

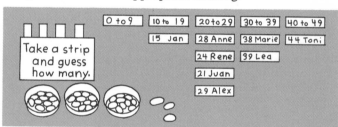

Each week place a container of materials for children to examine and estimate the quantity. (Change the size and shape of the container every few weeks.) It is the children's responsibility to record an estimate at one point during the week. If you build the counting day into your week, the children will be ready with their estimates. Before you call the children together to count the materials, you may wish to ask volunteers to sort the paper slips into the appropriate columns. You might also consider assigning the task of counting the objects to children. They could have all the items grouped in cups of 10 before you gather the children together. You can then proceed by asking, How many tens? How many ones? How many in all? These questions can form the basis of your discussion in ensuing weeks after the objectives of the next section have been presented.

- *Was your estimate greater or less than the actual number?*
- *How many people estimated there were between 30 and 40 items in the jar? Did more people estimate that there were between 40 and 50 items?*
- *Were there more than 23 items in the jar? Less than 40?*

Variation

Have the children count the items aloud by twos, fives, or tens. When counting by twos, move 2 items aside at the same time. To count by fives or tens, have the children first make groups of 5 or 10, then count aloud with the children. Say, **There are 37 peanuts. How many tens? How many ones?**

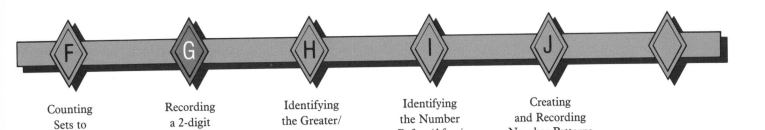

13. Shipping Yard

For this activity, each child will need an order booklet, a copy of Line Master 89 or 90, and access to numeral cards from 0 to 50. Gather the children around you and remind them that when someone wants to order things from a factory, they send in an order form. When the orders are filled, they are loaded on trucks, trains, ships, or planes and sent out to the people who ordered them. Tell the children that today they are going to load the orders for shipping. Show them a copy of the order form and turn up a card from a set of numeral cards. Say, **This is our first order.** Demonstrate how to fill out the order on a posted order form (Line Master 86). Ask, **How many tens are there? How many ones? Where do we print that on the order form?** Ask, **How many tens do we need to cut out for the first order? How many ones? How is the order being shipped?** Draw an outline of the mode of transportation identified and label the load with the appropriate numeral. Direct the children to work areas where they have access to numeral cards and paper. Have them select a numeral card to indicate the order, record it on an order form, cut out the appropriate number of objects, glue them on a sheet of paper, outline the mode of transportation, and label their sheet.

Note that the children may enjoy loading their orders on different modes of transportation.

14. What Did I Make?

Provide each child with a copy of Line Master 89 or 90. Direct small groups of children to work areas where scissors, glue, and pencils have been placed. Invite the children to print a numeral from 20 to 50 on their sheet of paper and then turn the paper over. On the reverse side, have them illustrate this numeral by cutting and pasting objects from the line master. Gather the children together when they have completed this activity, and invite volunteers to display the illustration of their number. Have them ask, **What did I make?** Encourage the children to explain their answers. For example, **You made 36. There are 3 tens and 6 ones.**

These sheets will form the basis of Activity 2 in Section 3, page 272. Store them for later use.

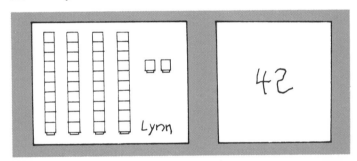

15. Ideas that Count

G

These suggestions further reinforce the skill of counting sets to 100 and the concept of place value. You may wish to set up any or all of these activities at centers. Direct children to pursue them independently or in small groups.

Children fill the packages with the appropriate number of objects. The package is then passed to another child who checks the contents by emptying the container and forming groups of tens and ones. The child then records the number on an inspection slip. The inspection number and label on the package should match.

Children select an inventory sheet and proceed to complete it. You might suggest that they keep a tally of the objects they are counting. Set up a signing out system to keep track of those children leaving the room.

Children create pattern trains with interlocking cubes and then record how many cubes of each color they used.

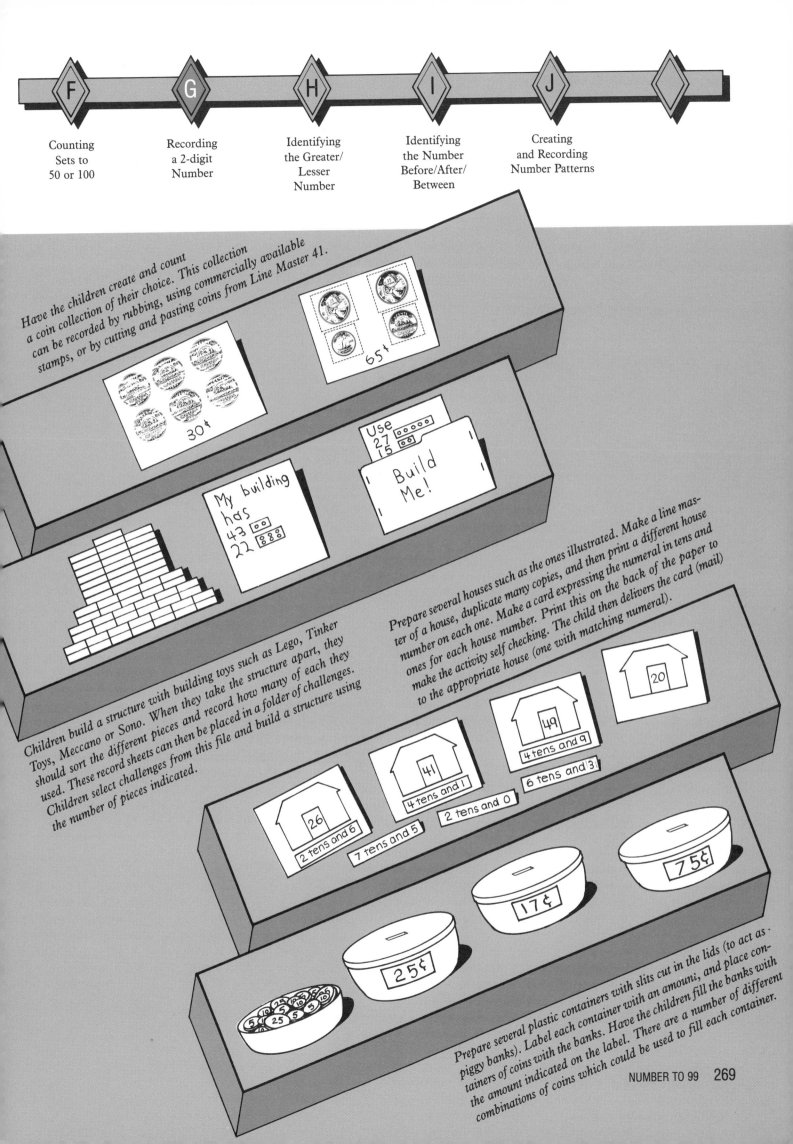

Have the children create and count a coin collection of their choice. This collection can be recorded by rubbing, using commercially available stamps, or by cutting and pasting coins from Line Master 41.

65¢

30¢

Use
27
15

Build
Me!

My building
has
43
22

Children build a structure with building toys such as Lego, Tinker Toys, Meccano or Sono. When they take the structure apart, they should sort the different pieces and record how many of each they used. These record sheets can then be placed in a folder of challenges. Children select challenges from this file and build a structure using the number of pieces indicated.

Prepare several houses such as the ones illustrated. Make a line master of a house, duplicate many copies, and then print a different house number on each one. Make a card expressing the numeral in tens and ones for each house number. Print this on the back of the paper to make the activity self checking. The child then delivers the card (mail) to the appropriate house (one with matching numeral).

20

49
4 tens and 9

41
4 tens and 1

6 tens and 3

26
2 tens and 6

2 tens and 0

7 tens and 5

75¢

17¢

25¢

Prepare several plastic containers with slits cut in the lids (to act as piggy banks). Label each container with an amount, and place containers of coins with the banks. Have the children fill the banks with the amount indicated on the label. There are a number of different combinations of coins which could be used to fill each container.

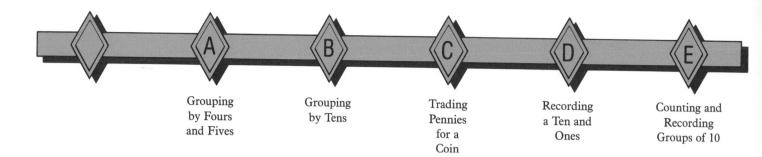

A — Grouping by Fours and Fives

B — Grouping by Tens

C — Trading Pennies for a Coin

D — Recording a Ten and Ones

E — Counting and Recording Groups of 10

Section 3

Planning the Section

Objective	Level	Activity	Grouping	Program *or* Management Suggestions
H Identifying the Greater/ Lesser Number	Concrete Pictorial Symbolic	1. Yours and Mine 2. Compare Us 3. Number Sort 4. Call Out	👥👥👥👥👥👥👥 👥👥👥👥👥👥👥 👥👥👥👥 👥👥👥👥	Activities 1 and 2 are teacher directed whereas the children can pursue Activities 3 and 4 with a partner. Activity 2 requires a recording made previously in Activity 14, Section 2.
I Identifying the Number Before/After/ Between	Concrete Symbolic	5. Before, After, Between 6. Open the Book 7. Undercover Number 8. Hundreds Board Jigsaw 9. Puzzle Pieces	👥👥👥👥 👥👥👥👥👥👥👥 👥👥👥👥👥👥👥 👥👥👥👥👥👥👥 👥👥👥👥	Activities 5 and 6 are teacher directed and focus on the language before, after, and between. Activities 8 and 9 are outgrowths of Activity 7. You might consider storing the puzzles children use in Activity 9 in an accessible spot so that they can continue to use them independently.
J Creating and Recording Number Patterns	Concrete and Pictorial Symbolic	10. Growing Patterns 11. Hundreds of Patterns	👤 👥👥👥👥👥👥👥	Post the patterns created in Activity 10. Many children will be motivated to create other chart patterns. Materials should be available for interested children to pursue charted patterns. Activity 11 should be repeated frequently.

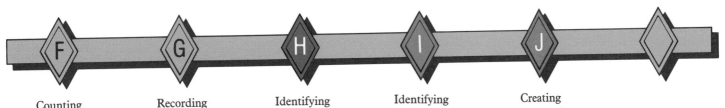

About this Section

Children should have a solid grasp of the place value concepts presented in the previous section before participating in any of the activities of this section. Those concepts are applied in each of the activities of this section.

The first 2 objectives of this section have been introduced in Unit 3, Numbers to 10. In this section, children apply those concepts to numbers greater than 10. Children have also explored the concept of pattern extensively prior to this section. In this section they apply and extend their patterning skills to include number patterns.

Observations and Evaluation

Many of the activities may be used for group evaluation. Yours and Mine, page 272 will allow you to assess a child's grasp of the concept of greater/lesser at the concrete stage, while Number Sort, page 273 may be used at the symbolic level. Before, After, Between, page 274 may be used to assess number before, after, and in-between at the concrete level; Undercover Number, page 274 may be used for the symbolic level.

These key questions could form the basis of further evaluation.

- **Did you make a number greater/less than mine?**
- **How do you know it is greater? Less?**
- **Show me a number greater/less than mine. What did you make?**
- **Point out a number greater/less than (42). How do you know it's greater/less?**
- **What did you do to make the number after? The number before?**
- **Is this the number after (26)? How do you know?**
- **Is this the number before (38)? How do you know?**
- **What is the number between (27) and (29)?**

Suggested Materials

- A large collection of bean sticks and beans, ten packs, and interlocking cubes or any other base 10 materials [Activities 1 and 5]
- A set of numeral cards ranging from 0 to 100 [Activities 1, 3, 4, and 5]
- 2 sorting mats such as large sheets of paper or cardboard for each pair of children [Activity 3]
- A large hundreds chart or hundreds board for demonstration [Activities 7 and 11]
- 2 large blank hundreds squares [Activity 8]
- Pieces of cardboard cut into different arrangements to cover numerals on a hundreds chart [Activity 8]
- A large quantity of translucent chips or squares cut from colored acetate [Activity 11]

Line Masters

Line Master **14**
Activity 10
A large quantity

Any of Line Masters **30** to **35**
Activity 10
A large quantity

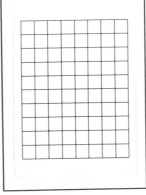

Line Master **26**
Activity 10
A large quantity

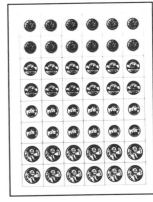

Line Master **41**
Activity 10
A large quantity

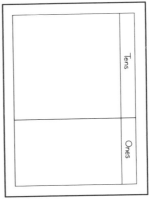

Line Master **88**
Activities 1 and 5
1 per child

Line Master **91**
Activities 9, 10, and 11
1 per child

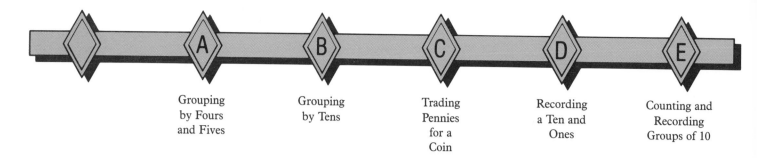

A	B	C	D	E
Grouping by Fours and Fives	Grouping by Tens	Trading Pennies for a Coin	Recording a Ten and Ones	Counting and Recording Groups of 10

Activities

1. Yours and Mine

H

Gather the children together around a work area and provide each child with a place value mat (Line Master 88). Put a collection of ten trains and interlocking cubes within easy reach of each child. Place a set of numeral cards ranging from 0 to 100 in a container. Pass this container around to the children and invite them to select a card. Ask them to show the number they selected with ten trains and interlocking cubes on their place value mats. While they are making their numbers, select a card and show it on a demonstration place value mat. When all the children have created a display of the number they selected, ask, **Is your number greater or less than mine?** Encourage each child to compare and describe her or his set with yours using the vocabulary greater and less. **I made 53. You made 47. My number is greater than yours. Your number is less than mine.** Ask, **How can you tell that 53 is greater than 47?** A child may respond, **I know, because 5 tens is more than 4 tens.** Ensure that all the children have the opportunity to compare their number with yours. Repeat this activity as long as interest is sustained.

You may wish to keep a record of the statements the children contribute. On a chalk board or chart paper, record your number and draw large circles on either side of it. Label the left circle less and the right circle greater. Record each numeral in the appropriate set.

Meeting Individual Needs

If a child is having difficulty identifying the greater or lesser number, have her or him take the trains of cubes apart and match the cubes one for one.

2. Compare Us

H

For this activity, each child will need the recording they made in What Did I Make?, page 267. On the chalk board print the headings greater and less. Invite 2 children to stand in front of the group holding their pictorial display of the number they made previously. Ask, **What is Sophie's number? What is Ronnie's number?** Ask, **Which number is greater? Which is less?** When the children have agreed to an answer to these questions, ask the children to record their number under the appropriate heading. Have the children read the recording on the board, e.g., **41 is less than 63.** Continue this process until each child has had the opportunity to participate at least once. Intermittently, draw the children's attention to the number of tens and ones as the sets are compared to emphasize further how one identifies the greater/lesser number.

You may wish to make a chart as shown which will ensure that each pair of numbers is lined up for easy reading. Vary the position of the columns so that the greater column is sometimes to the right of the less column to give children the opportunity to read a statement such as, 23 is greater than 19.

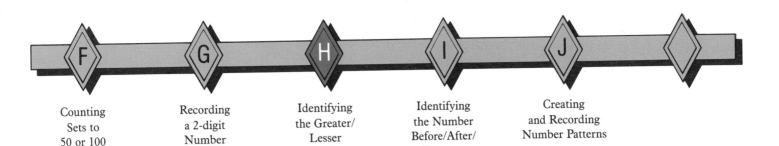

F — Counting Sets to 50 or 100

G — Recording a 2-digit Number

H — Identifying the Greater/ Lesser Number

I — Identifying the Number Before/After/ Between

J — Creating and Recording Number Patterns

3. Number Sort   PS   H

Provide each pair of children with a set of numeral cards ranging from 0 to 100 and 2 sorting mats. Have the children label one mat greater and the other mat less. Explain that today they are going to sort numbers. Have the children place the 2 sorting mats on either side of their pile of shuffled cards. Tell them to select a card from their deck and place it face up in-between the 2 sorting mats. They can then begin to turn over a card one at a time. Each card is to be compared to the one selected initially and then placed on the appropriate sorting mat. Encourage the children to explain to each other the reason for the placement of each card. **47 goes on the greater mat because 47 is greater than 29.**

You may wish to have the children record the result of their sorting. Have them draw 2 large circles on a piece of paper, print the reference number in-between them, and then record where each card was placed. You could also have them record their sorting on Line Master 45. Note that each time a new reference card is selected this activity changes.

4. Call Out   H

This is a partner game. Each pair of children will need a stack of 10 to 20 numeral cards ranging from 0 to 100 and cards labelled greater and less. Have the children place the shuffled cards face down and decide whether they are going to identify the greater (or lesser) numeral. To play, both children turn up a card simultaneously and glance at their card and their partner's card. The child who has the numeral card identified (that is the greater numeral if they decided to identify the greater of the 2) calls out, **Mine is greater. 50 is greater than 41.** Play continues. When the children have exhausted their stack, the cards may be reshuffled and play resumed.

Have the children place each pair of cards under cards labelled greater and less as they are turned over. This enables you to observe at a glance the decisions made during the game as you circulate among the children. Encourage the children to describe their findings. **54 is greater than 43. 43 is less than 54.**

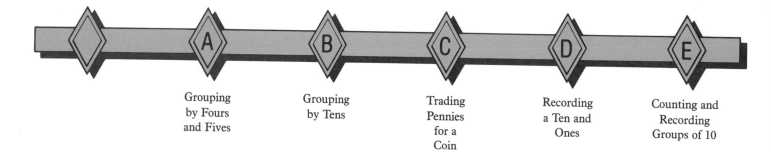

A	B	C	D	E
Grouping by Fours and Fives	Grouping by Tens	Trading Pennies for a Coin	Recording a Ten and Ones	Counting and Recording Groups of 10

5. Before, After, Between

Invite the children to sit around a work area where they are within easy reach of ten trains and interlocking cubes. Provide each child with a place value mat (Line Master 88). Select a numeral card, hold it up (42), and, say, **Make this number.** Wait until each child has made the number with the concrete materials. Ask, **How many tens did you use? How many ones did you use? What number comes before 42? Show it to me. What did you do to make 41?** Children respond, **We took one cube away.**

Continue to turn over numeral cards, ask the children to show the number, and then show the number that comes before or after it. To extend the activity to include discussion of the number in-between, have the children show you 2 numbers, e.g., 23 and 25. Ask them to make the number in-between. Discuss how the numbers are the same and how they are different.

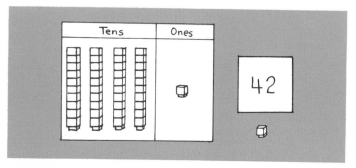

6. Open the Book

Have the children come to a circle with a book of their choice. (Make sure the book has numbered pages.) In turn, have each child open her or his book and say, **I opened my book at page 33. Which page comes before it? Which pages comes after it?**

*You may also wish to compare the number of pages in each book. Have 2 children tell how many pages are in their respective books and then ask, **Which book has more (less) pages?***

7. Undercover Number

Display a large hundreds chart (or hundreds board) so that everyone can easily read the numerals on it. (An overhead projector works well.) Give the children a few moments to study the chart. Ask them to close their eyes as you cover a numeral with a piece of paper, counter, or any small opaque object. (If you are working on a hundreds board, turn the tag over). Invite the children to look at the board again and ask, **Which number is the undercover number?** Encourage the children to explain how they know which is the undercover numeral using the vocabulary before, after, and between. **53 is the undercover. I know because 53 comes after 52 (before 54; between 52 and 54).** Repeat this activity as long as interest is sustained.

Meeting Individual Needs

Those children having difficulty determining the hidden numeral may benefit from focussing on fewer numerals. Display only a portion of the hundreds chart. Increase the number of squares displayed as the children feel comfortable.

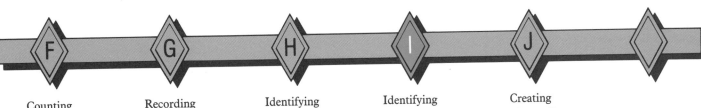

F	G	H	I	J
Counting Sets to 50 or 100	Recording a 2-digit Number	Identifying the Greater/ Lesser Number	Identifying the Number Before/After/ Between	Creating and Recording Number Patterns

8. Hundreds Board Jigsaw

Ahead of time, prepare 2 large blank hundreds squares. Post one square and fill in some numbers at random on the other square. Cut the numbered square into strips of varying lengths so that each strip has at least one of the recorded numerals. Distribute a piece of the cut up hundreds square to each child. Invite the children to fill in the blank squares on their strips. Circulate among the children to provide help when necessary. If children are having difficulty, draw their attention to the numbers on their strip. **What comes before (36)? After (36)? Start at the number given and count on. Print the numbers you say. Count back from the given number and record what you say.**

When everyone has completed their strip, gather the children together around the posted blank hundreds square. Explain that as a group you are going to put the cut up hundreds square back together again. Ask, **What numbers do you think begin the first piece? Who has the first piece?** Post the first piece and encourage the children to read it aloud, e.g., **1, 2, 3, 4, 5, 6.** Ask, **What number starts the next piece? How do you know? Who has the second piece?** Continue in this fashion until the hundreds square is complete.

9. Puzzle Pieces

Ahead of time, prepare several pieces of cardboard in a variety of shapes. These pieces should fit on the display hundreds chart so that the numerals are covered as shown. Gather the children around a posted hundreds chart (or hundreds board). (An overhead projector is a very useful way of displaying this chart.) Select one of the smaller cardboard pieces and place it anywhere on the hundreds chart. Ask, **What numbers are hidden? How do you know?** Encourage the children to describe the hidden numbers as coming before, after, or between the ones that are visible. Continue this activity with other cardboard pieces.

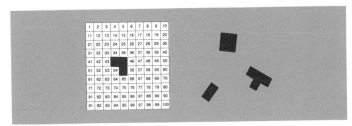

Provide each child with a copy of Line Master 91 after they have had opportunities to describe hidden numerals as a group. Have them cut out the puzzle pieces. The children can now continue to play Puzzle Pieces in pairs. Some may enjoy adding their own puzzle pieces to the activity.

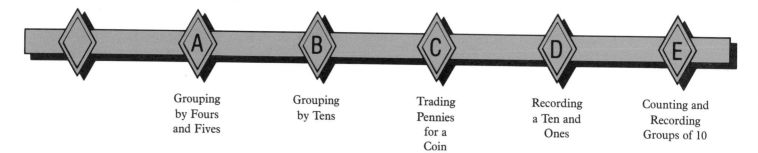

A	B	C	D	E
Grouping by Fours and Fives	Grouping by Tens	Trading Pennies for a Coin	Recording a Ten and Ones	Counting and Recording Groups of 10

10. Growing Patterns   PS J

Gather the children around a bin of interlocking cubes. Build a tower of 2 cubes and say, **Here is a 2-story tower.** Build a tower of 4 cubes and place it beside the first tower. Point to each tower as you say, **A 2-story tower and a 4-story tower.** Build a tower of 6 cubes and place it beside the other towers. Encourage the children to describe the towers aloud with you.

A 2-story tower, a 4-story tower, and a 6-story tower. Ask, **What kind of tower would come next in this pattern?** Invite a child to build the tower and place it in position. Have the children read the pattern aloud. Continue to build the pattern by adding and describing towers until at least 8 towers are in place. Repeat the process with towers of different heights.

Direct children to work areas where they can build their own patterns of towers. These patterns are easily recorded by cutting and pasting strips cut from Line Master 26. Have the children record patterns by printing corresponding numerals under each tower. Provide the appropriate section from the hundreds chart (Line Master 91) for them to paste at the bottom of their recordings. Ask them to circle those numerals which describe their pattern.

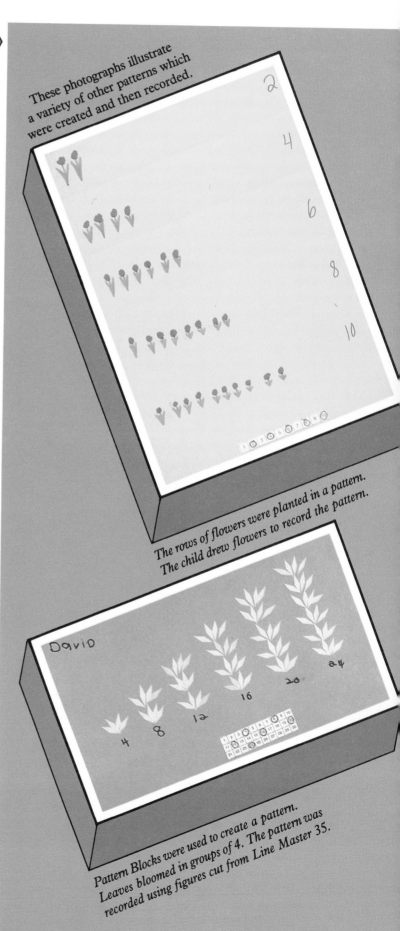

These photographs illustrate a variety of other patterns which were created and then recorded.

The rows of flowers were planted in a pattern. The child drew flowers to record the pattern.

Pattern Blocks were used to create a pattern. Leaves bloomed in groups of 4. The pattern was recorded using figures cut from Line Master 35.

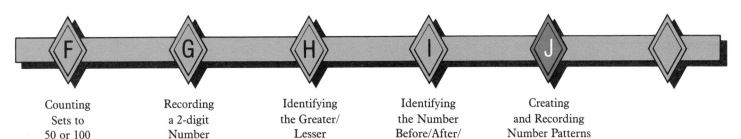

F	G	H	I	J
Counting Sets to 50 or 100	Recording a 2-digit Number	Identifying the Greater/ Lesser Number	Identifying the Number Before/After/ Between	Creating and Recording Number Patterns

Nickels were used to create a pattern. The child earned a nickel a day. The pattern was recorded using coins cut from Line Master 41.

The imps (cut from Line Master 14) lined themselves up in a pattern.

11. Hundreds of Patterns PS J

Gather children around a hundreds chart or display one on an overhead projector. Start to place translucent bingo chips or squares cut from colored acetate on the even numbers. After you have covered all even numbers to about 14, ask, **What number do you think I'm going to cover next? Why? And next? And after that?**

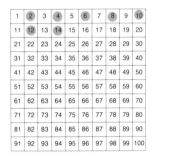

1	2	3	4	5	6	7	8	9	10
11	12	13	14	15	16	17	18	19	20
21	22	23	24	25	26	27	28	29	30
31	32	33	34	35	36	37	38	39	40
41	42	43	44	45	46	47	48	49	50
51	52	53	54	55	56	57	58	59	60
61	62	63	64	65	66	67	68	69	70
71	72	73	74	75	76	77	78	79	80
81	82	83	84	85	86	87	88	89	90
91	92	93	94	95	96	97	98	99	100

Continue the pattern to at least 30 and then have the children chant the pattern. Clear the board and repeat the process with a new pattern.

1	2	3	4	5	6	7	8	9	10
11	12	13	14	15	16	17	18	19	20
21	22	23	24	25	26	27	28	29	30
31	32	33	34	35	36	37	38	39	40
41	42	43	44	45	46	47	48	49	50
51	52	53	54	55	56	57	58	59	60
61	62	63	64	65	66	67	68	69	70
71	72	73	74	75	76	77	78	79	80
81	82	83	84	85	86	87	88	89	90
91	92	93	94	95	96	97	98	99	100

When children are familiar with the process, distribute hundreds charts (Line Master 91) and translucent markers. Invite them to create their own patterns. Encourage the children to frequently ask each other, **What number do you think I'm going to cover next?**

Children can record these patterns by coloring in squares as they remove each marker. They could also print the shaded numbers at the bottom of the paper. Have the children read their patterns aloud.

Number Across the Curriculum

Language Arts

- Lead a discussion on what the world would be like if there were no numbers. Encourage the children to describe the problems, humorous situations, potential differences in events, or actual objects. Have the children illustrate any of their anecdotes or begin a collective story about characters living in a world with no numbers.
- Invite the children to write and/or illustrate improbable world records. Begin by reading some actual world records (involving number) from an almanac or record book to provide motivation.

- Prepare a concentration game of numerals and number names on cardboard.

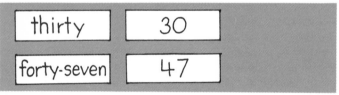

- Have the children identify their favorite number. Ask them to make up a story using this number several times.
- In conjunction with this unit, you may wish to read this book (see page 318 for an annotated bibliography): *The Most Amazing Hide and Seek Counting Book* by Robert Crowther.

Social Studies

- Display an abacus and demonstrate how it can be used as a counting machine. Explain that it was used long before calculators were invented. Encourage children to experiment with an abacus. You might consider having children make their own abacus out of straws and Plasticine.

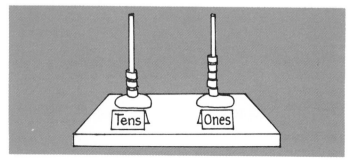

- Have the children go on a number search. Provide a variety of magazines, catalogues, newspapers, brochures, old telephone books, and old storybooks for the children to cut up. These numbers can be posted on a bulletin board, pasted in a scrapbook, or form a collage.

- Have the children observe where numbers are used in their environment. Speed limit signs, house numbers, room numbers, capacity and mass recorded on packages, clocks, bus route, and licence plates are only a few of the places where children may observe numbers. You might take the children on a neighborhood walk to collect this information or invite them to add to a list entitled Numbers Around Us.

Science

- In class ask the children to estimate quantities of different objects found outside such as trees or flowers in the schoolyard, posts in the fence, houses on the block, cars in the parking lot, or concrete slabs in the sidewalk. Take the children outside to count the different items. Record the discoveries and post them on a chart entitled Outdoor Inventory.

Extension Project

- Bring into class, a pumpkin, watermelon, or a quantity of pea pods. Invite the children to estimate how many seeds (or peas) there are in the item displayed. Scoop the seeds out of the pumpkin, have a watermelon for a snack, or shell the peas. Have the children group the seeds (or peas) in groups of 10 to facilitate counting. Count the seeds (or peas) and record your findings.

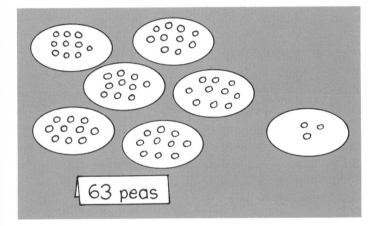

Physical Education

- Place a hula hoop or mark off an area with masking tape on the gym floor to act as a target. Distribute up to 9 (blue) bean bags and 9 (red) bean bags to the children. Have the children try to toss the bean bags into the target. After all bean bags have been tossed, announce the value of each color bag. For example, blue bags in the target are worth 10 points, whereas, red bags are worth only 1 point. Have the children count the points scored and record the total. Continue the activity, ensuring that all children participate. Compare the group's score of each throw with the previous total. Change the value of the bags often so that the color of the bag does not become an issue for the children when you distribute them.

- Place a variety of catalogues, newspapers, magazines, and brochures at a center. Have the children create a flyer of items that cost less than 99¢. They should cut and paste the object and the price on the flyer. Encourage them to find as many items as they can for these flyers.

  Provide wallets (envelopes) with different coin collections (real or coins cut from Line Master 41) up to 99¢. The children should select a wallet and a flyer (their own or a classmate's), count the coins, record the amount on a sheet of paper and all the items they could buy for that amount. A child may choose to list the choices he or she has or total the cost of several items.

Measurement

Unit Objectives

Section 1

A Telling Time to the Hour
B Recording Time to the Hour

Section 2

C Estimating and Comparing Length in Non-standard Units

Section 3

D Creating and Interpreting a Bar Graph

About this Unit

Time

Children have been involved in several activities in which they sequenced events and measured time in non-standard units. They have heard you make frequent references to the passage of time as well as to the actual time. For example: **It took us a very long time to clean up after activities today. In a few minutes we must start to get ready for gym. It's 11 o'clock; time to line up for assembly.** Children develop a sense and appreciation of time through these frequent incidental and functional exposures to time. In this unit events are linked to time, e.g., **It's 3 o'clock; time to start clean up.** Children learn to tell time and develop a sense of when events occur if events and times are connected repeatedly. For example, **When it's 11 o'clock, the real clock will look like this.** (Set a demonstration clock.) **It will be time for our trip.**

Length

Children have participated in many activities where they estimated, compared, and ordered objects by length on a base line. The activities of this unit provide opportunities for children to use non-standard units to measure objects. This method of measuring allows them to consider: how long/short an object is, how much longer/shorter one object is compared to another, and compare and measure objects which physically cannot be placed side by side. Children estimate and measure objects using a variety of non-standard units. The activities lead the children to discover that the length of the room is 12 of their footsteps long while their friend measures it as 16 footsteps long. These measurement experiences form the foundation for the concept of standard units introduced next year.

Graphing

To date, children have had several opportunities to create and interpret concrete graphs and pictographs. The last section of this unit presents children with opportunities to create and interpret bar graphs. Each colored square on a bar graph represents a concrete object, or an individual's response to a question. These graphs require few materials and therefore can be created quickly with little prior preparation. Children initially participate in creating concrete graphs with interlocking cubes. These graphs are then transferred to paper as paper square graphs and then finally as colored bars. The same type of questions asked of concrete graphs and pictographs initiate discussion to interpret the bar graphs created.

Problem Solving

Children practice their skill of obtaining information from a chart as they participate in the activity What Are We Doing?, page 289. In Unit 4 and in many Five Minute Math Activities children have sequenced events. The activity My Guide, page 290 provides an opportunity for children to link the time to events they sequence as they create a booklet. In addition, activities provided in Five Minute Math, page 283 develop these problem-solving skills:

- sorting
- solving story problems
- identifying likenesses and differences
- developing observation and listening skills

Vocabulary

- Hour
- Length
- Measure
- Minute
- Unit

Planning Ahead

The next unit focusses on addition and subtraction facts for 11 and 12 and is appropriate for those children who have a solid grasp of the addition and subtraction facts to 10. Assess or reassess any children about whom you need more information as you engage in the measurement activities of this unit.

Ongoing Objectives

- Ordering days of the week and months of the year
- Counting
- Identifying the number before/after/between and the greater/lesser number
- Counting coin collections
- Problem solving
  - Sorting
  - Solving story problems
  - Identifying likenesses and differences
  - Developing observation and listening skills

Five Minute Math

Calendar Activities

- To help children see the cycle of the days of the week as a pattern, prepare at least 3 sets of cards for the days of the week. Have the children post the cards as illustrated. Read the cards aloud with them. Ask, **How many weeks are posted? How did you figure that out?**

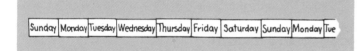

- Post the months of the year and seasons as shown. This display illustrates how the months of the year are tied to seasons. To initiate discussion, ask, **Is April a spring month? In what season does January come? What are the summer months?**

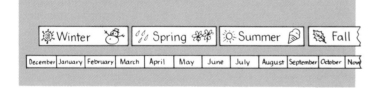

- Have the children identify cycles. They then chant at least 2 repetitions of each cycle. For example:
  - **Winter, spring, summer, fall, winter, spring, summer, fall,...**
  - **Morning, afternoon, evening, night, morning, afternoon, evening, night,...**
  - **January, February, March, April, May, June, July, August, September, October, November, December, January,...**
  - **Sunday, Monday, Tuesday, Wednesday, Thursday, Friday, Saturday, Sunday,...**

Counting Activities

- Invite a volunteer to display a set of bean sticks and beans or any other ten pack materials, page 255. Have the children identify the set, e.g., 53 and then count on to 100 or any other number you choose.
- Go on counting walks with the children. Before you set out, ask the children to estimate the number of steps they think they will take.
  - **How many normal steps do you think it will take to get from our door to the drinking fountain? Let's watch Lee walk and count her steps.**
  - **How many giant steps do you think it will take to go down the hall? Let's walk it and count our giant steps.**
- Have the children play Buzz. When they are comfortable counting by 5s, have them count by 1s, substituting the word buzz for every multiple of 5. This may be done as a circle game with children counting around the circle in turn. For example, **1, 2, 3, 4, buzz, 6, 7, 8, 9, buzz,...** . This game can also be played by substituting buzz for every even number, however, this is more difficult. For example, **1, buzz, 3, buzz, 5, buzz, 7, buzz,...** .
- Have the children use a calculator as they count by 1s, 2s, 5s, and/or 10s. For example:

To count by ones press

To count by twos press

![2][+][=][=][=] , ...

Have the children count aloud each time they press the = button. Note that the calculator must have an automatic constant feature in order to do this activity.

Number Activities

- Distribute to each child either a numeral card from 1 to 9 or a multiple of 10 card. Ask, **Do I need your card to make 47?** Have the children who respond cooperate to form the number requested with their cards.

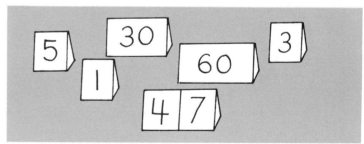

- Ask riddles such as these:
  - **I'm thinking of a number with 8 tens. What number am I thinking of?**
  - **I'm thinking of a number with 5 tens and 2 ones. What number am I thinking of?**
  - **I'm thinking of a number between 43 and 45. What number am I thinking of?**
  - **I'm thinking of a number 1 greater than 62. What number am I thinking of?**

Money Activities

- Cut a slit in the top of a plastic food container, and tape a coin to the top of the container. Have the children identify the taped coin. Invite a volunteer to drop a corresponding amount using different coins into the container. Have the child count aloud as he or she drops each coin. For example, if a dime was taped to the container, a child could drop a nickel and 5 pennies in and say, **5 cents, 6 cents, 7 cents, 8 cents, 9 cents, 10 cents**. Empty the container and place that collection to one side. Invite another child to try and deposit a different collection.

- Place a penny, nickel, dime, and quarter in a bag. Have a volunteer close her or his eyes and take a coin out of the bag. Ask, **What coin did you choose?** Wait for the child's response before asking, **Why do you think it is the (penny)?** Alter the game by asking the children to select a specific coin from the bag. Say, **Close your eyes, put your hand in the bag, and find the nickel**.

Problem Solving Activities

Sorting

Draw illustrations such as these on the board.

Have the children choose the Glib from the 4 additional figures drawn to one side. Ask, **Why is it a Glib? Why is this not a Glib?** as you point to each of the other figures not selected. Invite all children to draw another Glib for the Glib family. Involve the children in a variety of these exercises before you ask them to contribute their own similar problems for their classmates to solve. These may be used for similar exercises.

Solving Story Problems

Tell problems with missing information for the children to discuss. You might act out the stories with small objects as you tell them. Encourage the children to explain what else they need to know in order to answer the question.

- **There are 4 children playing on the teeter-totter. How many girls are playing?**
- **Michael had 7 hockey cards. He gave some to Anna. How many does he have left?**
- **Jeanne bought 5 presents. Does she have enough to give a present to each friend?**

Identifying Likenesses and Differences

Ask a volunteer to put both hands behind her or his back. Have another child place an Attribute Block in the volunteer's hands. Ask the volunteer to tell you about the block. Encourage the child to describe the block's size, thickness, and shape. If necessary, ask, **Is it large or small? Is it thick or thin? What shape is it?** On subsequent days, have the volunteer describe 2 figures. Encourage the child to describe the figures in comparison with each other. For example, **I'm holding a triangle and a square. The triangle is larger than the square. The square is thicker than the triangle.**

Developing Observation and Listening Skills

Display an object such as a chair. Have the children describe it without saying what it is so that their description fits only the chair. For example, this discussion could take place.

Child: **It is made of plastic and metal.**
Teacher: **That's right. Is anything else in our room made of plastic and metal?**
Child: **Yes, the bookshelf.**
Teacher: **What else can we add to our description?**
Child: **It's made of plastic and metal and has 4 legs.**
Teacher: **Good! Does that describe anything else?**
Child: **Yes, the table.**
Teacher: **What else can we add so that our description fits only the chair?**
Child: **It's made of plastic and metal. It has 4 legs and we sit on it.**
Teacher: **Is there anything else in the room which is made of plastic and metal, has 4 legs, and is made for sitting on?**
Child: **No, only the chair.**

Using the Poem

The poem Please Tell Me the Time relates important events in Ted's day to specific times. A discussion of the time of events in Ted's day can be extended to include questioning on the time certain classroom activities and routines take place. This discussion may be used as the basis for a simple time line or time chart as suggested in the activity What Are We Doing?, page 289. The children could illustrate their own simple time lines.

You may wish to designate one group of children to ask the question and another to call out the time in each verse, or you may wish to divide the class and have each group read alternate lines or verses.

Verses may be added to focus on other times which are particularly significant for the children, e.g.,

The school bell is clanging,   Our work is complete now,
The doors are all banging,   The classroom is neat now,
   Please tell me the time.   Please tell me the time.
   9 o'clock! Everybody,   4 o'clock! Everybody,
   Now it's school time!   That's going home time!

Supplementary Material

Ted is my Friend: Mathematics Activity Book, pages 89-92; and graphing mat, pages 38 and 55.

Please Tell Me the Time

The birds are all twittering,
Tiny footsteps are skittering!
Please tell me the time.
7:30! Troll-teddy,
That's our wake-up time!

Our porridge is steaming,
The sunlight is beaming,
Please tell me the time.
8 o'clock! Troll-teddy,
That's our breakfast time!

The snowflakes are falling,
The chickadee's calling,
Please tell me the time.
9 o'clock! Troll-teddy,
That's our play time!

My tummy is rumbly,
My fingers are fumbly.
Please tell me the time.
12 o'clock! Troll-teddy,
That's our lunch time!

The fire is glowing,
Muffin pans are overflowing,
Please tell me the time.
3 o'clock! Troll-teddy,
That's our baking time!

I'm setting the table,
As fast as I'm able,
Please tell me the time.
5:30! Troll-teddy,
That's our supper time!

We've told a long story,
There's no time for morey,
Please tell me the time.
8:30, Troll-teddy,
That's . . . our . . . zzzzzzz!

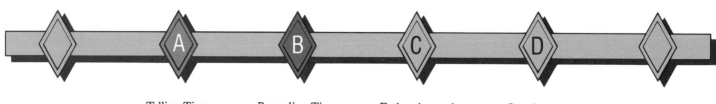

Section 1

Planning the Section

Objective	Level	Activity	Grouping	Program *or* Management Suggestions
A Telling Time to the Hour	Pictorial Concrete	1. Clock Search 2. The Clock 3. Build a Clock 4. Build Your Own Clock 5. What Time Is It Mr. Wolf?	♦♦♦♦♦♦♦ ♦♦♦♦ ♦♦♦♦♦♦♦ ♦♦♦♦ ♦♦♦♦	Activity 1 draws the children's attention to the reasons why they need to tell time using a clock. Repeat Activities 2 and 3 until children are comfortably reading times to the hour. As children build their own clocks in Activity 4, you may need to assist them in spacing the numerals and affixing the hands.
B Recording Time to the Hour	Pictorial	6. What Are We Doing? 7. My Guide 8. Time Well Spent	♦♦♦♦♦♦♦ ♦ ♦♦♦♦	In Activity 6, a class time table is recorded. You may wish to do this daily to create a week's schedule. Activity 8 offers a number of suggestions to reinforce reading and recording time to the hour. These should be prepared ahead of time.

About this Section

In Unit 4 and throughout the Five Minute Math Activities, children have been exposed to questioning and experiences to develop their awareness of time. In this section, children are formally introduced to reading a clock to the hour. This skill often proves to be a difficult one to master. To help simplify the task, try to obtain a large, simple demonstration clock with hands that are easy to manipulate.

Engage the children in clock reading exercises daily and continue the incidental references to time throughout the day. Comments such as these help establish a link between an event and a time on the clock. **It's 10 o'clock; time to get ready for library. It's a few minutes to 12. Let's start to get ready for lunch.**

Today, many clock radios, car clocks, and watches show time in digital notation. Many children are now more familiar with the digital clock than they are with the standard clock. Nevertheless, the standard clock is used to introduce the telling of time for several reasons. The movement of the hands is a more visual representation of the passage of time. The sequencing of the numbers on the face provides a model for the sequencing of times: 1 o'clock, 2 o'clock, etc. The digital clock introduces a level of precision that is confusing for children. 11:59 looks very different from 12:00 on a digital clock. It is, however, important to link the standard and digital presentations. This can be accomplished by: having a digital and standard demonstration clock in the classroom; recording the time in digital notation when reading a standard clock; having the children participate in the matching activities suggested in Activity 8.

Observations and Evaluation

These key questions help focus the children's attention on reading the clock.

- **Which is the hour hand? Show me.**
- **Which is the minute hand? Show me.**
- **Which number is the hour hand closest to?**
- **It's exactly 10 o'clock. What number is the hour hand pointing to? And the minute hand?**
- **It's almost 12 o'clock. Which number are both hands pointing to?**

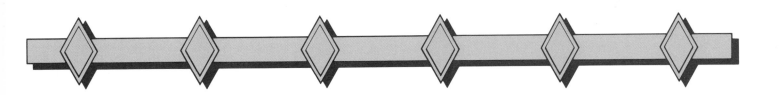

Suggested Materials

- A collection of magazines and catalogues [Activity 1]
- A large demonstration clock [Activities 2 and 3]
- A paper plate for each child [Activity 4]
- A brass fastener for each child [Activity 4]
- A set of clock concentration cards [Activity 8]
- A set of domino clock cards [Activity 8]
- A self–checking clock sheet [Activity 8]
- A grandfather clock [Activity 8]
- A clock puzzle [Activity 8]
- A collection of TV Guides [Activity 8]

Line Masters

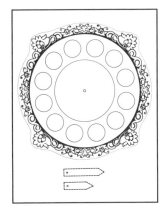

Line Master **92**
Activity 4
1 per child

Line Master **93**
Activities 7 and 8
1 per child

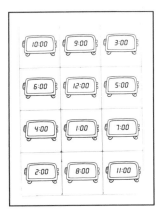

Line Master **94**
Activity 8
A few copies

Line Master **95**
Activity 8
A few copies

Activities

1. Clock Search

Gather the children around a demonstration clock and engage them in a discussion about when and why they would need to use a clock. You may wish to record their responses on a chart.

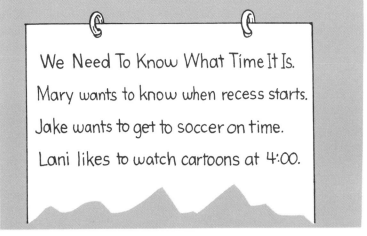

We Need To Know What Time It Is.

Mary wants to know when recess starts.

Jake wants to get to soccer on time.

Lani likes to watch cartoons at 4:00.

Have the children cut different clocks from magazines and catalogues. Discuss the similarities and differences of the clocks they discover. Sort them into groups based on their observations. Paste the clocks onto the class chart.

A	B	C	D
Telling Time to the Hour	Recording Time to the Hour	Estimating and Comparing Length in Non-standard Units	Creating and Interpreting a Bar Graph

2. The Clock

Gather the children around a demonstration clock. Discuss with them the different parts of the clock and the purpose of each. Ask the children to make observations about the hands and the numerals. Point out that when an hour is just beginning, the short hand will point to the name of the hour and the long hand will point to the 12. Provide several examples on the clock and have the children tell you the time.

To add variety and interest to the examples, ask the children to suggest an event from their day. Display the closest hour on the clock. Have the children tell you the time shown. Or have the children chant this rhyme to identify the time.

When the big hand points straight up,
The little hand tells the time.
It's (6) o'clock, it's (6) o'clock,
Listen for the chime.

The children can clap 6 times to represent the chimes of the clock.

Meeting Individual Needs

A child who appears confused distinguishing between the hands on the clock may benefit from focussing on a simpler clock. Present a clock with only the hour hand. When the child is comfortable reading this spinner clock, introduce the minute hand. Alternatively, accentuate the hands by creating a demonstration clock with hands of 2 different colors.

3. Build a Clock

Ahead of time draw a large circle on the chalk board and mark the appropriate position for the numerals on a clock. Engage the children's interest by telling them that they are going to play a game that will turn the circle into a clock. Explain that you are going to set a time on the demonstration clock. When someone tells what time it says, he or she can add a number to the clock on the board. The game is over when the clock is drawn with all the numerals in place.

Guide and discuss the correct positioning of the numerals as the children build the clock. Frequently draw the children's attention to the position of the hands on the demonstration clock.

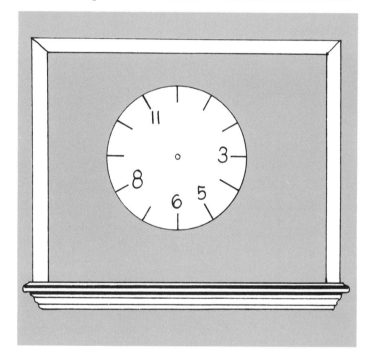

4. Build Your Own Clock

Provide each child with a copy of Line Master 92. Guide the children in printing the numerals on their clocks. Have them cut out the clocks and glue them on a paper plate. Assist the children in securing the hands to the clock with a brass fastener. The children may wish to decorate the rims of their clocks.

Once the children have made their own clock, have them practice positioning the hands on their clocks. Begin by providing a model on the demonstration clock. Ask the children to identify the time and show the same time on their clock faces. After several examples, say a time and invite the children to manipulate the hands to show it on their clocks.

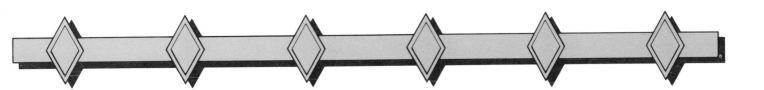

5. What Time Is It Mr. Wolf? A

Invite the children to sit in a circle with the clocks they made in Activity 4. Have the children set their clocks to any hour. Tell them to hold the clocks so that no one can see the time they have set. Explain that you are a shepherd who must find out if there are any wolves hiding in the flock of sheep (the children). Print a time on the board (2:00) and ask, **What time is it Mr. Wolf?** The children who had set their clocks to 2 o'clock should stand, display their clocks, and respond, **It's 2 o'clock!** Invite one of these children to assume the role of shepherd and decide on the time for the next round of the game. If necessary, help the child print the time on the board. Continue this activity as long as interest is maintained.

6. What Are We Doing? PS B

Prepare a chart with the children to record their activities at the different hours of the day.

Time	Monday	Tuesday	Wednesday	Th
9:00	Gym	Class Circle	Class Circle	
10:00	StoryWriting	Library	Music	
11:00	3 1 7 5 4 Math Activity	Gym	Math Activity	
12:00	Lunch	Lunch	Lunch	

Ask questions such as these:

- **What time did we go to the library?**
- **What did we do at 9 o'clock?**
- **Did we go to the gym today?**
- **What did we do before Math Activities? And after Math Activities?**
- **What did we do first? Second?**
- **Which days did we have gym?**
- **How many times this week did we go to the library?**

Encourage the children to make up questions for their classmates to answer.

You may wish to set an alarm clock which will signal the hour for you. To make this chart a cumulative record, record the activities the children engage in for each hour of the week. This could provide a basis for discussion or graphing.

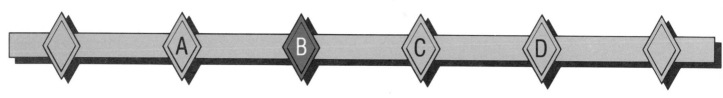

A	B	C	D
Telling Time to the Hour	Recording Time to the Hour	Estimating and Comparing Length in Non-standard Units	Creating and Interpreting a Bar Graph

7. My Guide   PS B

Provide each child with a copy of Line Master 93. Ask the children to record the times and cut out the clocks. Invite the children to create a guide to their day. Have them paste the clocks on separate sheets of paper, assemble them in order, and staple them into a booklet. Encourage the children to draw a picture of what they might be doing at each time. Gather the children together and give them an opportunity to read their guides to each other.

Provide paper for covers. The children could use their initials in the title, e.g., D.P. Guide. You may wish to encourage children to focus on a school day, a weekend day, or an imaginary day.

Meeting Individual Needs

If children experience difficulty determining what they do at different times, they may benefit from referring to the chart developed in Activity 6.

8. Time Well Spent   B

Line Masters 93 to 95 can be used to create a variety of motivating activities to reinforce telling and recording time to the hour. Make all or any of the activities described and place them at a center.

Make cards from Line Masters 93 and 94. The children can play Concentration with these cards by matching a standard clock with a digital clock.

Paste the clocks from Line Masters 93 and 94 on 2 separate strips of paper. Have the children manipulate strips so that they both show the same time.

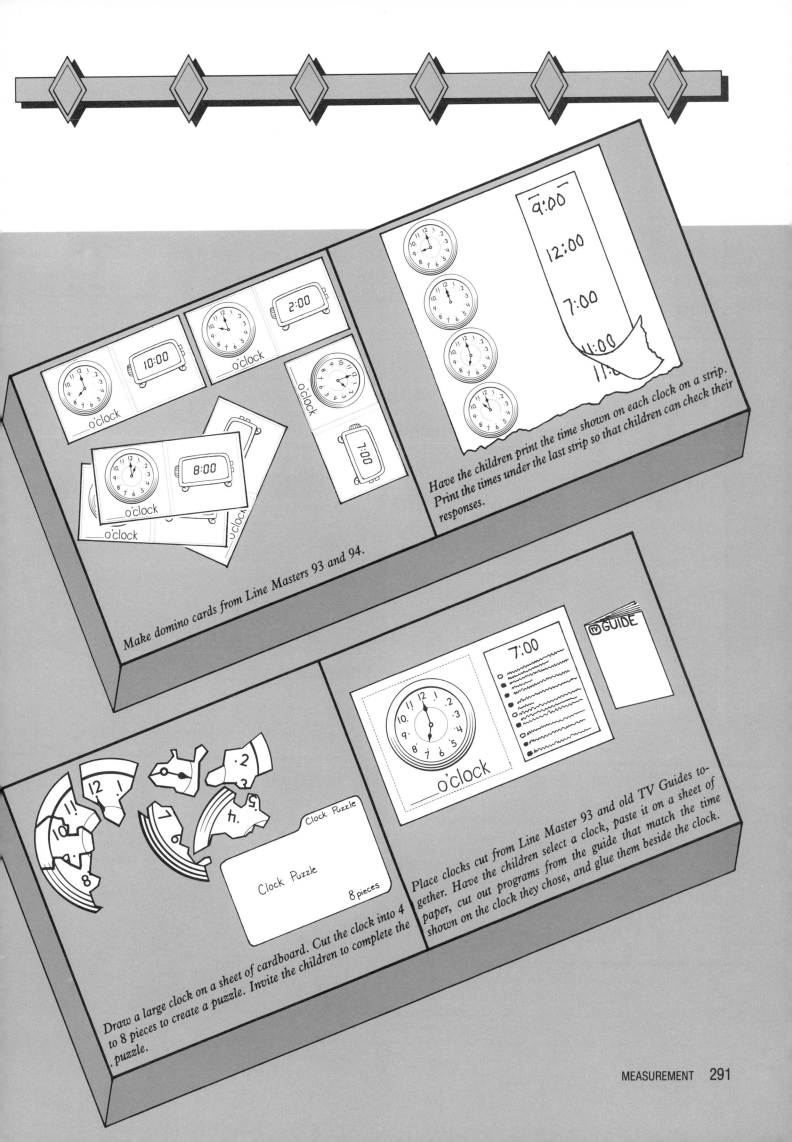

Make domino cards from Line Masters 93 and 94.

Have the children print the time shown on each clock on a strip. Print the times under the last strip so that children can check their responses.

Draw a large clock on a sheet of cardboard. Cut the clock into 4 to 8 pieces to create a puzzle. Invite the children to complete the puzzle.

Clock Puzzle

Clock Puzzle

8 pieces

Place clocks cut from Line Master 93 and old TV Guides together. Have the children select a clock, paste it on a sheet of paper, cut out programs from the guide that match the time shown on the clock they chose, and glue them beside the clock.

o'clock

7:00

TV GUIDE

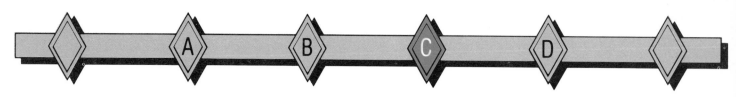

A	B	C	D
Telling Time to the Hour	Recording Time to the Hour	Estimating and Comparing Length in Non-standard Units	Creating and Interpreting a Bar Graph

Section 2

Planning the Section

Objective	Level	Activity	Grouping	Program *or* Management Suggestions
C Estimating and Comparing Length in Non-standard Units	Concrete	1. How Long Is It? 2. More Measuring 3. Guess, Then Check 4. Imprinted Snakes 5. Body Rulers 6. Tape Measure Making 7. My Measurements	ꝉꝉꝉꝉꝉꝉꝉ ꝉꝉꝉꝉꝉꝉꝉ ꝉꝉꝉꝉꝉꝉꝉ ꝉꝉꝉꝉꝉꝉꝉ ꝉ ꝉꝉꝉꝉ ꝉ	In Activities 1 to 3, the children use several units to measure different objects. Activity 2 builds on the experience of Activity 1. The technique of using a single unit to measure the length of an object is taught in Activity 4. Activity 5 introduces the idea of using body parts as units of measurement. Suggestions for different tape measures are offered in Activity 6. Place the required materials at a center so that children can continue to make different tape measures.

About this Section

In Unit 4 and through various Five Minute Math Activities, the children have estimated, compared, and ordered objects according to length and/or height. Through these exercises the children have developed a vocabulary of comparisons. They should now be comfortable in identifying and describing objects as longer, shorter, taller, longest, shortest, and tallest. In this section the children are introduced to measuring objects in non-standard units. This measuring skill allows the children to compare the length of objects without placing them side by side. It also enables them to consider these questions: **How long? How short? How much longer? How much shorter?**

When the children use units to measure length, they should be reminded to: place the first unit at the end of the object, have each unit touch the unit placed before it, and describe the length of the object to the nearest unit. Children are often encouraged to estimate before they measure the objects.

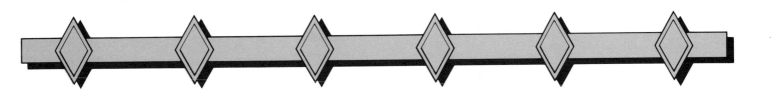

Observations and Evaluation

Circulate among the children to ensure that they are using non-standard units properly. Check that they are placing the units end to end without leaving space or overlapping units. It is also important that the units be placed in a straight line. Observe whether children have selected appropriate units for measuring different objects. For example, are they attempting to measure the length of a room with toothpicks or the length of a crayon with a straw? If necessary, lead a discussion on which units are appropriate for measuring long and short objects. As children measure with non-standard units, they will encounter situations where measurements are not exact but only approximate. Model language such as, **Almost 3 toothpicks, between 6 and 7 handspans, close to 8 paper clips,** or **about 20 straws.**

These key questions will initiate further discussion.

- **How many (units) long do you think this is?**
- **Is it longer or shorter than you thought?**
- **Would it be better to use paper clips or straws to measure this? Why?**
- **Measure this (object) with paper clips. How long is it? Measure it with popsicle sticks. How long is it?**

Suggested Materials

- A large quantity of items for measuring in non-standard units such as flat toothpicks, popsicle sticks, paper clips, coffee stirrers, or straws [Activities 1, 2, 3, 6, and 7]
- A piece of Plasticine for each child [Activity 4]
- A paper clip for each child [Activity 4]
- A large quantity of long paper strips [Activity 6]
- Fingerpaint [Activity 6]
- An inkpad [Activity 6]

Activities

1. How Long Is It?

At different work areas place large sheets of newsprint and units for measuring such as flat toothpicks, popsicle sticks, paper clips, coffee stirrers, or straws cut to the same length. Gather the children together around one of these areas. Engage their interest by telling them that today they are going to discover how long certain things are using the items they see on the table. Select an object such as a tissue box, place it on the sheet of newsprint, and trace around it. Explain that this will enable them to keep a record of their discoveries. Hold up a toothpick and ask, **How many toothpicks long is this tissue box? Make a guess.** Give each child an opportunity to guess before you actually start to measure. Discuss how you could find out the length of the tissue box in toothpicks. Have the children demonstrate their suggestions. Through this process, establish that each unit must touch, must be placed end to end (not overlapping), and must be in a straight line. Probably the box will not be exactly a certain number of toothpicks. Discuss that, **It is between (6) and (7) toothpicks;** or, **It is almost (7) toothpicks long.** To keep a permanent record of the number of toothpicks, either glue them in place, mark with a pencil the beginning and end of each one, or record a statement to summarize your findings.

As you circulate among the work areas, discuss the children's discoveries.

- **What are you using to measure things?**
- **What have you discovered?**
- **Which is longer the (book) or the (stapler)?**
- **What is the longest/shortest thing you have measured?**

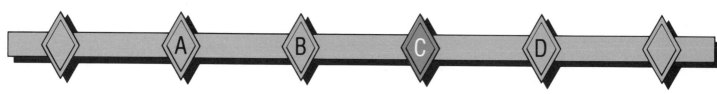

	Telling Time to the Hour	Recording Time to the Hour	Estimating and Comparing Length in Non-standard Units	Creating and Interpreting a Bar Graph
	A	B	C	D

2. More Measuring

Distribute the records the children made while participating in the activity How Long Is It?, page 293. Direct children to work areas where units for measurement have been placed. Explain that today they should choose a different measurement unit. Demonstrate how they could lay the second unit under the first one recorded or along the opposite side of the object.

As you circulate among the groups, focus the children's attention on the relationship of the 2 different units.

- **What did you measure the tissue box with yesterday?**
- **What are you using today?**
- **How many toothpicks long is the box? How many paper clips?**
- **We know the box was the same length yesterday as it is today. Why do we have 2 different measurements?**

3. Guess, Then Check

Engage the children's interest by telling them that today they are going to go on a measurement hunt in the classroom. Demonstrate how they should draw the chosen object on a sheet of paper and then print how many (toothpicks) long or wide they think it is. The children should then measure the object and record their discovery. Place bins of units of measurement in central places and invite the children to begin.

Some children may require additional help when they encounter objects that must be rounded off to the nearest unit. Encourage the children to describe the length as between (3) and (4) toothpicks.

Variation

Have the children hunt for objects of a specific length. For example, they could search for objects that are longer than 5 toothpicks; shorter than 8 toothpicks; as long as 4 toothpicks; or between 5 and 10 toothpicks.

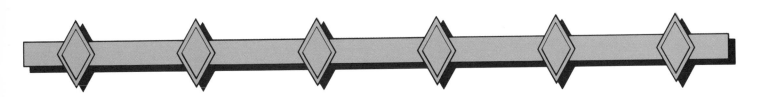

4. Imprinted Snakes

Provide each child with a piece of Plasticine, a sheet of newsprint to work on, and a paper clip. Have the children break off a piece of Plasticine and roll it into a snake. Ask, **How many paper clips long is your snake? Make a guess. How could you find out using only 1 paper clip?** Explore the different suggestions. If necessary, suggest pressing the paper clip in the Plasticine to make imprints which go from one end of the snake to the other. Remind the children that they must make the first imprint so that the end of the paper clip is at the end of the snake and that each imprint must touch the one before it. Invite the children to measure their snakes using a single paper clip. Have them make another snake and repeat this imprinting process.

You may wish to challenge the children to roll a snake that is a specific length. **Roll a snake that you think is 8 paper clips long. Make paper clip imprints to check your guess.** *Children could continue this activity with a partner. Each child could challenge their partner to make a snake of a specific length. They could then check each other's snakes by imprinting with paper clips.*

5. Body Rulers

Gather the children together and begin a discussion by asking, **What have we used to measure the length of things?** List the different responses to compile a comprehensive list. Ask, **Have you ever used something else to measure length? Have you ever measured something with your fingers, hands, or feet?** Explain that people used to rely heavily on using body parts to measure. Ask, **What body part could you use to measure the length and width of the room? A piece of paper? The chalk board ledge?** Have volunteers demonstrate their responses and ensure that each unit touches the one before it.

Invite the children to measure classroom objects using body units. They can follow the same procedure for recording their estimations and measurements as outlined in Guess, Then Check, page 294. Encourage them to measure using different body units. Children may discover that longer units are more efficient for measuring longer distances.

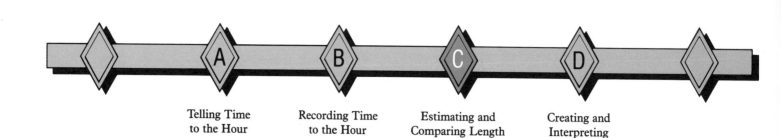

C

6. Tape Measure Making

At different work areas place various items children can use to make their own tape measures. Remind the children before they begin that each unit must touch the one adjacent to it, the units must be placed in a straight line, and specify a minimum number of units for each tape measure. You may wish to have the children make any of the tape measures illustrated. After the tape measure is complete, demonstrate how the children can number the units. Discuss how numbering the units facilitates measuring. On a subsequent day have the children use their tape measures to measure classroom objects. Their discoveries can be recorded following the procedure outlined in Guess, Then Check, page 294.

These tape measures can be clipped to hangers for easy storage. Some children may enjoy making several different tape measures.

296

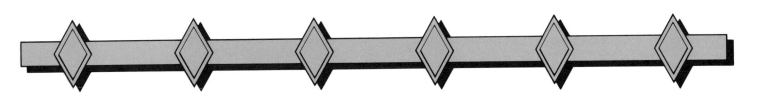

7. My Measurements

Provide each child with a large piece of paper and drawing materials. Invite the children to draw a large picture of themselves. Have them measure their body parts using a variety of units of measurement such as toothpicks, popsicle sticks, handspans, finger widths, or tape measures. Ask the children to record each measurement on their drawing.

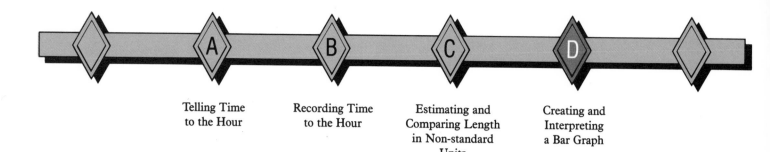

Section 3

Planning the Section

Objective	Level	Activity	Grouping	Program *or* Management Suggestions
D Creating and Interpreting a Bar Graph	Concrete	1. Stacking and Linking	♦♦♦♦♦♦♦	Each activity offers a variety of graphing ideas. Activity 1 presents a concrete bar graph created from interlocking cubes. In Activity 2, each child places a paper square to create a bar graph while in Activity 3 children color squares on the graphing mat. Remember that these graphing experiences are intended to be carried out over an extended period of time.
		2. Paper Squares	♦♦♦♦♦♦♦	
	Pictorial	3. Color a Square	♦♦♦♦♦♦♦	

About this Section

In this section, children continue to develop their graphing skills as they create and interpret bar graphs. Each activity suggests many different questions to initiate a graph. It is suggested that you involve the children in creating and interpreting a graph on an average of once a week. Make graphing mats (Line Master 70) available so that interested children can independently pursue graphing activities when they wish.

Initially begin by posing questions which can be graphed on 2-column graphs. When children demonstrate that they can read 2-column graphs comfortably, introduce 3- and 4-column graphs. Ensure that each graph has a title and that columns are labelled with an appropriate picture or word.

It is important that children continue to create and interpret concrete graphs and pictographs even after they are familiar with the bar graph. The usefulness of each particular type of graph becomes more evident in light of the children's additional graphing experiences. Intermittently, have the children create and interpret a concrete graph, pictograph and bar graph for the same question. Have the children consider whether each graph presents the same information and which of the graphs is most convenient.

Observations and Evaluation

These key questions can form the basis of a discussion on the various bar graphs created in this section.
- **What does this graph tell us?**
- **Which column has more (less, most, least)?**
- **Are any columns the same? What does that mean?**
- **Are there more (less) _____ than _____? How many _____?**
- **How many more (less) _____ than _____? How many _____?**

Suggested Materials

- An interlocking cube for each child [Activity 1]
- A large quantity of paper squares [Activity 2]
- A graphing mat [Activities 2 and 3]

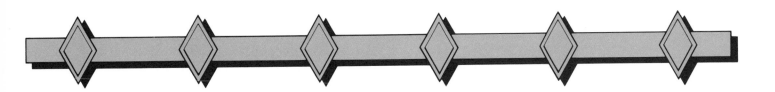

Activities

1. Stacking and Linking   PS D

Gather the children together. Provide each child with an interlocking cube. Recall the types of graphs you have made as a group and individually to date. Explain that today they are going to make graphs where their choice is shown by a cube. Discuss how these graphs are convenient as they do not take a lot of time or require many materials.

Pose a question which can be graphed on a 2-column graph. These questions are suggested for 2-column graphs.

- **Do you have a brother (sister)?**
- **Have you ever been to a zoo?**
- **Have you ever travelled on an airplane?**
- **Would you rather go to the police station or the fire station on your next class trip?**
- **Do you like to play tag during recess?**
- **Which do you like better; ice cream or popsicles?**
- **Are there more children wearing shoes with laces than there are wearing shoes without laces?**

Place labels for each column on a flat surface. Have the children identify them. In turn, have the children stack their cubes in the appropriate columns.

When the graph is complete, ask questions such as these:

- **Which column has the most/least? Show me.**
- **How many more children have brothers than don't have brothers?**
- **How many children have brothers?**
- **How many children don't have brothers?**
- **Can you tell me who has a brother by looking at this graph?**
- **What can you tell me about this graph?**

There are other materials which can be used as substitutes for inter-locking cubes. For example, by stacking wooden blocks or milk cartons and/or linking paper clips or paper strips, comparable graphs can be created. Pose questions which can be graphed on a 3-column graph after children are familiar with 2-column graphs.

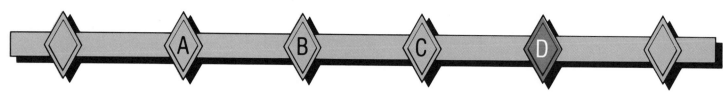

2. Paper Squares   PS D

Present the children with 3 colors of construction paper and ask them to consider the colors and choose a square of the color they like best. Post a graph divided into 3 columns the same width of the squares. Discuss which labels should appear under each column and print them. In turn, have the children tape their squares in place. When all squares have been placed, lead a discussion about the graph.

*Have the children participate in creating a variety of paper square graphs. You may wish to post a question and a graph with labelled columns, paper squares, and tape in a spot easily accessible to the children. Read the question aloud with the children. Explain that they should consider the question and respond to it by a specific time (e.g., Friday morning). On Friday morning, gather the children around the displayed graph and ask, **What can you tell me about this graph?** You may wish to record all of the children's responses to this question. These comments can then be posted beside the graph. Note that stickers are good substitutes for paper squares. Have the children give suggestions for the questions you post.*

Have you been on an airplane ?

yes

no

Airplane Trips

More children have not been on a plane.
7 children have been on a plane.
12 children have not been on a plane.

paper squares

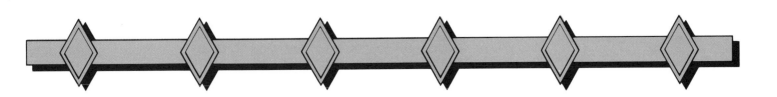

3. Color a Square

Ahead of time, make a large graph for demonstration such as the one shown. Explain that today you are going to create graphs similar to the paper square graphs. Instead of taping a paper square to show the information, you are going to color squares. Pose a question such as, **Are there more children wearing striped shirts than there are wearing checked shirts?** Discuss the appropriate labels for the columns and record them. Ask all children wearing striped shirts to stand. In turn, have each of these children color a square in the appropriate column. Repeat the process for children wearing checked shirts. When all the information is recorded, lead a discussion on the graph.

To maintain a high level of interest, it is important to keep a quick pace. It is recommended that you ask questions which do not involve a response from every child in the class so that the children do not have to wait for a long period of time as the information is recorded.

After the children have had ample opportunity to see a number of bar graphs created and participated in interpreting them, pose questions which involve the children in collecting information from their environment. These questions are representative of an unlimited number you could ask:

- *Are there more 2-door cars than there are 4-door cars in the parking lot?*
- *Are there more trees in the front or back yard of school?*
- *What is the most common color front door on our street?*
- *Do more cars pass our window in the first 5 minutes of school or the last 5 minutes?*

Before you go to collect information, ensure that the children understand the question and have seen the graph that is going to be completed. It is suggested that initially you record the children's observations on a class graph. Later you might consider having the children make their own bar graphs of the observations on Line Master 70.

Measurement Across the Curriculum

Language Arts

- Have the children complete any of these sentences. You may wish to have the children write a story or illustrate their ideas.

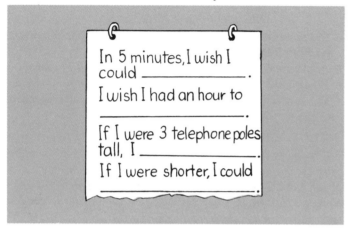

- In conjunction with this unit, you may wish to read any of these books (See page 318 for an annotated bibliography):

    - *Mouse Days* by Leo Lionni
    - *The Scarecrow* by George Mendoza
    - *Wake Up, City* by Alvin Tresselt

Science

- Have the children construct a sundial. Place a stick in the ground and tack a large sheet of mural paper on the ground as shown.

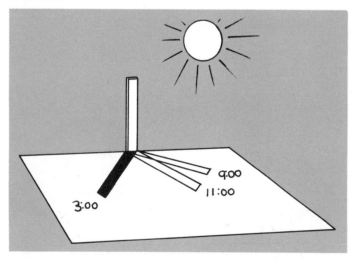

Trace the shadow that is cast each hour on the mural paper and record the time. Alternatively, cut and stake pieces of string the length of each shadow and label them with the time. When the sundial has been recorded for a day, have the children observe it on the hour for a few days to see how precise it is.

- Have the children find out how long it takes them to do any of these things:

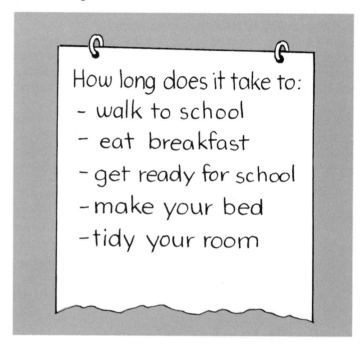

- Have the children measure the height and/or length of their pets with their non-standard unit tape measures. These measurements can be posted and then used to generate comparisons. **My dog is 18 toothpicks long. It is 2 toothpicks longer than Daniel's cat.**
- Have the children use a variety of non-standard units to measure items on the nature or science table.

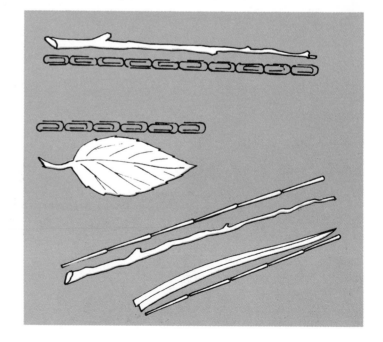

Extension Project

Social Studies

- Have the children observe and record how many cars drive by in 1 minute and in 5 minutes at different times during the day.

> How many cars pass our school in 5 minutes?
> 9:00 to 9:05   ⩀⩀ ⩀⩀ II
> 12:00 to 12:05 ⩀⩀ III
> 3:00 to 3:05   ⩀⩀ ⩀⩀

- Lead a discussion on how people used to tell time before clocks were invented. Remind the children of the different timing devices they used to measure time in Unit 4. Discuss the limitation of such devices.

- Pose a daily home measurement problem for the children to consider. For example, **How many steps are there from your bedroom to the front door? How many steps from the refrigerator to the kitchen table?**

Music

- Adjust a metronome to different tempos and have the children play various rhythm band instruments in time with the beat. Invite some children to move to the tempo while others play the instruments in time.
- In conjunction with this unit, you may wish to teach these songs:

    - Brush Your Teeth by Raffi
    - Walk, Walk, Walk by Raffi
    - Paper Clocks by Hap Palmer

Art

Have the children design a clock or watch which they would like to buy.

Physical Education

Have the children measure various distances in the gym using different movements. They could measure the distance from the black line to the white line using baby steps then giant steps. They could count the number of hops and then leaps it takes them to travel from one wall to another.

Involve the children in researching what other children do at specific hours during the day. For example, a child may choose to investigate how her or his classmates spend their time at 5 o'clock in the evening. The child would interview as many children as he or she wishes and record the findings on a chart or graph as shown.

Set aside time for the children to present their reports to the class. These reports could be called the 5 o'clock News and consist of a child displaying the chart or graph, telling how the information was collected, and answering questions from the class.

Note that it may be interesting for children to visit other classrooms to carry out interviews.

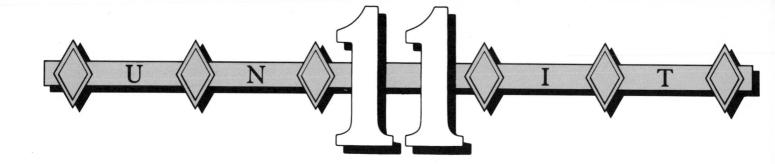

Addition and Subtraction to 12

Unit Objectives

Section

A Combining and Separating Sets to 11 and 12

B Recording Sums and Differences to 11 and 12

C Creating and Solving Story Problems

D Solving Number Sentences to 12

About this Unit

Addition and Subtraction

In Units 5 and 7 children participated in a variety of activities to develop addition and subtraction facts to 5 and 10 respectively. This unit presents a new set of activities in which children manipulate objects to generate the addition and subtraction facts for 11 and 12. Children who have not yet mastered facts to 10 should engage in these new activities, but at their own level. By participating in these activities, children will feel they are keeping pace with other children who are ready to move on. Children who master the objectives of this unit may be given the opportunity to generate addition and subtraction facts for 13 through 18. Children can generate these facts as they manipulate objects in 2 colors on boards as shown.

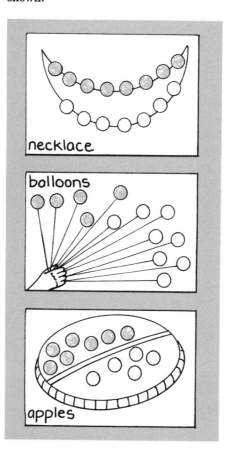

necklace

balloons

apples

Problem Solving

Children have additional opportunities to create and solve story problems as they engage in Let's Show Stories and Read All About It!, page 314. In addition, activities provided in Five Minute Math, page 307, develop these problem-solving skills:

* sorting
* identifying, extending, and creating patterns

Ongoing Objectives

- Reading and creating a calendar
- Estimating and counting
- Estimating and comparing length
- Reading a thermometer
- Telling time
- Identifying geometric figures or geometric solids
- Problem solving
  - Sorting
  - Identifying, extending, and creating patterns

Five Minute Math

Calendar Activities

- Make up calendar riddles which the children solve.
  - **I'm thinking of a rainy Tuesday. What date am I thinking of?**
  - **I'm thinking of the day which is 3 days after Brian's birthday. What day am I thinking of?**
  - **I'm thinking of the day which is 5 days before we went to the zoo. What day am I thinking of?**
  - **I'm thinking of last month. What month am I thinking of?**
  - **I'm thinking of the month that comes after May. What month am I thinking of?**
  - **I'm thinking of the season that comes before summer. What season am I thinking of?**
- Provide the children with a blank calendar (Line Master 98) and have them complete it. Encourage the children to record personal events on the calendar and/or to keep track of the weather. You could have the children make a calendar as a present; they could record special chores they will perform.

If you think the task of completing the calendar is too difficult for the children, fill in some or all of it before you make copies.

Sunday	Monday	Tuesday	Wednesday	Thursday	Friday	Saturday
			1	2	3	
		7			10	11
12		14	15			
19	20					25
	27	28		30		

Counting Activities

- Provide opportunities for counting objects. For example, ask,
  - **How many counters do you think are in this box? Let's count and find out.**
  - **Do you think 15 interlocking cubes will fit in this box? Let's count them and find out.**
  - **How many windows do you estimate are in our school? Let's walk around the school and count them. We will keep a tally of the windows as we count them. 1, 2, 3, 4, 5, 6, 7, 8, 9, 10, 11, 12, 13, 14, 15, 16, 17, 18. How many does our tally show? 5, 10, 15 and 3 more, 16, 17, 18. Our school has 18 windows.**

- Count books, floor tiles, beads, or blocks and make a tally as you and the children count aloud. When you have finished counting the objects, check the total by counting the tallies by fives **5, 10, 15, 20, 25, 26**
- As an enrichment activity, encourage children to count by tens beginning with a number other than 10. For example, 2, 12, 22, 32, 42, 52 ... . Use the hundreds square as a focus for the activity.

Measurement Activities

- Provide the children with access to interlocking cubes. Display a popsicle stick and say, **Make a train of interlocking cubes as long as this popsicle stick.** When everyone has finished, ask, **How many cubes did you use?** Distribute popsicle sticks so that the children can check to see if their train of interlocking cubes is as long as the popsicle stick. Ask, **Did you make it as long as the popsicle stick? Is it longer or shorter? How much longer (shorter)?** Display a different object and repeat the activity.
- Have the children measure the temperature of a glass of hot water and a glass of cold water. Record the temperatures. Ask the children to predict the temperature of the water after you pour the hot water into the cold water in a separate container. Measure the temperature. Discuss whether the estimates were high or low.
- Measure the temperature of a glass of hot water. Have the children measure and record the temperature of the water at 5 minute intervals for 15 minutes. Assist the children in reading the thermometer.
- Indicate a time to the hour on a large demonstration clock. Have a volunteer pantomime an activity that would take place at that particular time. Encourage the audience to first read the time and then guess the activity.

Geometry Activities

- Display a large piece of paper and a set of geometric figures or geometric solids. Have the children follow oral directions to locate a geometric figure and place it on the paper. **Place the large blue circle in the bottom left corner. Place the small red square beside the large blue circle.** Encourage children to give directions, as well. If possible, play this game so that each child has a piece of paper and a set of geometric figures. Have the children compare their papers after you have given the last direction.
- Give each child in the circle a geometric figure or geometric solid. Have a volunteer stand with her or his hands behind her or his back. Give this child a geometric figure. Invite the child to guess who in the circle has the same figure.

Problem Solving Activities

Sorting

Draw 2 circles with numbers in them on the chalk board as shown.

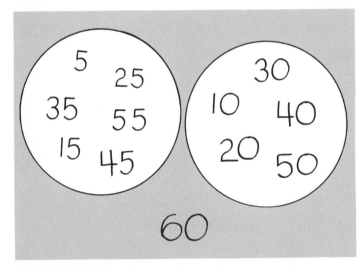

Print 60 outside the circles and, ask, **Which circle does the 60 belong in? Why?** Invite a child to print it in the appropriate circle. When it has been added to the appropriate set, erase the 60 and print another multiple of 5 (from 65 to 100) and repeat the process.

Identifying, Extending and Creating Patterns

- Print number patterns such as the ones shown on the chalk board. Invite the children to fill in the blanks. Have the children contribute their own patterns for their classmates to solve.

```
2  4  6  8 __ 12  14  16 __ 20
5  10  15 __ 25 __ 35  40 __ 50
10  20 __ __ 50 __ 70 __ 90
```

- Post a chart such as the ones shown. Complete at least one chart as a group. You may wish to illustrate the charts with concrete sets. Leave other charts posted and encourage the children to solve them before a specific day, e.g., the end of the week.

Number of Children	Number of Fingers
1	10
2	20
3	30
4	
5	
6	

Number of Stickers	Cost
1	5 ¢
2	10 ¢
3	15 ¢
4	
5	
6	

Using the Poem

The poem My Garden may be used as an introduction to addition and subtraction to 12 by having the children discuss the poem and their experiences with planting seeds. In the activity My Garden, page 312, children plant and then pick flowers from Ted's garden. You may wish to follow up this activity by planting a given number of seeds and use the experience as a daily basis for mathematical problems. For example: **How many seeds do you think will come up?** Compare with how many actually come up. **What day do you think the first one will come up? How many days is that from now? What day do you think the last one will come up? How many days is that from now? How many days between the first and last? How can we find out? How many seeds are up today? How many did we plant? How many more are there still to come up?**

You may wish to have a class garden, or allow each child to have a flower pot and make observations about her or his own garden. The children can construct charts to show how many seeds took 3 days, 4 days, 5 days, etc., to come up.

My Garden

Twelve little brown seeds
Planted in a row,
It's time just to sit still
And watch my garden grow.
One daisy, two daisies
Three daisies, four . . .
If I sit here longer,
Surely there'll be more.

Eight little daisies
Peeking through the ground,
Where are the other ones?
Four can't be found!
Are they hiding in the brown earth?
Or eaten by a grub?
Did someone take those four away
And hide them in the tub?

Oh! Four more little green shoots
Are growing in my plot.
Since four and eight are twelve, you see,
I'm certain that's the lot!
Now, twelve white daisies
Are blooming in the sun.
If I should give eleven to you,
Why then I'd still have one.

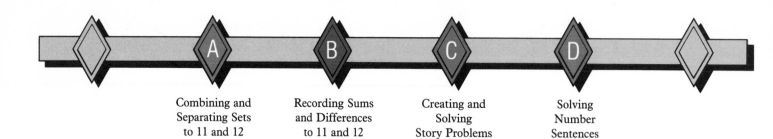

A	B	C	D
Combining and Separating Sets to 11 and 12	Recording Sums and Differences to 11 and 12	Creating and Solving Story Problems	Solving Number Sentences to 12

Section

Planning the Section

Objective	Level	Activity	Grouping	Program *or* Management Suggestions
A Combining and Separating Sets to 11 and 12	Concrete	1. My Garden 2. Sell and Buy	♦♦♦♦ ♦♦♦♦	Children manipulate sets to generate the addition and subtraction facts for 11 (12) as they engage in Activities 1 and 2.
B Recording Sums and Differences to 11 and 12	Concrete, Pictorial, and Symbolic	3. Recording the Games	♦	Children should begin to record the games only after they have played Activities 1 and/or 2 several times.
C Creating and Solving Story Problems	Semi-concrete and Symbolic	4. Let's Show Stories 5. Read All About It!	♦♦♦♦ ♦♦♦♦	As small groups of children participate in Activities 4 and 5, other children can continue to engage in Activities 1 to 3.
D Solving Number Sentences to 12	Concrete and Symbolic	6. Find the Solution	♦♦♦♦	Activity 6 offers suggestions for reinforcement games. Children should be directed to the games only after they have participated in Activities 1 to 5.

About this Section

Many activities from Units 5 and 7 can be adapted and extended to include number sentences to 12. It is recommended that you select the children's favorite activities from those units and use them to introduce and reinforce the concepts of this unit.

Children should engage in Activities 1 and/or 2 frequently to experience combining and separating sets of 11. The children should then participate in Activities 3 to 5 to further establish understanding of addition and subtraction facts of 11. This sequence should then be repeated to develop the addition and subtraction facts of 12.

The process for Activities 1 and 2 differs somewhat from previous manipulating games in that the child making the sets verbalizes the combination during the demonstration. The group then repeats the combination as it is pointed out a second time. This is necessary because the number in each subset can not be visualized at a glance and the speed at which children count varies.

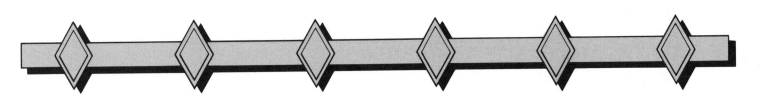

Observations and Evaluation

If a child appears to be having difficulty with the objectives of this unit, consider whether he or she is actually ready to proceed with this material. Line Masters 71 and 72 present addition and subtraction facts to 10. The child should be able to complete these sheets comfortably and also successfully show, using concrete materials, any number sentences you select randomly.

These key questions can form the basis of your discussions as you circulate among the children.

- **Show me a combination for 11. Can you show me another combination? And another?**
- **Place 11 counters in front of you. I'm going to take away 3 counters. How many counters are left? What number sentence tells about what just happened?**
- **Look at these number sentences:**

11 − 6 = 5	2 + 9 = 11.

  Could you show them to me using counters?

Suggested Materials

- A Styrofoam food tray to act as a garden for each child [Activities 1 and 3]
- A large collection of pipe cleaners, party toothpicks, straws, or popsicle sticks in 2 colors to act as flowers [Activities 1, 3, and 6]
- A large collection of egg cartons [Activities 2 and 3]
- A large collection of counters, cubes or small objects in 2 colors [Activities 2, 3, 4, and 5]
- A collection of objects priced from 1 cent to 10 cents [Activity 6]
- File folder self-checking puzzles [Activity 6]
- A collection of number sentence cards for facts of 11 and 12 [Activity 6]

Line Masters

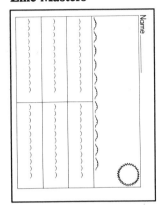

Line Master **96**
Activity 3
1 per child

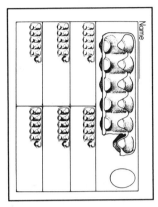

Line Master **97**
Activity 3
1 per child

Any of Line Masters **18** to **23**
Activities 4 and 5
1 per child

Line Master **52**
Activity 5
1 per child

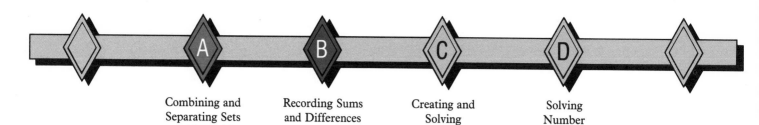

A	B	C	D
Combining and Separating Sets to 11 and 12	Recording Sums and Differences to 11 and 12	Creating and Solving Story Problems	Solving Number Sentences to 12

Activities

1. My Garden

Invite a small group of children to sit in a circle. Provide each child with a garden (a Styrofoam food tray with 11 small holes in it) and a collection of flowers in 2 different colors (pipe cleaners, party toothpicks, straws, or popsicle sticks).

Engage the children's interest by telling them that in the early spring Ted planted 11 seeds in his garden. Invite the children to suggest what kind of flower the seeds might grow into, e.g., daisies. Have the children "grow" 11 daisies in the garden.

In turn, the children describe the flowers in their gardens in terms of color and number. **There are 6 yellow daisies and 5 white daisies in my garden. There are 11 daisies altogether. 6 plus 5 equals 11.** Have the other children repeat the number sentence as the gardener (the child who is demonstrating) points to each set. Invite the children to show different combinations for 11 flowers. Ensure that they verbalize each combination they create.

When children are familiar with the addition action of the game, introduce the subtractive action. Have the children set up their gardens so that there are 11 flowers in 2 colors. Explain that Ted likes to pick flowers from the garden to put in his vase. As you pick 3 white flowers from a demonstration garden, say, **Ted was delighted to see 11 beautiful flowers in his garden. He decided to pick 3 white flowers.** Point to the remaining 8 yellow flowers and continue, **There are still 8 yellow flowers in the garden. 11 minus 3 equals 8.** Have the children repeat, **11 minus 3 equals 8.** In turn, have children pick flowers from their gardens and describe the action and result. The other children repeat the number sentence as the gardener displays the picked flowers and the ones remaining in the garden.

When children are familiar with the addition and subtraction processes, have them play the game in small groups or with a partner.

2. Sell and Buy

Invite a small group of children to sit in a circle. Provide each child with an egg carton cut in 11 sections and a handful of red and green counters. Tell them that today they are going to be fruit farmers packaging baskets of red and green apples to send to market. Have the children sort their apples into 2 piles, according to color. Fill a demonstration basket with green and red apples so that all counters of each color are grouped together as shown.

Point to each set of apples as you say, **My basket has 8 red apples and 3 green apples. There are 11 apples altogether. 8 plus 3 equals 11.** Point to the sets of apples and the whole basket a second time and encourage the children to repeat, **8 plus 3 equals 11.**

Have the children package their baskets with red and green apples. In turn, have them describe their baskets in terms of color and number. Encourage the group to repeat the combination as the sets are pointed out a second time.

When the children are familiar with the addition action of the game, introduce the subtractive action. Have the children fill their baskets with red and green apples. Explain that these baskets are now at the market. As you remove 4 red apples from a demonstration basket say, **The 11 apples looked delicious. A shopper bought 4 red apples.** Point to the remaining 7 green apples and continue, **There are 7 green apples left. 11 minus 4 equals 7.** Have the children repeat, **11 minus 4 equals 7.** In turn, have children buy apples from their baskets and describe their action and result. Have the other children verbalize each action demonstrated.

When children are familiar with the addition and subtraction process of the game, have them play with a partner. One child can be the fruit farmer who packages the apples, while the second child buys apples from the basket. They should reverse roles.

When you play this game to develop combinations for 12, distribute a complete egg carton and a handful of small objects such as beans in 2 colors. Tell the children that they are egg farmers packaging cartons with white and brown eggs.

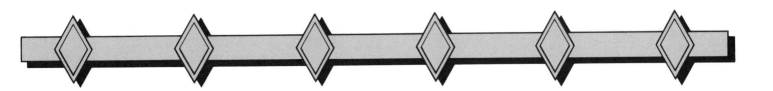

3. Recording the Games

B

After children have had many opportunities to play My Garden and Sell and Buy, begin invoving them in keeping a record of the number stories they generate. Line Masters 96 and 97 are provided for recording purposes. The large top frame should be used as a working space for placing the concrete materials used in the game. This frame accommodates the first step of transferring the action to the page.

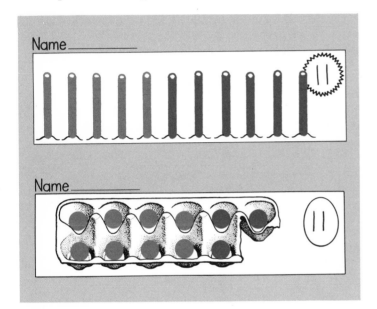

When children have demonstrated that they can transfer their actions to the page with concrete materials, have them keep a more permanent record by drawing a pictorial representation of the action and the corresponding number sentence.

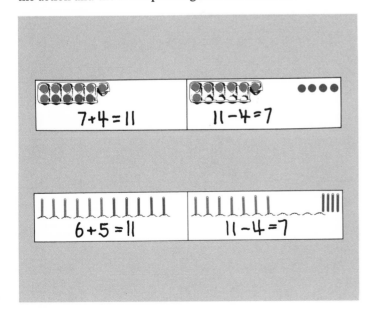

In the final recording step, the children simply record the number sentence that tells their action.

Line Masters 96 and 97 have been developed for recording combinations of 11. To adapt these recording sheets for recording combinations of 12, draw a twelfth hole in the garden and/or a twelfth section for the carton before making copies.

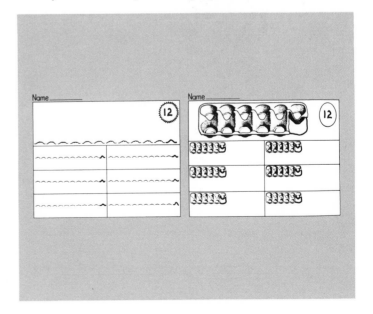

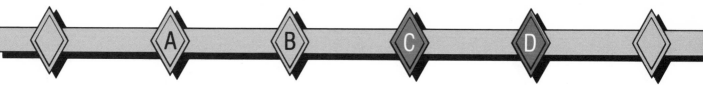

A	B	C	D
Combining and Separating Sets to 11 and 12	Recording Sums and Differences to 11 and 12	Creating and Solving Story Problems	Solving Number Sentences to 12

4. Let's Show Stories — PS C

Provide each child with a story board (Line Masters 18 to 23) and at least 12 small objects. Tell a story which involves additive and subtractive action. This story, told using objects to represent shells on the beach story board (Line Master 22), is representative of an unlimited number of stories the children can act out.

It was a beautiful day at the beach. A wave washed 5 shells onto the sand. Another wave brought 6 more shells onto the sand. What number sentence tells this story? (5 plus 6 equals 11.) **A little boy saw the 11 shells and decided to take 3 home to put with his collection. What number sentence tells this story?** (11 minus 3 equals 8.) **Another child came by, saw the 8 shells, and took 4 of them home. What is the number sentence of this story?** (8 minus 4 equals 4.) **Another wave washed in 7 more shells beside the 4 shells. What is a number sentence for this story?** (4 plus 7 equals 11.) **A strong wind blew and covered 6 shells with sand. . . .**

Tell a continuous story as long as interest is maintained. Encourage the children to participate as storytellers.

When the children are comfortable verbalizing the appropriate number sentences, ask them to build the sentences using cards cut from Line Master 53. On other occasions, ask the children to be authors and record the stories as the action occurs (see Authors Wanted, page 207).

5. Read All About It! — PS C

Provide the children with access to different story boards (Line Masters 18 to 23), a variety of small objects, copies of the mini-story boards, (Line Master 52), and large sheets of newsprint.

Guide the children to select a partner and a work space. Tell them that everyday problems and situations occur that are reported in the newspaper. Explain that today is a special day because everything is happening to 11. Have one child tell and act out a story about 11 on a story board while the other child acts as a reporter and records the story on a mini-story board or a large story board. Have the children reverse roles.

Invite the children to glue their reports on sheets of newsprint. You may wish the children to include a headline for each news item. Encourage the children to discuss their stories. Leave the story boards out so that children can contribute to the news board as they wish.

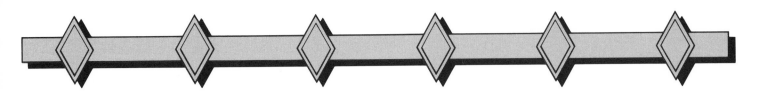

6. Find the Solution

D

At a center, provide any or all of the reinforcement games suggested in this activity. These games provide children with the opportunity to recall number sentences from this unit as well as the number sentences developed in Units 5 and 7. Remember that these games are intended to reinforce the concepts, not teach them. You can also extend the games of Unit 7 to include number sentences to 12.

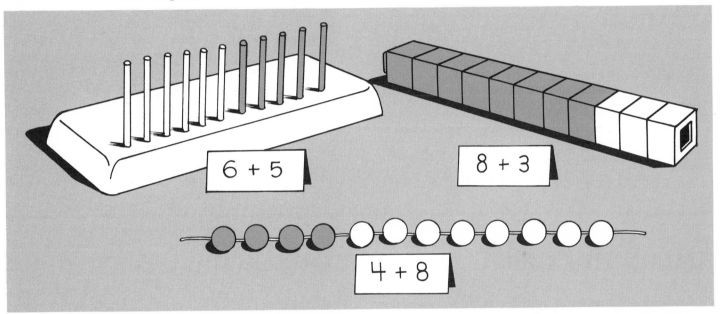

Children choose a number sentence card and plant a garden, make a train of interlocking cubes, or string beads in 2 colors to show the sentence.

Children create booklets which contain different names for 11 and/or 12.

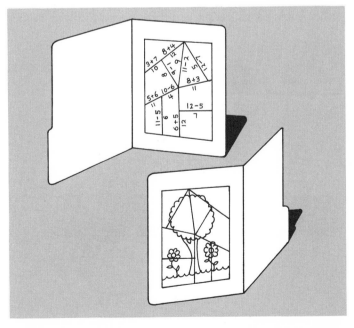

Children solve the puzzle by aligning each question with an answer. To check, the child closes the folder, turns it over and opens it. If the picture is completed properly, the child knows the solution was correct.

Addition and Subtraction Across the Curriculum

Language Arts

- Have the children contribute to a continuous story involving 12 children.

  There were 6 boys and 6 girls in one large family. There were 12 children in all. One day, 3 of the children decided to play in the tree fort. The other 9 children went to the park . . . .

- Have the children select a picture from an old story book, calendar, or magazine and encourage them to identify sets of objects in the picture. The children then create a story about the identified set becoming larger and smaller.
- In conjunction with this unit, you may wish to read these books (see page 318 for an annotated bibliography).

  - *The Most Amazing Hide and Seek Counting Book* by Robert Crowther
  - *Henny Penny* by Paul Galdone
  - *The House that Jack Built* by Paul Galdone

Social Studies

Have the children make up stories about their families and/or other families they know. Have them include the number of adults, the number of children, and the total number of people.

Physical Education

Have the children total their personal scores as they knock down bowling pins with a ball or throw bean bags on to a target.

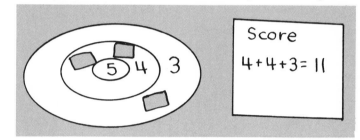

Extension Project

At a center, place a variety of small objects labelled with prices from 1¢ to 10¢, strips of paper (pieces of adding machine tape work well), a calculator, and wallets (envelopes) with coin collections ranging from 5¢ to 20¢. Invite the children to select a wallet, count the collection, and then decide which objects they could buy from the display. They should make a bill on a strip of paper to show total cost before checking their calculations with the calculator. The children should then use the bill they created to make up an advertisement such as the one shown for the priced objects.

Sample Letters to Parents

It is important to the children's success in mathematics that their parents be supportive of the program. Sending letters home at regular intervals will help keep parents informed of the goals of the program as well as enabling them to become involved in their children's learning. Here are four sample letters which you may wish to use as models for this purpose.

Dear Parent or Guardian:

This year your child will be involved in an activity-based mathematics program called *Explorations*. An activity-based program requires many materials, so we are asking for your help. Lots of things that you might consider "junk" would be very valuable to us! Here are just some of the things we can put to good use:

- containers (egg cartons, boxes of all sizes, milk cartons, yogurt containers, ...)
- scraps (fabric, wallpaper, wrapping paper, ribbon, yarn, ...)
- small objects to sort and count (bottle caps, buttons, old keys, bread tags, twist ties, shells, screws, bolts, ...)
- magazines and catalogues
- odds and ends (old costume jewelry, plastic cutlery, party favors, greeting cards, playing cards, ...)

Please send any materials that you think we might use to school with your child.

Occasions will undoubtedly arise throughout the year when I could use assistance in the preparation of materials for the program. If you wish to participate, please call the school and let me know.

Thank you in advance for your help.

Sincerely,

P.S. Ask your child to tell you about Ted the Troll!

Dear Parent or Guardian:

Thank you for the various items you donated to our math collections. Because the children have brought them in, they feel they have made an important contribution to the program.

We have been using some of these materials in our sorting and patterning activities. A great deal of time has been spent on these topics because they develop important skills which will help the children solve problems.

Being able to sort will help the children arrange and organize information, ideas, and objects around them. For example, our math collections have been carefully sorted and labelled so that we know where everything is when we need it and where to put it when we are finished.

Our number system—in fact, all of mathematics—is built on patterns. So children who are able to recognize patterns will be more successful in mathematics. Also, recognizing patterns in events such as daily routines, in the days of the week, etc., enables children to predict what should happen next.

It is important that children see how their work in mathematics relates to the world around them. Here are some ways you can help your child do this.

- Ask the child to identify and describe patterns found in your home, e.g., wallpaper, carpets, routines, and place settings.
- Encourage your child to identify places where objects are sorted in the home, e.g., the cutlery drawer, dresser drawers, linen closets, and cupboards. You may wish to ask your child to suggest other ways the objects may be sorted.

If you have questions about the program, please don't hesitate to call.

Sincerely,

Dear Parent or Guardian:

Your child has been working on many activities related to number. Although we adults tend to think of number as a very simple idea, it is really quite complex. We often assume that because a child can count to 10, or even beyond, he or she understands numbers. In fact, when questioned further, we find that many children may not realize that the number of objects in a set doesn't change when the arrangement changes. Many young children think that there are more objects in a set like this: (o o o o o) than in one like this (ooooo) or one like this (8 o 8). In our math program, we have provided many opportunities for your child to explore this and other important ideas related to number.

The children have made a record of some of their activities. Today, your child is proud to bring some of these records home to share with you. Please ask her or him to describe some of the pages to you.

If you have any questions about the program, please do not hesitate to call.

Sincerely,

Dear Parent or Guardian:

"What did you do in school today?" "Nothing!" How often have you heard that response? Fortunately, there are ways that you can help your child to recall and describe some of the interesting activities that he or she participated in at school. Here are some questions that will help you do this:

- Tell me what you did in math today.
- Did you talk about number? Shapes? Measuring?
- What materials did you use?
- Did you record your work today? How did you do it?
- Did you share your work with your friends today? What did you share? With whom? What did you say about your work?
- How did you feel about your work today? What did you like (not like) about it? Why?
- Did you have a story today? Tell me about it.
- What did you do at the calendar today?
- What were some of the other activities you could have chosen?

Once you are aware of topics your child is working on, encourage her or him to extend the experience at home. Here are some ways in which you can do this:

- Borrow and read related books from the children's section of the public library.
- Identify where number is used in your home, neighborhood, and local stores.
- You may engage your child in specific activities such as:
  - Count these for me.
  - How many glasses do we need to set the table?
  - What do you see that is the same shape as the dining room table?
  - How many socks are in the drawer? Count them by twos.

These activities will help your child to realize that math happens all around her or him; not just at school!

Sincerely,

Annotated Bibliography of Children's Literature

Problem Solving

Sorting

Ahlberg, Janet and Allan. *The Baby's Catalogue*. Boston: Little Brown & Co., 1983.

Illustrations pertaining to a wide range of topics associated with babies have been sorted in various ways.
Children could discuss sets of pictures and identify the sorting rule. Children could contribute items for a 'baby's collection.' Items could then be sorted and classified in various ways or graphed.

Ahlberg, Janet and Allan. *Each Peach Pear Plum*. New York: Scholastic, 1985.

The characters in this story are familiar folk from nursery rhymes and fairy tales.
Children could sort the characters using various criteria, e.g., scary / not scary; animals / people; young / old.

Hoban, Tana. *Is it Red? Is it Yellow? Is it Blue?* New York: Greenwillow Books, 1978.

This book contains vivid color photos of actual objects in bright colors.
Children could create their own collections of things to sort by color.

Hoberman, Mary Ann. *A House is a House For Me*. New York: Viking-Penguin, 1978.

A collection of houses of various kinds is included in this book.
Children could sort the houses using various criteria, e.g., homes for animals / homes for birds, shapes, location, size.

Patterning

Alderson, Sue Ann. *Bonnie McSmithers, you're driving me dithers*. Edmonton: Tree Frog Press, 1974.

Bonnie's mother uses patterned language to express her loving exasperation with her rambunctious daughter.
Children could chant the rhyme, emphasizing the pattern by stressing appropriate syllables.

Emberley, Barbara. *Drummer Hoff*. Spokane: Treehouse Productions, 1967.

Rhyming couplets tell the story of how the characters worked together to fire a cannon. In this cumulative pattern, the character's name rhymes with what the character does. ("Drummer Hoff fired it off!")
Children could use their own names to make rhymes using this pattern.

*These books are out of print but will be available at many public and school libraries.

*Krauss, Ruth. *Bears*. New York: Scholastic, 1970.

This book begins and ends with the pattern "Bears, bears, bears, bears, bears, bears." In the middle, the bears are described in various ways, e.g., "under chairs", "collecting fares", "millionaires". All of the descriptions rhyme.
Children could adapt the pattern to a variety of topics.

Martin, Bill Jr. *Brown Bear, Brown Bear, What Do You See?* New York: Holt, Rinehart, & Winston, 1983.

The pattern in this book is a favorite! ("Brown Bear, Brown Bear, What do you see?" etc.)
Children could easily adapt the pattern to other topics and make up their own verses, e.g. Astronaut, Astronaut, what do you see?

*Yabuki, Seiji. *I Love the Morning*. Cleveland: World Publishing Co., 1969.

The simple pattern in this book ("I love the _____ because … ") lends itself to the creation of original verses.
Children could compose their own stories about the things that they love.

Graphing

Cleaver, Elizabeth. *ABC*. Toronto: Oxford University Press, 1984.

Each page contains a beautiful illustration including various numbers of objects beginning with each letter of the alphabet in turn. The words are listed on the opposite page.
Children could make a bar graph which shows the number of words beginning with each letter, then compare numbers in the various sets.

*Duvoisin, Roger. *Our Veronica Goes to Petunia's Farm*. New York: Alfred A. Knopf, 1962.

Veronica, a hippopotamus, finds herself on a farm and gradually makes friends with the farm animals.
Using pictures, children could sort and graph the 14 farm animals in this story using a variety of criteria, e.g., 4 legs / 2 legs; feathers / fur.

Slobodkina, Esphyr. *Caps for Sale*. New York: Scholastic, 1976.

The main character, a hat vendor, has his hats stacked on his head.
Using pictures, children could graph the hats according to color and compare the sets. Children could bring their own hats to sort and graph.

Other Skills and Strategies

• **Identifying likenesses and differences**

Hutchins, Pat. *Titch*. New York: Macmillan, 1971.

Titch, the youngest child, has an older sister and brother.
Children could discuss similarities and differences in the activities of the three children.

• Ordering objects and events

*Carle, Eric. *Pancakes, Pancakes*. New York: Alfred A. Knopf, 1970.

> A young boy successively seeks out the various ingredients he needs to make pancakes with his mother.
> *Children could order ingredients and steps in the pancake-making process.*

• Selecting relevant information from pictures

Hutchins, Pat. *Rosie's Walk*. New York: Macmillan, 1968.

> Rosie the hen has a number of near escapes from the fox, evident in the illustrations, though never mentioned in the text.
> *Children could discuss or write about the activities of the fox in these illustrations.*

• Looking for possibilities

Spier, Peter. *London Bridge is Falling Down*. New York: Doubleday, 1967.

> There are several possibilities for repairing London Bridge, but each has its problems.
> *Children could suggest other solutions.*

Measurement

Size

*Merriam, Eve. *Do You Want to See Something?* New York: Scholastic, 1965.

> In each of several verses, the reader is asked if he or she wants to see something very small, e.g., "Do you want to see a dancing flea?" Then in six seriated steps, from largest to smallest, the reader is led to the exact location of the object, e.g., "In the tent there's a ring. In the ring there's a pony. On the pony there's a lady. On the lady there's a poodle. On the poodle there's a mouse. And on that mouse there is a dancing flea."
> *Children could make up their own verses seriating along several dimensions.*

Wildsmith, Brian. *The Apple Bird*. Toronto: Oxford University Press, 1983.

> In this wordless picture book, a little bird eats a big apple and each changes shape.
> *Children could compare and discuss the illustrations with respect to changes in shape and size.*

*These books are out of print but will be available at many public and school libraries.

Length

Krauss, Ruth. *The Carrot Seed*. New York: Harper & Row, 1945.

> This book deals with the steps in the process of planting, tending, and growing a carrot.
> *Children could compare and seriate stages in the growth of the carrot seed, noting changes in length. Seeds could be grown, cared for, observed, and measured in the classroom.*

Mass

Leaf, Munro. *The Story of Ferdinand*. New York: Viking, 1936.

> Ferdinand grows larger and larger as this story progresses.
> *Children could note and compare the changes in Ferdinand's mass as he grows.*

Galdone, Paul, (ill.) *The Three Billy Goats Gruff*. San Antonio: Willow Publishing Co., 1981.

> Three billy goats cross a bridge, under which lives the mean, ugly, old troll, in order to get to greener pastures on the other side.
> *Children could note and compare the mass of the three goats. How does their mass affect the sound they make crossing the bridge? The mass of the goats could also be compared with that of the troll.*

Time

• Sequencing events

Galdone, Paul, (ill.) *The Little Red Hen*. New York: Seabury Press, 1973.

> This story deals with the steps involved in growing wheat and grinding it into flour to make bread.
> *Children could sequence these steps and discuss the passage of time through several seasons as this story takes place.*

• Telling time

Galdone, Paul, (ill.) *The Three Little Pigs*. New York: Seabury Press, 1970.

> The third little pig cleverly outwits the wolf by rising one hour earlier than the appointed time to gather his apples and turnips.
> *Children could dramatize and improvise upon this part of the story using a variety of times.*

*Mendoza, George. *The Scarecrow Clock*. New York: Holt, Rinehart, and Winston, 1971.

> Each hour a scarecrow is asked where a passing creature has gone. The scarecrow replies and demonstrates the time with its arms.
> *Children could anticipate the hour as the story is told. They will enjoy demonstrating the hours with their arms.*

*Tresselt, Alvin. *Wake Up City*. New York: Lothrop, Lee, and Shepard Co., 1957.

> The early morning activities which take place in a city are described and illustrated.
> *Children could describe their early morning activities. The activities could be illustrated and sequenced. Children could investigate what time they did each of the activities they describe. This information could be collected and displayed on a class graph or chart.*

- **Days of the week**

Carle, Eric. *The Very Hungry Caterpillar*. New York: Putnam Publishing Group, 1969.

> On each day of the week the hungry caterpillar nibbles his way through ever-increasing quantities of food.
> *Children could anticipate the days of the week as the story is told, and try to recall them afterward.*

- **Months of the year**

*Lionni, Leo. *Mouse Days*. New York: Pantheon Books, 1980.

> Each month of the year is illustrated. These illustrations are accompanied by a description of activities and weather particular to the month.
> *Children could illustrate their favorite time of year. These illustrations could be posted to reflect the order of the months of the year. You may wish to construct a graph of favorite months and / or weather.*

Sendak, Maurice. *Chicken Soup with Rice*. New York: Harper and Row, 1962.

> A nonsensical rhyme for each month of the year reflects the changing seasons as well as some characteristics, celebrations, and activities.
> *Children could anticipate the months of the year as the story is being told, and note the details used to describe each month.*

Temperature

Fujikawa, Gyo. "The Sun and the Wind." In *Fairy Tales and Fables*. New York: Putnam Publishing Group, 1970.

> The sun and the wind try to prove which is more powerful by trying to make a traveler take off his coat. Several changes in temperature occur as the tale progresses.
> *Children could discuss this aspect of the story.*

Money

*Domjan, Joseph. *I Went to the Market*. New York: Holt, Rinehart, & Winston, 1970.

*These books are out of print but will be available at many public and school libraries.

In this old Czechoslovakian folk song someone goes shopping with a brand new penny.
> *With help, children could adapt this song by substituting other coins and thinking of original items to buy.*

Galdone, Paul. *Jack and the Beanstalk*. San Antonio: Willow Publishing Co., 1982.

> In this story, the Giant takes out his money bags and counts piles of coins until he falls asleep.
> *Children could dramatize this part of the story while counting or trading equivalent piles of coins.*

Number and Place Value

One-to-One Correspondence

Galdone, Paul. *The Three Bears*. New York: Seabury Press, 1972.

> There is one bowl, one chair, and one bed for each bear.
> *Children could use flannel board cutouts to match and determine equivalent sets.*

Obligado, Lilian. *The Three Little Kittens*. New York: Random House, 1974.

> There are two mittens and one piece of pie for each kitten.
> *Children could compare and identify which sets have more, less, or the same number of members.*

Number to Ten

Anno, M. *Anno's Counting Book*. New York: Harper and Row, 1977.

> This picture book contains colorful, detailed illustrations that take the reader through a year in a small village.
> *The children could count the items on each page, comparing the numbers in each set.*

Carle, Eric. *The Very Hungry Caterpillar*. New York: Putnam Publishing Group, 1969.

> This book follows the progress of a hungry little caterpillar who eats his way through different numbers of foods for a week, then spins a cocoon and turns into a butterfly. This book also reinforces the names of the days of the week.
> *Children could label and identify sets and count as they enjoy the story.*

*Francoise. *Jeanne Marie Counts Her Sheep*. New York: Charles Scribner's Sons, 1951.

Jeanne Marie imagines that her sheep has 1 to 10 lambs and thinks about all the things she could buy with the money

from the wool.
Children could identify, count, and compare sets.

Gretz, Suzanna. *Teddybears One to Ten*. Tonbridge, Kent: Ernest Benn, 1969.
Teddy's 1 through 10 are involved in a variety of antics.
Children could identify, count, and compare sets when discussing this book.

Hutchins, Pat. *1 Hunter*. New York: Greenwillow Books, 1982.
In this counting book, one hunter passes by increasing numbers of jungle animals, 2 to 10, and does not detect any of them until the end of the story.
Children could identify, count, and compare sets.

Langstaff, John. *Over in the Meadow*. New York: Harcourt, Brace, Jovanovich, 1967.
Various meadow animals have different numbers of offspring, 1 through 10.
Children could identify and compare sets when discussing this poem.

Quackenbush, Robert M. (ill.) *Poems for Counting*. New York: Holt, Rinehart, & Winston, 1963.
This book contains a poem for each of the numbers 1 to 10.
Children could count, identify sets with more or less, identify numbers before, after, between, refer to ordinal position, etc., in relation to these poems.

Number to 99

Crowther, Robert. *The Most Amazing Hide and Seek Counting Book*. New York: Viking-Penguin, 1981.
This pop-up book deals with numbers to 100.
Illustrations lend themselves to counting, grouping, and composing number sentences.

Fractions

Greenaway, Kate. *A-Apple Pie*. New Jersey: Castle Books Inc., 1979.
Illustrations in this ABC book show a pie divided into pieces in various ways.
Children could identify the number of pieces and the fraction each piece represents.

*These books are out of print but will be available at many public and school libraries.

Operations

Addition

Adams, Pam. *There Was an Old Lady Who Swallowed a Fly*. Sudbury, Massachusetts: Playspaces International, 1973.
In addition to the fly, this lady swallowed six more animals with disastrous results.
Children could identify how many animals have been swallowed as each one is added.

Galdone, Paul. *Henny Penny*. New York: Seabury Press, 1968.
Henny Penny successively adds all the farm fowl to her search party to find the king so that she can tell them that the sky is falling.
Illustrations lend themselves to writing number sentences.

*Galdone, Paul. *The House that Jack Built*. New York: McGraw-Hill, 1961.
Ten characters, including Jack, are added one at a time as this tale is told.
Children could identify the number of characters as each new character is added.

Tolstoi, Alexei. *The Great Big Enormous Turnip*. London: William Heinemann, 1968.
One more character is added successively until the whole group is able to cooperatively tug the huge turnip out of the ground.
This situation lends itself to writing number sentences.

Subtraction

Adams, Pam. *There Were Ten in the Bed*. Sudbury, Massachusetts: Playspaces International, 1979.
Each time the ten children roll over, one more falls out of the bed until all are on the floor and none are in the bed.
The book is illustrated in such a way that children can actually turn a cardboard wheel that makes the children fall out of the bed, one by one. Illustrations lend themselves to writing number sentences.

Burningham, John. *Mr. Gumpy's Outing*. Markham, Ontario: Penguin, 1984.
One by one, the animals board Mr. Gumpy's raft until the crowd begins to jostle and they all fall off.
Children could identify the number of animals on the raft as each new animal is added. The accident provides an opportunity to subtract.

de Paola, Tomie. *Pancakes for Breakfast*. New York: Harcourt, Brace, Jovanovich, 1978.
An old woman decides to make pancakes for herself and successively seeks out all the different ingredients, but unfor-

tunately her pets eat the ingredients before she has a chance to make the pancakes.
Illustrations lend themselves to writing number sentences.

Galdone, Paul. (ill.) *Jack and the Beanstalk*. San Antonio: Willow Publishing Co., 1982.
The Giant has three treasures which he loses one by one as Jack steals them.
Children could discuss this aspect of the story and write number sentences.

Geometry

Hoban, Tana. *Circles, Triangles, and Squares*. New York: Macmillan, 1974.
Circles, triangles, and squares can be found within the objects photographed.
Children could recognize and sort geometric figures.

Hoban, Tana. *Shapes and Things*. New York: Macmillan, 1970.
Black and white photos of actual objects contain various geometric shapes.
Children could identify the geometric figures.

Hutchins, Pat. *Changes, Changes*. New York: Macmillan, 1973.
Geometric solids are manipulated to form different objects.
Children could identify the different geometric solids.

Pienkowski, Jan. *Shapes*. New York: Harvey House, 1975
Various shapes are shown in this book.
Children could recognize and sort geometric figures.

*Sullivan, Joan. *Round is a Pancake*. New York: Holt, Rinehart, & Winston, 1963.
Shapes are related to everyday objects.
Children could generate their own examples, or adapt this pattern to other topics, e.g., square is a _____.

*These books are out of print but will be available at many public and school libraries.